Doomsday

Doomsday

Britain after Nuclear Attack

STAN OPENSHAW, PHILIP STEADMAN
AND OWEN GREENE

Basil Blackwell

First published 1983
Basil Blackwell Publisher Limited
108 Cowley Road, Oxford OX4 1JF, England

British Library Cataloguing in Publication Data
Openshaw, Stan
    Doomsday: Britain after nuclear attack.
    1. Atomic warfare   2. Soviet Union—Military
    policy   3. Great Britain—Military policy
    I. Title   II. Steadman, Philip
    III. Greene, Owen
    355'.0217   UF767

    ISBN 0-631-13393-3
    ISBN 0-631-13394-1 Pbk

Typeset by Katerprint Co Ltd, Oxford
Printed in Great Britain by Billing and Sons Ltd.

Contents

Acknowledgements

We are grateful to our colleagues in Scientists Against Nuclear Arms (SANA) for advice and information on all of the subjects covered in this book. We would like to thank in particular Mike Pentz, Azzam Qasrawi and Neil Turok, as well as other members of the 'Hard Luck' working group. Azzam Qasrawi and Colin Wymer gave valuable assistance with the design of parts of the computer model described in chapter 6. Thanks are also due to Terry Ratcliffe of NUMAC for help with the computing work. Duncan Campbell gave us the benefit of his unrivalled knowledge of civil defence matters and of the siting of military targets in Britain. Barbara Pearce helped with editorial work and drew some of the figures. The manuscript was typed by Kime West, Ann Earls, Di Perry and Lynn Camborne-Paynter. We also thank the staff of Basil Blackwell Publisher for their help and hard work. Finally, we are grateful to the following individuals and organizations for their kind permission to reproduce copyright material: the International Institute for Strategic Studies for figure 3.1, the Superintendent of Documents (US Government Printing Office) for figures 6.2 and 6.3, HMSO for figure 9.1, Mr S. F. Butler for figure 9.4 and table 9.3, and Mr P. R. Bentley and the SRDB for figure A4.1.)

1
Introduction

It is almost exactly 900 years since William the Conqueror ordered a survey to be made of the land which he had conquered and of the people under his rule. Only much later did the survey come to be known as 'Domesday', that is the 'day of judgement' — a reckoning to be compared with those books described in Revelation by which 'the dead were judged out of those things which were written.' If Britain were to be 'conquered' again, this time with nuclear weapons, what would be the condition of its land and how many people might be left living? These are the questions which this new 'Doomsday' book sets out to answer.

This book provides for the first time, in the open literature, a detailed comprehensive account of the effects of nuclear attack on Britain, both nationally and locally. Perhaps comparable studies exist within the Ministry of Defence, or the Home Office, but they have not been made public. Other authors have described what nuclear weapons would do to single cities or to regions in Britain[1] — indeed one such local study, of *London after the Bomb*,[2] has been made by a group which included one of the authors (Owen Greene) of the present volume. There have also been discussions in broad terms by various authors of the level and nature of nuclear attack which this country might face.[3] This book is different.

It begins by considering the size of nuclear attack which the UK could expect, and the targets which would be destroyed. At first sight this might appear to be an impossible task — so many alternatives can be imagined. Western nuclear policy envisages attacks ranging from a single 'warning shot' over a remote area or against a city, through various levels of 'limited' nuclear war, to an all-out attack. The Home Office has talked of attacks ranging from conventional bombing raids right up to 3,000 megatons — a fifth of the entire Soviet nuclear arsenal — being detonated over Britain.[4] Careful consideration however shows many of these alternatives to be fanciful.

The obvious first step is to examine how the US, NATO and especially the Soviet Union envisage fighting a nuclear war. Chapter 2 provides an account of their various strategies, drawing largely on military writings from American and Soviet sources. A large number of Soviet military documents are now available in the West. They are quite clear about how the Soviet Union plans to fight a nuclear war, should one break out. The Soviet strategy is different from that of the US and NATO. It shares few of the latter's comfortable assumptions. Chapter 2 ends with a brief description of the trends in modern nuclear weaponry.

Since plans made in peacetime are not always adhered to in war, chapter 3 examines how a nuclear war might start. It discusses the factors which tend to escalate a conflict or exacerbate a crisis, and some of the technological developments which are making unintentional nuclear war more likely. This provides a context within which to assess how a nuclear war is likely to proceed. Can it be limited or is it likely to escalate into all-out war? How will it affect Britain?

In all the scenarios and discussion it is assumed that it is the Soviet Union which launches an attack on Britain. This is simply an acknowledgement of current political and military realities, and should not be read as a statement, one way or the other, about any possible aggressive intentions on its part. At some future date it is conceivable, though let us hope not inevitable, that Britain might come to face other potentially hostile powers with nuclear weapons. For the present book we are concerned with what might happen should nuclear war occur in the immediate future.

In chapters 4 and 5, therefore, we describe the numbers and characteristics of the nuclear weapons which the Soviet Union is thought to have currently available for use against Western Europe, and we estimate what proportion of these is likely to be allocated for use against the UK. Soviet military literature is explicit about the range of targets they would be directed against. By looking in detail at the military, industrial and civilian targets in mainland Britain, we construct a series of some 11 patterns of attack of differing magnitude. Some of these are, we believe, plausible examples of the sort of attack the UK could actually expect. Others are much less plausible, but are included in order to give a systematic overall picture of the consequences of increasing levels of bombardment, with different military objectives and directed against different classes of target.

We also look at a specific pattern of attack intended to destroy ground-launched cruise missiles dispersed on their launch vehicles to a number of sites scattered through southern England. And we consider what is, in nuclear terms, a very small retaliatory strike by the Soviet Union directed exclusively at cities and the energy industry on the assumption that the bulk of their weapons have already been destroyed in a US/NATO first strike.

Finally, we contrast these attack patterns with some analysis of the scenarios devised for the purposes of civil defence exercises conducted over the last 25 years, of which the most recent are the 1980 'Square Leg' and the (cancelled) 1982 'Hard Rock' exercises.

In chapter 6 we consider methods for predicting in detail the effects of the explosion of nuclear weapons, principally those of heat, blast and radiation from fallout. We describe how it is possible to calculate, albeit approximately, using standard and generally accepted methods, the numbers of people who would be killed and injured by the immediate effects of attack, the levels of damage which would be caused to buildings, and the extent of the areas over which radioactive contamination would spread. Because these calculations are somewhat complex and are made in detail for every part of the country, they are only practicable using computers. We describe a series of computer programs which we have developed over the last two years specially for the purpose.

Chapter 7 analyses the results from these calculations, in terms of resulting numbers of casualties and areas of damage. The predictions are broken down by counties to give the local as well as the national picture. Chapter 8 follows through, in a rather more speculative way, some of the medium- and longer-term consequences which might follow in the aftermath of attack. Subjects discussed include the destruction of housing and industry, effects on agriculture, some of the complex ecological and environmental damage brought about by a large-scale attack (including the special problems of radioactive contamination where nuclear power stations are targets), and the prospects for the health of those people who escape death or injury in the attack itself.

Predictions of casualties and of the extent of damage in a nuclear attack on Britain are also made by the Scientific Research and Development Branch of the Home Office, for the purposes of civil defence planning. The Home Office has published rather little in detail about this work, but it has released two papers, of which one describes its methods of calculation,[5] and the other gives summarized results at the national level.[6] The Home Office makes use of computer programs which are similar to our own in general structure, although very different in some of the numerical values taken for certain critical factors. These Home Office methods of calculation, and the results which they produce, are discussed and contrasted with our own findings in chapter 9. Finally in chapter 10 we give a brief account of current civil defence preparations in the UK, and the other measures which might in principle be taken but are not at present envisaged, and we assess their likely effectiveness.

At no point in the book do we raise the question of nuclear disarmament, or discuss any of the routes by which this might be achieved. Nevertheless, questions of the likely level and effects of attack on Britain, and the practicability of civil defence, have become hotly contested because of their bearing on the disarmament issue. Government officials and members of the wider civil defence community have been making public statements on these topics, many of them based on the work of the Home Office Scientific Research and Development Branch already mentioned. Others, including ourselves and our colleagues in the organization Scientists Against Nuclear Arms (SANA) — of which two of

the present authors (Philip Steadman and Owen Greene) are members —
have been publishing very different findings. Since we are highly critical
here of government statements, and are sceptical about the value of
current civil defence plans in the UK, it is possible that our involvement in
such controversies may raise doubts in the minds of some readers as to the
reliability of the data which we use as the basis of our findings. We have
therefore laid out all our assumptions, figures and methods of calculation
for inspection, so that they are open to challenge on issues of legitimate
scientific debate.

We emphasize all uncertainties and areas in which variable factors may
affect our conclusions. Where there is scientific controversy we have made
conservative assumptions. And we have used the most authoritative
sources of information available. For example, our methods of calculation
of the direct effects of nuclear explosions are drawn almost exclusively
from publications of the United States Department of Defense and other
American government sources, in particular Glasstone and Dolan's *The
Effects of Nuclear Weapons*.[7] This is the standard work and contains the
most complete compilation of scientific findings from the experience of the
bombings in Japan, from the programme of American weapons tests, and
from theoretical studies. If anything, it is to be expected that these
American figures err on the conservative side. A number of ways in which
nuclear weapons can cause death and damage have further been omitted
from the calculations, not because they are unlikely to occur, but because
of the difficulties of quantitative prediction.

Most important is the fact that our methods of calculation have, as a
matter of public record, been endorsed both by the British Medical
Association (BMA) and by the Home Office Minister responsible for civil
defence, who has conceded by implication that those of his own
Department are not to be believed. When the BMA was conducting its
enquiry into *The Medical Effects of Nuclear War* during 1982, we gave
written and oral evidence, together with other colleagues, based on the
study of *London after the Bomb* and on papers published (by Stan
Openshaw and Philip Steadman) in specialized journals.[8] In their report[9]
the BMA compared the methods of calculation used by ourselves and by
the Home Office, and contrasted the resulting predictions of numbers of
casualties in an attack on Britain. Roughly speaking, the differences
between the Home Office computer programs and ours are such that they
predict half, or less than half, the numbers of deaths and injuries for an
identical pattern of attack that we do. Full details are given in chapter 9.
The BMA wrote in the conclusion to their report that:

There are discrepancies between the projections for blast, heat and radiation
produced by the Home Office and Scientists Against Nuclear Arms (SANA). The
latter rely on methods and figures derived for the most part from the United States

Department of Defense and the US Office of Technology Assessment. We have examined the methods for calculating the projections used by SANA, and the Working Party believes, on the evidence it has received, that the projections from SANA give a more realistic estimate of the blast, heat and radiation effects of nuclear weapons. We understand that the Home Office is currently revising its calculations.[10]

Following the publication of the BMA report, Mr Patrick Mayhew, then Minister of State at the Home Office and responsible for civil defence, was interviewed on BBC Radio's *The World This Weekend*. *The Times* reported that '. . . he did not take issue with any of the calculations in the BMA's report'.[11] These are precisely the techniques of calculation used in the present book.

The truth of the matter is that there is no need for those who take the consequences of the use of nuclear weapons on Britain as an argument for the urgency of nuclear disarmament, to exaggerate their effects. As we demonstrate, even a moderate, realistic, level of attack would be likely to result in at least four-fifths of the country's population being killed and injured by the direct effects, 65 per cent of all buildings in the country being seriously damaged, set on fire or demolished, and 70 per cent of the inhabited land area of Britain being subjected to levels of radiation from fallout which would be fatal to any person (and most animals) in the open.

It is because of this that successive governments have thought it prudent, in order to maintain political support for the continued possession of nuclear weapons by this country, to discourage public discussion of the consequences of nuclear attack. Where discussion has been unavoidable, the effort has been made to play down the effects through a bland and selective presentation of the facts, or by misrepresentation. We see this in the suppression of the BBC's *War Game* and the attempt to censor other television programmes; in the fatuities of the *Protect and Survive* leaflet[12] ('On hearing the all-clear . . . you may resume normal activities'); and, as we show, in the published work of Home Office scientists.

The reaction of the Government to the publication of the BMA's report is instructive. The Home Office Minister was quoted as saying that the danger of the report was that 'it gave the impression that a 200 Megaton attack could be expected' (this is the level which, until around 1982, the Home Office have themselves taken as a basic assumption); and that it could be used as an argument to 'go neutral, non-nuclear and pull out of NATO'.[13] Not that the BMA's analysis was faulty, note, but that these were not matters to be discussed in front of the children. Whatever position one takes on the disarmament question, it is surely deeply disturbing that in a democratic society it is felt necessary to suppress the facts or discourage discussion of the truth, lest popular support for Government policy be undermined.

Over the last two years discussion in the press and on television has become somewhat more open — largely as a result of the activities of the peace movement. As independent scientific assessments have become available and widely publicized, the Government has been obliged to engage in some public debate on the issues. However, there is still a dismaying reluctance on the part of the Home Office, or regional Emergency Planning Officers, to adopt an open and serious approach to discussion. New regulations were laid before Parliament, in July 1983, placing legal obligations on local authorities to take part in civil defence plans in which very many of them have no confidence. Despite the statement by the Minister, and despite Home Office scientists' own indications that they intend to make changes in their methods of estimating the consequences of nuclear attack, there are as yet no public signs that such changes have been instituted. Indeed it appears that all the official forms of advice given out to local authorities and to civil defence workers — the handbooks, the calculators, the tables of data — which all incorporate these now discredited figures, continue exactly as before.

The purpose of the book is therefore to present as realistic, detailed and reliable a set of predictions about the effects of a nuclear attack on Britain as the current state of scientific knowledge permits. We hope that it may find readers among the general 'uncommitted' public, against which they can assess the likelihood of nuclear war, and can decide on the most effective way of responding to that threat.

Supporters of the peace movement should, we believe, find the book especially useful. One of the attack scenarios which we consider in particular detail was devised (in collaboration with Neil Turok and Azzam Qasrawi) and analysed during the summer of 1982. It was subsequently made use of by CND, who dubbed it 'Hard Luck' in response to the official (and later cancelled) 'Hard Rock' exercise and took it as the basis for their 'Operation Hard Luck' in September 1982. For this and all the other attacks considered, we have broken down the casualty estimates geographically so that, in conjunction with the weapons effects data provided in chapter 6, a detailed picture can be built up of the impact of attack on any chosen local area.

Although we are highly critical of current civil defence preparations, we hope that our work may still prove useful to Emergency Planning Officers, DHSS 'war planners', Home Office scientific advisers and other civil defence workers. They will discover detailed information here of a kind which the Home Office presently fails to supply. Perhaps they may be convinced that measures very different from those planned at present would be a more appropriate response to the realities of nuclear attack; or even that their time and effort would be better devoted to prevention rather than treatment. At the very least the book provides a more realistic set of casualty estimates for their plans and war games; and should bring home the enormity of the difficulties facing civil defence in a nuclear war, and banish for ever the currently prevailing official assumptions that for planning purposes '75 to 90 per cent' of the population might be expected to survive.

Lastly, we hope that these studies may interest academic workers in a number of fields: students of strategy, war and peace, as well as geographers and planners. The subject of the book is intrinsically geographical, and yet this is an area which geographers in their professional capacity have largely ignored, and in which many possibilities for further research exist. The mathematical and computer models which are employed are in many ways crude by comparison with contemporary work in regional and urban studies, and might benefit from the application of newer and more sophisticated techniques.

Some people in Britain today, including many politicians and members of the civil defence community, seem truly to think that a nuclear attack will be rather like the Blitz, if slightly worse, and that so long as our determination and morale do not fail, then we can pull through. Such people believe that to argue the contrary is 'defeatist', if not downright treacherous. For them the findings of this book will be news. In the Blitz, throughout the whole of the war, the Germans dropped some 70,000 tons of high explosive on Britain. The smallest single Russian warhead assumed to be used in the attack scenarios considered here — that of the SS20 — has more than twice that explosive power. Overall, in the attacks on Britain which we analyse, the explosive used — in the course of a few hours or days — would be equivalent to perhaps *50 times* the quantity used in all the countries involved throughout the entire World War II. It will not be the same as the Blitz.

Many other people know in their hearts the truth of what a nuclear war will do, and yet because the truth is so unimaginably horrific they continue to banish it from their consciousness. We have found ourselves while working on this study, that although we have become intellectually familiar with and even blasé about the effects of nuclear weapons, we are still being continuously appalled by the enormity of our own findings. Even those who really know, need to be continuously reminded. Britain is perhaps uniquely badly situated in relation to nuclear attack — because of its small land area, its high population density, and its concentration of strategically important targets mixed in closely with those centres of population. Britain truly has become it seems the Oceanian 'Airstrip One' or Orwell's *Nineteen Eighty-Four*. Only the Germanies are arguably in a worse position.

The survey of the British people which was compiled into the Domesday Book did not provide a complete count of their numbers in 1086; but on the partial evidence which the book gives, the total population at that date has been estimated at around 1¼ million. It is quite conceivable that a nuclear attack of the magnitude we face today would leave, at the end of the following year, say, only a comparable number surviving, under conditions which would make the daily life of the eleventh century seem like a paradise by contrast.

2

Nuclear Strategies

The immense destructive power of nuclear weapons has changed the way war can be fought and makes it doubtful that military force can ever rationally be used to resolve direct conflicts of interest between nuclear weapon states. The US and the USSR have over 50,000 nuclear warheads between them with a total explosive power of some 20,000 megatons, equivalent to 1.5 million Hiroshimas. A fraction of these would be sufficient to kill hundreds of millions of people and to devastate large areas of the world.

Nevertheless, the superpowers continue to develop their nuclear arsenals and to produce increasingly sophisticated means of delivering these weapons to their targets. Conflicts of interest will continue to exist in the world for the foreseeable future and Warsaw Pact and NATO governments obviously have not abandoned the idea that the possession of nuclear weapons can influence the outcome of these to their own advantage. Accordingly, they have both developed nuclear policies indicating how they intend to use, or threaten to use, their nuclear weapons if the need arises. In this chapter we review these policies. This will provide a background for discussions in later chapters on how a nuclear war might start, how it would be fought and on the probable characteristics of any resulting nuclear attack on the UK.

There are two sides to nuclear policy. The first relates to the way nuclear weapons can be used for the prevention of war, for nuclear blackmail, or for 'crisis management' — that is, the art of handling a confrontation to advantage. The second is concerned with how to use nuclear weapons to advantage if 'deterrence fails' and war breaks out. For most of the time since World War II neither the US nor the USSR has found the demands of these two aspects of nuclear policy contradictory. They have worked on the classical military assumption that the best way to prevent war is to convince their opponent of their capability to wage nuclear war effectively.

However, as we shall see, their nuclear policies are different in many important respects. This is not surprising since they are in different strategic situations and have different histories, military traditions and social structures. For example, until the end of the 1960s the nuclear forces of the USA were clearly perceived by both superpowers to be larger and more capable than those of the USSR, making the Americans more inclined towards the politics of brinkmanship and nuclear blackmail. Further, since the US tries to use nuclear weapons to deter attacks against overseas allies, such as Western Europe, it has had to ask rather more of nuclear weapons than the Soviet Union. The threat to use nuclear weapons to retaliate against any attack on an overseas ally — so called 'extended deterrence' — has less credibility than a promise to respond to a direct attack on the homeland, and US nuclear doctrine has had to take this into account.

US NUCLEAR POLICY

During the 1960s, western strategists concentrated most of their attention on ways of avoiding strategic nuclear war. They thought about ways of reducing the risk of accidental nuclear war, about crisis management and about how to preserve the condition of Mutual Assured Destruction (MAD).

According to the MAD doctrine the strategic situation is stable provided both the US and the USSR are confident that the other is able to unleash a massive retaliatory nuclear attack against cities and industries, even after absorbing an all-out surprise attack. This implied that each side required only a few hundred nuclear warheads with accuracies of half a mile or so.

Since the early 1970s this has changed. Questions relating to the period *after* the onset of nuclear war are now of greatest concern. For instance, which targets should be destroyed and at what stage in the conflict? Can the escalation of the war be controlled? How can the war be terminated before each side is destroyed? The MAD doctrine did not survive this change of focus. Critics pointed out that it made nuclear weapons unusable should deterrence fail. If the USSR launched an attack on an American ally or against a limited number of targets in the US (avoiding American cities) MAD only offered the US President a choice between suicide or surrender. If the President responded by launching a massive attack on Soviet cities, America's own cities would certainly be destroyed in retaliation. Therefore the only rational decision would be to surrender, in which case the possession of nuclear weapons would have proved useless. Furthermore, they argued, since this is clear to the USSR, the US nuclear 'deterrent' lacks credibility under the 'inflexible' MAD doctrine and therefore does not prevent war.

In January 1974, the US Secretary of Defense James Schlesinger announced that the US had abandoned its declared policy of Mutual Assured Destruction in favour of a (purportedly) more usable strategy known as 'Limited Strategic Options'.[1] According to this, targeting plans had to be made which provided the National Command Authorities (NCAs) with a wide range of possible responses to Soviet attack. These could range from small, 'surgical', attacks, against a few military installations, to massive strikes against various combinations of military and civilian targets. The National Strategic Target List (NSTL) must therefore include *both* 'countervalue' targets such as power stations, oil refineries, industry, transport systems and administrative centres, *and* 'counterforce' (military) targets such as missile silos, command centres, airfields, naval bases and bridges. By offering the prospect of keeping the war limited, the strategy attempted to make it rational to use nuclear weapons after a conflict had begun.

In fact this doctrine was not entirely new. As Harold Brown, US Secretary of Defense, said in 1980: 'The US has never had a doctrine based simply and solely on reflexive massive attacks on Soviet cities. Instead, we have always planned more selectively (options limiting urban-industrial damage) and more comprehensively (a range of military targets).'[2] For instance, in 1962 the US Secretary of Defense, Robert McNamara, announced a 'no-cities' doctrine[3] according to which the US could respond to Soviet attack by launching a 'pure counterforce' strike on the USSR. By preserving Soviet cities and therefore holding them hostage to further attack, he hoped that the USSR would be deterred from devastating American centres of population. Although the US administration later officially abandoned this policy, the Pentagon continued to include such options in its Single Integrated Operational Plans (SIOPs) throughout the 1960s.[4] The policy which Schlesinger announced in 1974 re-established 'counterforce' nuclear strategies as the *declared* policy of the US, as well as the operational one. What was new was its emphasis on the development of a large number of limited nuclear warfighting 'options' and on the feasibility of bargaining during a nuclear war.

Since 1974, the Limited Strategic Options policy has been confirmed and developed by President Carter, in his (unpublished) *Presidential Directive 59* of 25 July 1980,[5] and by President Reagan's (also unpublished) *National Security Decision Document 13*, issued in the summer of 1982.[6] It is now known as the 'Countervailing Strategy'.

The central concept in the Countervailing Strategy is 'controlled escalation' (or more recently 'escalation dominance'). According to this, the US must be able to conduct limited, precise attacks against certain categories of target. A number of different levels of attack are identified. The US should have the capability to respond at the level of the initial enemy attack or at a higher level of its own choosing. The strategy specifically includes the option of being the first to use nuclear weapons in a conflict. This might involve using battlefield nuclear weapons in the European 'theatre' or elsewhere if conventional weapons did not appear to be sufficient to contain an enemy advance. Alternatively, a single nuclear weapon might be detonated inside the adversary's territory or at sea in order to demonstrate political resolve and remind them of the danger of continued provocation (a so-called 'warning shot'). At each stage, the US hopes to coerce the enemy into keeping the war limited and coming to a negotiated settlement by threatening to launch its remaining nuclear weapons against further targets which the adversary values highly ('intra-war deterrence'). If the war continues, then the US intends to escalate the war in a 'controlled' manner to a higher level, by attacking a wider area or more categories of target. The war would proceed until either a settlement acceptable to the USA was reached, or one side or the other (almost certainly both) was destroyed; and might be expected to continue 'over a protracted period'[7] of weeks or months. As a US Department of Defense report says, if nuclear war began, the American objective would be 'to deny the Soviet Union (or any other adversary) a military victory at any level of conflict, and force the earliest termination of hostilities on terms favourable to the United States'.[8] As for the possibility of limiting nuclear war, Secretary of Defense Schlesinger has said:

Many people believe that in all likelihood [a nuclear exchange] must go all the way, but there is some possibility that nuclear war could be constrained to a lower level. . . . If we were to maintain continued communications with the Soviet leadership during the war and if we were to describe precisely and meticulously the limited nature of our action, including the desire to avoid attacking their urban industrial base . . . political leaders on both sides will be under powerful pressure to continue to be sensible.[9]

To sum up, current US strategy calls for preparations to allow the US to fight limited nuclear wars, possibly only involving attacks on military targets such as missile silos or radar stations. It declares the US's willingness to use nuclear weapons first in a conflict and asserts that there is a possibility that nuclear war could remain limited and therefore that there are circumstances in which it is rational to use nuclear weapons.

It has been reported[10] that Reagan's *National Security Decision Document 13* calls for the capability to *prevail* (win?) in such a war — that is for 'escalation dominance' rather than simply 'escalation control'. However, that does not necessarily imply that the US *intends* to start such a war or believes that its benefits could outweigh its costs. Supporters of the US doctrine would say that, on the contrary, 'There is no contradiction between this focus on how a war would be fought and what its results would be and our purpose of ensuring continued peace through mutual deterrence.'[11] Nuclear weapons can only deter attacks, they argue, if the US is ready and able to fight limited nuclear wars, if it believes they can be limited and if this is made absolutely clear to the Soviet Union and any other potential aggressor.

NATO'S NUCLEAR STRATEGY

As already mentioned in the introduction to this chapter, the credibility of the US nuclear 'guarantee' to respond to attacks in Europe is a particular problem, since the US would be irrational to respond to a Soviet attack on Europe in a way which it believed would result in its own cities being destroyed. NATO governments have tackled this problem by adopting a nuclear strategy, known as 'flexible response', which is very similar to the Countervailing Strategy. The policy identifies a series of 'rungs' on a 'ladder of escalation', on which it is planned to exercise 'controlled escalation'. In chapter 3 we examine how a war in Europe might actually proceed; but NATO strategy envisages it developing as follows.

Suppose the USSR was to launch a conventional attack on Western Europe: NATO would first attempt to hold it back with conventional forces alone. If this failed, NATO would use its shorter-ranged, 'battle-field' nuclear weapons to disrupt the Warsaw Pact's attack — destroying advancing forces as well as targets well behind enemy lines such as communications centres, airfields, and weapons stores. If the Warsaw Pact responded in kind, then longer-ranged nuclear forces would be used. At some stage, the doctrine demands that the US escalates the conflict by using its long-range 'theatre' nuclear forces (LRTNF) — F111 bombers, Poseidon submarine-launched missiles and, if they are installed, the ground-launched cruise missiles and Pershing II missiles – to attack targets inside European Russia. (The UK and France could also use their 'independent' nuclear forces.)

Since the US cannot be expected to launch such an attack unless there is some prospect of American territory remaining unharmed, 'flexible response' envisages the possibility that a war involving European Russia and Europe, but excluding the USA, might remain limited. This is possible, the doctrine claims, provided US 'strategic' nuclear forces are not used and instead only 'theatre' nuclear forces are launched. The belief is that this would signal to the USSR that all-out war was still avoidable, and that the threat posed by the remaining US strategic missiles would coerce the Soviets into stopping the war at that stage.

This rather absurd belief is of critical importance to NATO unity. The governments of its European members look to 'flexible response' to demonstrate clearly to the Soviet Union the costs of any attack on Western Europe. A nuclear war in Europe which excludes the territories of the US and the USSR is obviously completely unacceptable to them. They have therefore been continually looking for a guarantee that the US would attack Soviet territory as a result of such a war, believing that such a guarantee would 'strengthen deterrence' and make war less likely. Thus, for the sake of NATO unity, the US declares its belief that there is a possibility that a war involving only European Russia and Europe can remain limited, and is therefore willing to launch the attack its NATO partners wish.

This is probably the least plausible of any of the limited nuclear war scenarios envisaged in present US and NATO doctrine. It relies upon the USSR choosing not to retaliate against the American mainland after a US attack on the most highly industrialized and populated regions of its territory, containing a large proportion of its nuclear and conventional forces, simply because NATO has used the missiles and bombers which it has labelled 'theatre' rather than 'strategic'. In fact, it appears glaringly obvious that the Soviet Union will respond according to which country ordered the attack and which targets were destroyed. It has repeatedly declared that any nuclear attack on its territory will be considered to be strategic, and will inevitably result in targets being attacked in the US in return. The rationale for this is so convincing that it seems inevitable that the US leadership has long abandoned any belief in this particular aspect of 'flexible response' doctrine, and will only choose to attack the USSR if it is prepared to sacrifice targets in the USA and believes that strategic nuclear exchanges can be limited.

The European NATO governments, therefore, appear to be in search of a chimera. The US nuclear 'guarantee' is probably little more than a myth. As Henry Kissinger puts it '. . . our European allies should not keep on asking us to multiply strategic assurances that we cannot possibly mean, or if we do mean, we should not wish to execute because if we execute, we risk the destruction of Civilization . . .'[12] However, a war limited to Europe but excluding the superpowers appears at first sight to be much more plausible, and therefore those aspects of flexible response which relate to this possibility have more credibility.

It can be seen that the concept of 'escalation control' is central to NATO's 'flexible response' policy, as well as to the American Countervailing Strategy. In the next chapter we shall argue that it would probably be unworkable in reality. Nuclear war would be likely to escalate rapidly into global conflict, however limited it was initially. However, even if we were to neglect all of the technical, military and political reasons for this, there remains one absolutely critical factor — Soviet nuclear strategy.

The control of nuclear war requires *all* the participants to be willing and able to exercise restraint. The Soviet Union must, therefore, recognize the US's thresholds and target distinctions and (at least tacitly) agree to fight the war according to them.[13] It must be willing to accept the risks inherent in such a war and refrain from attacking military installations even though they might well be used to attack the USSR later. Above all, it must agree to leave its opponent's command and control centres intact in the hope that control can be maintained and that bargaining will end the war before everything is destroyed. That is, in order for 'controlled' escalation to work, the USSR must believe in limited nuclear war.

SOVIET STRATEGIC DOCTRINE

Soviet strategic commentators are all united in their rejection of the possibility of limited nuclear war and have shown no inclination to fight any war according to US rules.

In a nuclear war, if one breaks out, the combatants will use from the very beginning all the conceivable forces and means at their disposal, above all strategic nuclear means. (Major General V. Zemskov)[14]

If a nuclear war breaks out in Europe or elsewhere, it will necessarily and unavoidably become universal. (L. Brezhnev)[15]

The idea itself of introducing rules of the game and of artificial limitations 'by agreement' is based on an illusion and is without foundation. It is hard to imagine that nuclear war, if launched, could be held within the framework of the 'rules' and not grow into general war. (G. A. Arbatov, Director of the Institute of US and Canadian Studies, Moscow).[16]

None but utterly irresponsible individuals can claim that nuclear war can be fought under some rules established in advance whereby nuclear missiles will go off under a 'gentleman's agreement', only at specific targets without hitting the population in the process. (Marshal D. F. Ustinov, Minister of Defence, USSR)[17]

Could anyone in his right mind speak seriously of any limited nuclear war? It should be quite clear that the aggressor's actions will instantly and inevitably trigger a devastating counter-strike by the other side. (Marshal Ustinov)[18]

In fact, Soviet leaders regard the Countervailing Strategy as an attempt to legitimize nuclear war by making limited nuclear war appear feasible and more acceptable.[19] They believe it to be part of an attempt by the US to re-establish nuclear dominance and to use it to intimidate the Soviet Union in international diplomacy.[20]

Many western commentators have dismissed these Soviet statements as simple propaganda and have said that they do not necessarily reflect the beliefs of Soviet leadership. It was only to be expected, they argue, that the USSR would try to make US strategy appear unworkable in order to undermine the confidence of the United States's allies in its nuclear guarantee and to provide the Soviet Union with a diplomatic edge in any international crisis.

The possibility that these people are correct is remote. It is true that we have less detailed information on Soviet strategic policy than we have for the US. The USSR is a secretive society — indeed, the days of Soviet strategic inferiority and Khrushchev's policy of bluffing have had the effect of making secrecy a *part* of Soviet strategic doctrine. Nevertheless, there is quite enough information available to build up a coherent and convincing picture of Soviet nuclear policy. Besides a large number of openly available articles in papers and journals, there is a series of Soviet military text books which have been translated as part of the USAF's series *Soviet Military Thought*.[21] There are a number of other key texts, such as *Soviet Military Strategy* (prepared by a collective headed by Marshal V. D. Sokolovsky, one-time head of the Soviet general staff),[22] *The Offensive* by A. A. Sidorenko, the *Basic Principles of Operational Art and Tactics by* V. Ye. Savkin and others.[23] In addition, the issues of *Voyennaya mysl'* — *Military Thought* — between 1963 and 1973 are now available in translation.[24] This is a restricted or classified journal written for senior officers in the Soviet armed forces and is the official organ of the Soviet general staff. Since this journal and the texts named above were intended for Soviet officers and not for a western audience, they can be accepted as providing a reliable account of actual Soviet strategy.

Soviet military and political leaders agree that all-out nuclear war would be disastrous for both sides, and that it must therefore be avoided. They believe that starting a nuclear war is tantamount to suicide[25] and that nuclear war cannot rationally be used as an instrument of national policy.

In our time . . . there is no more dangerous an illusion than the idea that thermonuclear war can still serve as an instrument of politics, that it is possible to achieve political aims through the use of nuclear power, and at the same time survive; and that it is possible to find acceptable forms of nuclear war.[26]

Yet, although the Soviets regard Mutual Assured Destruction as a fact of present-day life, they reject the policy of minimum deterrence and the notion that it is sufficient to guarantee strategic stability.[27] Soviet history and doctrine has led them to prefer to rely on their own capabilities rather than on enemy rationality. They argue that since Capitalism and Communism have fundamental conflicts of interest, a nuclear attack on the USSR remains a possibility, either as a result of misperception or of escalation from a local war.

From the Soviet point of view, the most effective guarantee of national security 'is a force capable of decisively seizing the initiative at the brink of war and actually fighting towards specific political and military objectives'.[28] Such a posture, they argue, clearly demonstrates to an aggressor that it could not gain any advantage in such a war, and therefore is the strongest guarantee against misperceptions.[29] They believe that it is also the most responsible strategy to adopt should deterrence fail. As soon as the Soviet Union believes that it has incontrovertible evidence that the US (or China) has launched an attack, then Soviet strategy declares that it is rational to launch a massive damage-limiting nuclear strike. The objective is to disrupt the adversary's attack and reduce the damage that can be inflicted on Soviet territory.[30] It is therefore a 'counterforce' strategy in which facilities of military significance are targeted.

Once war has started, time is short. Quick action might catch bombers on the ground, military forces before they have dispersed, and missiles before they have been launched. 'The launching of the first massed nuclear attack acquires decisive importance for achieving the objectives of war.'[31] Soviet strategy constantly emphasizes the importance of surprise and decisive action. The emphasis is so overwhelming that Soviet strategy often appears to indicate a Launch on Warning (LOW) policy — where missiles are launched as soon as the early warning systems indicate an attack — if not one of anticipatory strikes. 'One of the decisive conditions for success in an operation is *the anticipating* of the enemy in making nuclear strikes, particularly against the enemy's nuclear missile weapons.'[32]

Mass nuclear missile strikes at the armed forces of the opponent and at his key economic and political objectives can determine the victory of one side and the defeat of the other at the very beginning of the war. Therefore, a correct estimate of the elements of supremacy over the opponent and the ability *to use them before the opponent does, are the key to victory in such a war.*[33]

Early warning systems and high levels of alert mean that Soviet missiles 'will have time during the flight of the missiles of the aggressor to leave their launchers and inflict a retaliatory strike against the enemy.'[34] Certainly, 'it is inconceivable that any Soviet leadership will countenance "absorbing" any initial strike'[35] as a MAD strategy would demand.

The initial Soviet missile attack would most emphatically not be restrained and restricted to a few selected categories of target. It would involve a massive attack on the 'aggressor's means of nuclear attack and a simultaneous mass destruction of vital installations comprising the enemy's military, political and economic might'.[36] The strategic missile forces 'are intended for the destruction of the enemy's means of nuclear attack, his large troop formations and military bases, the destruction of the aggressor's defence industry, the disorganisation of [his] state and military command and control, and of operations of his rear and transportation'.[37]

The power of nuclear weapons will be concentrated above all on destruction of the military-economic potential, defeat of the groupings of armed forces, and undermining of the morale of the population. Very important strategic missions of the armed forces can be the destruction of the largest industrial and administrative-political centres, power systems, and stocks of strategic raw materials and other materials; disorganisation of the system of state and military control; destruction of the main transportation centres; and destruction of the main groups of troops, especially of the means of nuclear attack.[38]

Command, control and communications centres would be high-priority targets since the adversary would have difficulty co-ordinating its forces without them. Population centres in themselves would be low-priority targets but they would not be avoided if they were near other targets. The finite size of the Soviet arsenal and targeting priorities obviously impose some constraints on the targets destroyed, as do military constraints such as refraining from destroying a bridge that might shortly prove useful. However, these are a far cry from the more artificial constraints required for 'controlled escalation'.

The initial nuclear exchange would have devastated the combatants' territories and much else besides, but Soviet strategy assumes that each side will retain some warfighting capability. So, 'in spite of the decisive role of nuclear weapons in battle, operation and war as a whole, ultimate victory can be achieved only as a result of using all branches of the armed forces'.[39] The Soviet 'combined arms' concept therefore involves all the other branches of the Soviet armed forces following close behind the initial nuclear strike to begin a second phase of the war which may 'drag out and require the protracted striving of all the forces of the Army and the Nation'.[40]

The main purpose of offensive combat is the complete destruction of a defending enemy, and will now be achieved first of all by strikes of nuclear weapons and firepower or other means of destruction, and by the growing [in force] swift actions of the motorized infantry and tank troops co-ordinating with infantry and parachute drops.[41]

The advance of these forces is to be swift, calling where necessary on further nuclear strikes against centres of resistance.[42] Much of the terrain on which they will be fighting will be a radioactive wasteland. 'Under the influence of nuclear strikes, the nature of the locale sharply changes.'[43] 'A new characteristic feature of the offensive in nuclear war is the conduct of combat actions under conditions of the presence of vast zones of contamination, destruction, fires and floods.'[44] To help overcome some of these obstacles and to speed the advance, air transport will be used.[45]

This is a strategy of total war and has little relation to the 'escalation control' and bargaining conducted during the war envisaged in the US's Countervailing Strategy and NATO's Flexible Response. Until about 1967 much of the Soviet military literature declared that any war, conventional or nuclear, between the Warsaw Pact and NATO would immediately and inevitably escalate into global nuclear war. Since that date, however, the USSR appears to accept the possibility that such a war might be confined to conventional weapons[46] — at least in its early phases. Warsaw Pact military exercises since 1967 have reflected this belief. In fact, the USSR has now made a pledge not to use nuclear weapons first in any conflict. Nonetheless, the Warsaw Pact exercises have invariably escalated into simulated nuclear exchanges[47] and the leadership obviously expects this to occur in reality.

The armed force deployments appropriate to conventional war are very different from those of the nuclear battlefield. The former requires concentrations of armed forces, whereas dispersal and rapid movement is vital for the latter in order to avoid presenting the opponent with convenient targets. Also it takes some time to change aircraft and artillery over from conventional to nuclear missions. The Soviet Union has chosen to adopt the force posture appropriate to nuclear war at some cost to its conventional capabilities, in order to avoid being surprised by a NATO first use of nuclear weapons.[48]

Some researchers into Soviet military strategy have detected some indication that it now also admits to some threshold distinction between theatre and intercontinental nuclear war.[49] However, as we have already mentioned earlier, the USSR categorically rejects the possibility of a war with the US in which targets within the Soviet Union are destroyed without retaliation against the American mainland. Therefore they would regard any missile or bomber attacking USSR territory as 'strategic' irrespective of where it was launched from or whether it was called 'theatre' or 'tactical'. So the threshold we are talking of here is between a nuclear war in the Middle East or in West and East Europe excluding Soviet territory, and a global war involving the territories of both superpowers.

The hint that Soviet strategists recognize the distinction between theatre and strategic war is, of course, no guarantee that they intend to fight according to it. It is also of no comfort to the UK since, as Lambeth says,

. . . within these three broad categories of conflict — theatre non-nuclear war, theatre nuclear war and central [strategic] nuclear war — the Soviets show no indication of endorsing any concept of restraint in the tempo and intensity of the conflict or any inclination to refrain from attacking certain target categories in the interests of collateral damage avoidance or intrawar coercive diplomacy.[50]

Soviet strategists regard the use of a nuclear weapon in a 'warning' shot, as envisaged in western strategy, as the 'height of strategic foolishness'.[51] It produces no tangible military advantage, and provides the adversary with every incentive to respond massively while it still has the strategic nuclear weapons to do so.

COMPARISON OF US AND SOVIET NUCLEAR STRATEGY

The leadership of both the US and the USSR, therefore, adopt the position that their nuclear 'deterrent' works best if it is able actually to be used to fight towards certain military and political objectives, should nuclear war break out. They believe that all-out nuclear war would be a catastrophe and that it must therefore be avoided. Nonetheless, nuclear war remains a possibility and each of the superpowers have adopted strategies which they expect to be most effective in limiting the damage inflicted upon themselves in the course of such a conflict. There is, however, a mismatch between their doctrines. The USSR regards the function of deterrence and coercive diplomacy to be confined to the period before nuclear war breaks out. Nuclear crises and brinkmanship are to be avoided unless one really has vital interests at stake and means business. Once nuclear war has started they plan to launch immediate, simultaneous, massive nuclear attacks in an attempt to destroy many of the opponent's military forces before they can be used, and to disrupt their attack. This would be followed up, where possible, by the remainder of their armed forces. It is a strategy of total war.

Although the word 'victory' appears in many of their writings, particularly the early ones, it is extremely doubtful whether there is any widespread belief in the meaningfulness of 'winning' such a war[52] or that the devastation of the Soviet Union could possibly be limited to acceptable levels. This pessimism would appear to apply to a war with China, let alone one with the US. The use of the word has been ascribed by many authors to the need to keep up morale in the armed forces and wider society, and to avoid any public suggestion that capitalist forces could possibly destroy the prospects for socialism. This interpretation is strengthened by the fact that the emphasis on the possibility of victory has been in inverse proportion to the size of the Soviet nuclear arsenal, and is now rarely heard.

Once nuclear war occurs, Soviet military objectives appear to be a desperate attempt to reduce the devastation inflicted on the USSR in the only way that appears to them to be feasible. They also aim to deny the aggressor any possible advantage even in the long term. In the knowledge that most of its own economic structures will be destroyed, the Soviet Union would aim to attack those targets which the enemy would require for long-term recovery. The Soviet strategy has a coherence and 'rationality' of its own given that it refuses to depend on any restraint by the adversary, preferring to rely only upon its own capabilities for its security once a nuclear war starts.

The US nuclear strategy is rather different, in that it envisages the possibility that all the adversaries in a nuclear war can be persuaded to exercise control and mutual restraint. It regards deterrence and coercive diplomacy to be applicable in the period after a nuclear war has begun as well as before. In the American strategy nuclear attacks are to be used in order to convey political messages to the opponent as well as to achieve military advantages. This involves preparing options to attack a wide range of 'target packages', each appropriate to a different level of war and political signal. Thus the Countervailing Strategy reduces emphasis on the significance of 'crossing the nuclear threshold'.

Of course, deft political signals and limited attacks are of no use if the adversary simply responds with massive attacks. Soviet warfighting strategy renders the US strategy unworkable in the reality of nuclear war. Further, the mismatch between the two strategies and the different historical and military traditions of the two countries will serve to make communication between them difficult both before and after war breaks out, fostering misperceptions and making crises more unstable.

Western strategists sometimes suggest that, once nuclear war actually broke out, self-interest would lead the Soviet leadership to abandon their own strategy and fight according to US rules. This is extremely doubtful.[53] Firstly, it is questionable whether the Soviet Union could fight a limited nuclear war even if it wanted to. Its military equipment, structure and training is appropriate to fighting according to its own strategy, not that of the US. For instance the Soviet command and communication system 'is weakest in the particular capabilities required for controlled escalation warfighting — such as timely intelligence, attack characterisation assessment, and targeting flexibility'.[54] Soviet targeting has taken no account of the need to reduce 'collateral damage' — that is, damage over and above that to the intended target — and cannot be much changed in the midst of war.

If the USSR opted to fight according to the controlled escalation strategy, it would be fighting according to rules for which it was ill-prepared and at a disadvantage and allowing the US to exploit all its strengths. It is an axiom of war that one does the opposite, and it is unlikely that the Soviet leadership would choose to ignore this principle.

Secondly, the stress of managing a crisis period means that this is the time when it is least likely that the leadership will abandon notions they are familiar with, and believe they understand, in favour of an alien and complex doctrine. Even if a few Soviet political leaders did have second thoughts, they would first have to persuade all of their colleagues. Then they would have to ensure that the massive military bureaucracy implemented the policy and acted with a restraint for which its staff had not been trained, and who would probably regard it as incomprehensible and contrary to all the 'common sense' built up over a lifetime in that military organization. Since leaders cannot possibly have a detailed knowledge of all the Soviet force capabilities, they would have to rely on military advice to assess the feasibility of a course of action. It is likely that all of these factors would prevent a rapid change of policy.

NUCLEAR WARFIGHTING WEAPONS

We finish this chapter with a brief description of a few of the most important characteristics of the superpowers' weapons systems.

Obviously, their nuclear strategies have little credibility unless they possess the military facilities with which to carry them out. This is not to say that the weapons were simply developed in response to the demands of strategy. History shows that things were more complex. It often appears to be closer to the truth to say that they were developed because of various technological, bureaucratic, political and industrial pressures (and commercial pressures in the case of the US); and then the nuclear strategy was adjusted in order to justify the weapons' capabilities.

The US and the USSR have strategies which call for weapons capable of destroying *counterforce* targets such as missile silos, airfields, weapons stores, command centres, troop concentrations and bridges, as well as *countervalue* targets such as cities or industrial and economic centres. We have already mentioned that the US targeting list (SIOP-6) identifies at least 40,000 such targets, and it is likely that the Soviet Union has listed a similar number. Obviously, many nuclear warheads are called for – the US and USSR have over 50,000 between them. Many of the targets are sufficiently close together that a single nuclear warhead can destroy several at once.

These enormous numbers demonstrate the great difference between counterforce strategies and those of minimum deterrence (MAD) where only a few hundred warheads are required to destroy most of the opponent's industry and cities. Once bridges, weapons stores, airfields, communications links and so on are targeted, the number of targets can be increased almost without limit.

Many of the 50,000 nuclear warheads are 'tactical' nuclear weapons intended for use against ships, submarines or planes; or they are carried on short and medium-ranged missiles and by bombers for use on a 'nuclear battlefield' in Europe or elsewhere. For instance, the US has about 6,000 tactical nuclear weapons in Europe and the USSR between 2,000 and 4,000. France and the UK add 1,000 or so to this figure.

The number of 'strategic' nuclear warheads carried on long-range missiles and bombers has also grown rapidly as illustrated in figure 2.1. The introduction of multiple independently-targetable re-entry vehicle (MIRV) technology by the US around 1970 and by the USSR a few years later led to a massive increase in the numbers of warheads during the 1970s. MIRV technology allows several warheads to be carried into space by a single missile, where they separate and proceed to their various targets. At the end of 1982, the US had about 9,700 such warheads and the USSR about 8,700.[55] As the pie charts in figure 2.2 show, the Soviet Union has most of these on land-based inter-continental ballistic missiles (ICBMs) while those of the US are more evenly spread amongst the three arms of its strategic nuclear forces – land, sea and bomber-based – the majority of them being on submarine-launched ballistic missiles (SLBMs).[56]

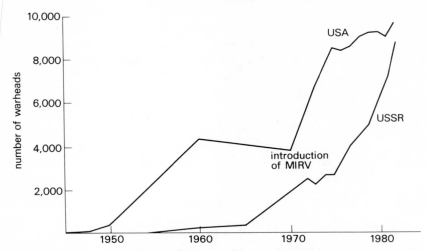

Figure 2.1   The nuclear arms race as revealed by the increase in numbers of strategic nuclear warheads in the arsenals of the US and USSR.

The explosive power or *yield* of a nuclear warhead is measured as an equivalent of tons of TNT. The units used are *kilotons* – thousands of tons – and *megatons* – millions of tons – of TNT equivalent. Most 'tactical' and 'strategic' nuclear warheads have yields of between 40 kilotons and 5 megatons.

Crude weapons with accuracies of half a mile or so are adequate to destroy countervalue targets such as cities or industrial centres, since they

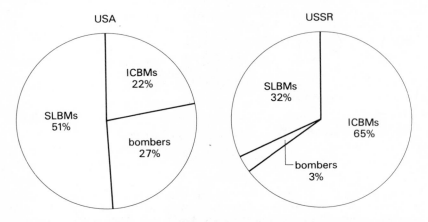

Figure 2.2   Proportions of the total numbers of strategic nuclear warheads carried on intercontinental ballistic missiles (ICBMs), submarine-launched ballistic missiles (SLBMs), and bombers in the US and Soviet arsenals.

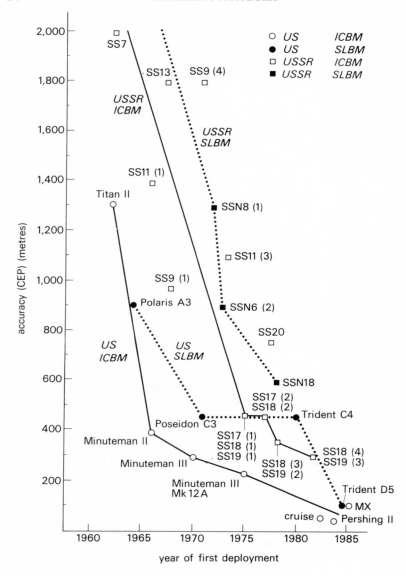

Figure 2.3 Trends in accuracy for US and Soviet land-based and submarine-launched missiles. Accuracy is measured in terms of 'circular error probable' (CEP): that is the radius of the circle around the target within which half of the missiles would be expected to land. Trends are shown separately for intercontinental ballistic missiles (ICBM) (solid lines), and submarine-launched ballistic missiles (SLBM) (dotted lines).

are unprotected ('soft') and cover a large area. However, much more sophisticated weapons are required to attack military (counterforce) targets, since these are usually smaller and less vulnerable to attack.

The capacity of a warhead to destroy a target by blast or ground shock depends primarily on its explosive power (yield) and on its accuracy or CEP. The CEP or 'circular error probable' is the radius of the circle around the target within which the warhead has a 50 per cent chance of landing. The accuracy is much the most important factor of the two — a twofold improvement in accuracy is equivalent to an eightfold increase in explosive yield.

Since the early 1960s missile accuracies have steadily increased to their present value of a few hundred metres (see figure 2.3). This accuracy is sufficient to give a single warhead a good chance of destroying 'soft' military targets such as bridges, aircraft on runways, radar installations and barracks. However, several such warheads would be required in order to be sure of destroying a 'hardened' target such as a missile silo or a protected command centre. Such a multiple attack would have the additional problem that incoming warheads might be incapacitated or deflected by the effects of earlier explosions (the so-called 'fratricide' effect). Uncertainties about the exact position of the submarine at the time of launching mean that submarine-launched ballistic missiles (SLBMs) have lower accuracies than the most modern land-based missile forces (ICBMs), and were therefore (in 1983) not a threat to the opponent's missiles.

Thus, in 1983, neither the US nor the USSR was in a position to launch a nuclear attack and destroy a high proportion of the other's command centres and nuclear forces. However, as chapter 3 shows, recent developments threatened to change this and created a much more dangerous, unstable, situation.

3
Possible Nuclear Wars

Until recently, the British government and civil defence organizations accepted that a nuclear attack by the USSR on the UK would be carried out along the lines described in the last chapter. For instance, a Home Office manual said in 1977:

The Home Defence assumption is that nuclear war poses the greatest threat. . . . Fear of retaliation would be a primary factor for consideration by any power about to engage in general war and it therefore seems likely that any initial nuclear strike would be a massive one aimed at making the country attacked totally ineffective militarily, politically and industrially.[1]

During 1982 and 1983, however, civil defence assumptions appear to have changed. Surprisingly, although Soviet strategy remains the same and the number of nuclear warheads available for use has continued to increase, smaller and smaller scales of attack are being presented as likely. In March 1983 the President, Chair and Vice-chair of the National Council for Civil Defence wrote in a letter to *The Times*: 'The greatest danger is therefore that of a conventional attack . . . Even the possibility of one or two bombs being dropped is also much more realistic than an "all-out" attack.'[2]

No reasons were given for this about turn. The arguments in the previous chapter that the USSR would not abandon its own strategy in favour of 'controlled escalation' continue to be valid. Further, in view of NATO's 'first use' policy, the notion that conventional attack poses the greatest threat to the UK seems to assume that NATO will abandon its own warfighting policy as well.

One does not have to appeal only to Soviet strategy, however, to show that any Soviet attack on the UK is almost certain to be massive and nuclear. Plans for limited nuclear attack are only likely to work in an imaginary world where wars are fought according to dictates of cost-benefit analysis and game theory, and remain completely under the control of rational well-informed leaders. In the real world things are different.

This chapter shows why nuclear wars between the major nuclear powers are very likely to escalate uncontrollably and how developments in nuclear weaponry are creating an incentive to launch a massive strike as soon as war appears inevitable, therefore increasing the chances of war by accident, fear or misjudgement. We argue that, although there is a small chance that the use of nuclear weapons at sea or in a battle in a region far from Europe may not escalate to involve Europe, any global or Europe-wide war will almost inevitably result in massive nuclear attacks on the UK.

The chapter begins by looking at the ways in which conventional wars, or periods of international tension, might escalate to involve the use of nuclear weapons. This is important because the prospects for limiting a nuclear war obviously depend upon the manner in which it started. If the nuclear threshold was crossed as a result of gross misjudgement, panic, or a breakdown of control, it is unrealistic to suppose that the war would, by a miracle, suddenly become controlled and 'rational'. This section also serves as a reminder of just how alarmingly possible nuclear war is.

NUCLEAR WAR BY ESCALATION

Every war or period of international tension involving nuclear weapons states or their allies threatens to escalate to nuclear war. Yet the superpowers' real or perceived conflicts of interest have set them on a collision course regularly in the past, and there is little prospect of this changing in the foreseeable future. Although the US and USSR have, naturally, been anxious to avoid direct military confrontations, there have been a number of occasions on which they have been prepared to risk global nuclear war in pursuit of shorter-term interests.

When the US and USSR get sucked into a war in the developing world fought between their respective allies or clients the situation becomes highly dangerous. Initially the superpowers could have very limited objectives: for instance, to defend their local interests, to stabilize the situation, or possibly simply to be seen to honour their commitments. But once a conflict starts, it can acquire a momentum of its own. Events would be driven by local factors and by the objectives of the clients, over which the superpowers could exert only imperfect control.

As the situation becomes more serious, each superpower is increasingly faced with two alternatives: either to back off and erode its international credibility (and possibly ruin the political careers of many in the leadership), or to back its ally to the hilt. As soon as neither of the adversaries feel able to back down, then they will be forced to try and 'manage' the crisis to advantage.

The threat to use nuclear weapons has become a standard part of the coercive diplomacy involved in handling such a crisis. Up to now their use has been either threatened, or formally considered, on about 30 different occasions by one or other nuclear power.[3] Some of these were the result of false alerts and others occurred while the US had a monopoly over strategic nuclear warheads. Alarmingly however, there remain several instances where nuclear war was deliberately threatened in spite of the risks of mutual annihilation.

Nuclear threats are intended to convey the message that the political leaders of the state believe that issues vital to its national interest are at stake, that they do not intend to back down and that the other side must therefore stop its provocations if nuclear war is to be avoided.

If the threat is believed, if each side maintains proper control over its forces and has an accurate perception of the situation, and if a compromise can be worked out that can satisfactorily accommodate both sides' perception of their national interest, then it is unlikely that the crisis will escalate. Indeed the nuclear threat may have encouraged the enemy to greater caution and to exert tighter control over their armed forces.

However, all these conditions are unlikely to be met. If they are not, then the nuclear threat intensifies the crisis and increases the pressures leading to nuclear war. Nuclear diplomacy is therefore an irrational business because it risks much more than could possibly be gained. The opponent is essentially being asked to act sanely in the face of a mad threat.

Two historical examples illustrate the processes we have outlined in this section so far — the 1962 Cuban missile crisis and the 1973 Arab-Israeli war.

The Cuban missile crisis began when the Soviet Union secretly began to install medium and long-range missiles in Cuba in the late summer of 1962. The US discovered the preparations and found out that the missiles, along with some nuclear-capable aircraft and other pieces of equipment, were being brought on ships to Cuba. After preparing a naval blockade, President Kennedy called for a Soviet withdrawal and announced that if they did not withdraw the US would prevent the ships reaching Cuba, and would take any military action necessary to ensure that all offensive weapons were removed from the island. For the following six days nuclear war seemed to be imminent. In the midst of the crisis, President Kennedy is quoted to have estimated the chance of nuclear war to be 'somewhere between one in three and evens'.[4] Robert Kennedy, the Attorney General, has reported of the President's call for a Soviet withdrawal 'it was a hope not an expectation. The expectation was a military confrontation.'[5] Khrushchev expressed similar opinions during and after the crisis.

Remarkably, however, neither side had a vital interest at stake. They both knew that the introduction of intercontinental ballistic missiles would mean that the USSR would soon be able to launch a missile attack on the USA. The installation of the Cuban missiles only brought that day forward by two or three years. In the US, Defense Secretary McNamara pointed this out early in the crisis. However, short-term political considerations meant that the point was quickly forgotten — soon both leaderships found themselves on a collision course from which neither found it easy to back down.

The crisis was resolved when Khrushchev backed down in the face of massive US strategic nuclear superiority and conventional superiority in the Caribbean region. We can only guess what might have happened if the balance of military capabilities had been more even and the crisis had been extended.

The October 1973 war between Israel, Egypt, and Syria was a war between clients of the superpowers.[6] The US provided Israel with arms and guaranteed its security while the USSR did the same for the Arab governments. On 5 October 1973 Egypt and Syria attacked Israel. However by 22 October the Arabs were on the retreat deep inside their own territory. After emergency negotiations between Kissinger and Brezhnev, the UN Security Council called for a ceasefire. The Israelis stopped fighting with the Syrians but chose to ignore the ceasefire in order to continue their offensive against the Egyptian Third Army. After ignoring a second ceasefire, by 24 October they had surrounded this army and were in a position to destroy it, leaving Egypt defenceless. Although the US had put pressure on its ally to observe the ceasefire, the Israelis obviously did not regard American concerns as decisive. The Soviet Union, however, suspected Kissinger of double-crossing them.

President Sadat called for a joint US-USSR peace-keeping force. This was immediately rejected by the US, but the USSR placed all seven of its airborne divisions (some 40,000 troops) on alert and prepared to intervene unilaterally to protect its ally. It sent a blunt letter to President Nixon to inform him of this. That night, around midnight, the Chairman of the Joint Chiefs of Staff, with Nixon's consent, moved all the US forces up by one level of readiness to defence readiness condition DEFCON III alert status. (There are five DEFCONS; DEFCON I indicates a state of war.)

After eight hours of official silence the US's team, led by Kissinger, sent a message to the Kremlin at 5.40 a.m. warning twice of the 'incalculable consequences' of any Soviet intervention. At noon the same day Kissinger gave a press conference in which he dwelt on the dangers of nuclear war and superpower confrontation. The crisis passed that afternoon as the Israelis stopped their military activities. An international peacekeeping force excluding both Soviet and American troops was organized.

Kissinger's nuclear threat was intended to raise the stakes sharply in the conflict so as to be sure that his 'message' got through.[7] It was not an indication that he thought that the issue warranted nuclear war. Since it did not result in nuclear war, and the crisis passed, it could be said that the tactic worked.

It was, however, a gamble. If the Israelis had continued to fight then the crisis could not have been resolved so quickly. The vulnerability of the Egyptian army meant that the USSR would have had to act quickly or not at all. If they had chosen to act, what would the US have done to back up its threat? Could Nixon, who was in the midst of the Watergate scandal, or the ageing Brezhnev, who might not have had more than a couple of hours' sleep over the past two days, have been relied upon to act sufficiently imaginatively and wisely to avoid war?

As it was, both sides unintentionally sent several 'messages' to the other which could have led to misunderstandings of each other's intentions. For instance the most visible action in the 'Middle East nuclear alert' was the shift of 50 to 60 B52 strategic nuclear bombers from Guam to the US — yet this was simply an unauthorized action by the US Department of Defense which took advantage of the crisis to relocate its forces in a way that had earlier been denied permission.[8]

US intelligence reported that a submarine carrying nuclear weapons had passed through the Bosphorus from the Black Sea to the Mediterranean.[9] Was this a routine mission? Was it an explicit threat to the US Mediterranean fleet or was it simply an error by the US intelligence? Nobody knows.

Similarly in the middle of the crisis, US intelligence 'lost' the Soviet airborne divisions that were on alert in the southern USSR.[10] At the time there was no way of telling whether this indicated that they were on their way to the Middle East or just that the intelligence services were inefficient. (The answer turned out to be the latter.) Such confusions are bound to arise in any crisis and will tend to result in an escalation since both sides are likely to make 'worst-case' assumptions.

CROSSING THE NUCLEAR THRESHOLD

There are several factors which tend to escalate wars, irrespective of the wishes of the political leadership. The control of the central command over the military forces tends to break down during a war, communications are often poor, and the information available is inadequate, leading to bad and possibly contradictory decisions. In addition, with the confusion and threat of sudden death, some battlefield commanders panic or ignore orders. These difficulties all contribute to the so-called 'fog of war' which tends to make conflicts unpredictable and unmanageable.

Another factor is the fine line between offensive and defensive military acts. For instance, US Secretary of Defense Weinberger remarked that, in order to deal with Soviet aircraft assigned to attack US shipping: 'Our preferred approach is to destroy enemy bombers before they can reach ASCM [air-to-surface cruise missile] launch range by *striking their bases* or destroying them in transit.'[11] [our emphasis] While this is probably the surest way to protect shipping, it is also escalatory, particularly since Soviet bombers are normally based inside the USSR. In general, actions that appear to the perpetrator to be a sensible defensive precaution are likely to be regarded as offensive and a signal of aggressive intentions by the victim, who will then respond accordingly.

This tendency to take the offensive is structured into the rules and guidelines, known as Standard Operating Procedures (SOPs), according to which armed forces are trained to carry out their operations. Since all modern military organizations are very large, complicated, and subject to several levels of command, it is impossible for the central political (or even military) command to be aware of, let alone control, all aspects of their SOPs and the manner in which operations are carried out. This means that, by authorizing a seemingly non-provocative operation, the political leadership may *unwittingly* have also ordered some act that is likely to trigger nuclear war.

The Cuban missile crisis illustrates this very clearly. During the crisis, President Kennedy and the Executive Committee went to enormous trouble to ensure that the naval blockade was implemented in a non-provocative manner. Soviet ships should not be harassed and the quarantine line was to be fixed so that the USSR had time to stand off and retreat without humiliation. However, the US Navy organized the blockage according to its traditional methods. Until well into the crisis, the Executive Committee was not aware that the US Navy was pursuing Soviet submarines in the North Atlantic in support of the blockade as part of its Standard Operating Procedures. In fact the Navy chose to conduct this operation very aggressively.[12]

Soviet submarines carrying cruise missiles with nuclear warheads were inevitably also a target.[13] Since these were the prime element of Soviet strategic forces at that time this was an extremely powerful coercive move. These submarines had to surface for some time before the cruise missiles could be launched. So the US Navy's action threatened the Soviet ability to launch a retaliatory nuclear attack on the US. This could have led them to conclude that the US intended war and to launch before it was too late. At the very least, it can be said that the US Navy's policy sent extremely strong signals to the Soviet Union which directly violated the spirit of the Executive Committee's intentions.

Another factor that makes war hard to control is the fact that conventional, tactical nuclear, and strategic nuclear military facilities are now so closely interrelated that it is difficult to disentangle them. Battlefield nuclear weapons are a standard part of the inventory of many NATO and Warsaw Pact divisions. Nuclear depth charges and nuclear-tipped missiles and torpedoes are routinely carried by many ships and submarines in Soviet and NATO navies. The aircraft that would be used for conventional war can also carry nuclear bombs. The same radar station would be used in conventional war as would provide strategic warning of a nuclear attack. Obviously, these connections make it harder to prevent a war from escalating to the nuclear level.

Even supposing that the political leadership is aware of all the implications of SOPs, and chooses to avoid all potentially escalatory actions (a most improbable situation), there are still great problems. For once actual military action begins, the armed forces become very impatient of what they see as piecemeal, 'half-hearted' measures. They will resist civilian interference within 'their sphere of competence' and, sometimes, may even choose to ignore orders. For instance, during the Vietnam War, General John Lavelle conducted 20 bombing raids into North Vietnam in 1971–72 without the knowledge or permission of American leaders.[14]

Doubtless, the military commanders would regard such actions as responsible attempts to protect their country's interests in spite of inadequate political leadership. When the US military chose to ignore President Kennedy's orders to halt reconnaissance flights by U2 spy planes over the USSR during the Cuban missile crisis, they probably thought that they were taking a sensible precaution by preparing for strategic nuclear war.[15] However, when one of these planes was shot down on Saturday, 27 October — the tensest day of the crisis — it could itself have triggered just such a war.

We now examine how these escalatory pressures apply to two examples of particular interest to the UK: a naval battle in the North Atlantic and a war in Europe.

NAVAL BATTLES AND THE NUCLEAR THRESHOLD

War at sea is particularly difficult to control. Invaluable surface vessels, such as aircraft-carriers or battleships, are sitting targets for modern guided missiles or torpedoes and their commanders will be anxious to destroy enemy submarines or aircraft as soon as they come into range. There will be a constant temptation to use nuclear weapons such as nuclear depth charges 'defensively' — to ensure that the enemy submarine, for instance, is destroyed immediately. Hunter-killer submarines and submarines carrying strategic missiles are in a similar situation. Their survival depends upon remaining hidden and on 'shooting first'.

Enemy hunter-killer submarines are, therefore, priority targets. Although tactical warfare is not the prime role of the strategic missile submarines, they do carry mines and torpedoes and so are also a direct threat. In any case many of the missile-carrying submarines are difficult to distinguish from hunter-killer submarines (for instance the Soviet Yankee II class). Consequently, as Vice Admiral Kaufman, Director of Command, Control and Communication for the US Navy, has said 'in a conventional war, all submarines are submarines. They are all fair game'.[16]

A few hunter-killer submarines on 'search and destroy' missions, each carrying about 20 torpedoes and able to remain submerged for weeks, can wreak considerable damage. They may well trigger nuclear war; either by sinking strategic missile-carrying submarines or by provoking the 'defensive' use of nuclear weapons.

To make matters worse, submarines would not be in contact with central command for long periods of time. Communications with submarines are tenuous at the best of times. During a war submarines would generally maintain radio silence and avoid extending an aerial for fear of revealing their position. In addition, some of the very low frequency transmission systems and the TACAMO ('take charge and move out') aircraft used for communicating with submarines may have been destroyed. Submarine commanders would therefore have to take decisions with little outside guidance. They might, for instance, continue their attacks unaware that a truce had been agreed, thus rekindling the conflict.

Any war between the Warsaw Pact and NATO is bound to involve naval battles in the North Atlantic. The following discussion of how such battles might escalate is largely inspired by a recent article by Posen.[17]

In order to protect the Shipping Lines of Communication (SLOC) across the Atlantic, which would be used to ship vital US reinforcements and supplies to Europe, NATO plans to 'bottle-up' Soviet hunter-killer submarines and the rest of the Soviet Northern fleet in the Barents Sea. Anti-submarine warfare (ASW) systems have been set up to detect and destroy Soviet submarines as they pass between Bear Island and the Northern Cape, and between Greenland, Iceland and Scotland (see figure 3.1). Aircraft and hunter-killer submarines would also be used to sink Soviet ships.

To reinforce this strategy and to put the Soviet navy on the defensive, the US Navy plans to attack the USSR's wartime 'sanctuary' in the Barents Sea itself. According to the US Deputy Chief of Naval Operations, hunter-killer submarines would be used in 'areas which are very contiguous with the home bases of an adversary.'[18] The US Chief of Naval Operations has said that the US Navy intends to 'seek out and destroy' Soviet naval forces, 'wherever they may be, even in Soviet coastal waters.'[19]

Such operations are bound to be regarded as extremely threatening by the USSR. About two-thirds of its strategic missile submarines are based in that region, protected by roughly two-thirds of the Soviet nuclear-powered hunter-killer submarines and the best quarter of their remaining fighting ships, diesel submarines and naval aviation forces.

In order to protect these forces, the USSR is almost certain to authorize the use of tactical nuclear weapons. They would probably suspect that the US intended to take advantage of the conventional phase of the war to attack or prepare to attack Soviet strategic missile forces. There would certainly be a strong incentive for the US to do so. The sonar receivers used to track enemy submarines are easily damaged by the use of nuclear weapons at sea and the communications systems on which ASW depends are extremely vulnerable to nuclear attack.

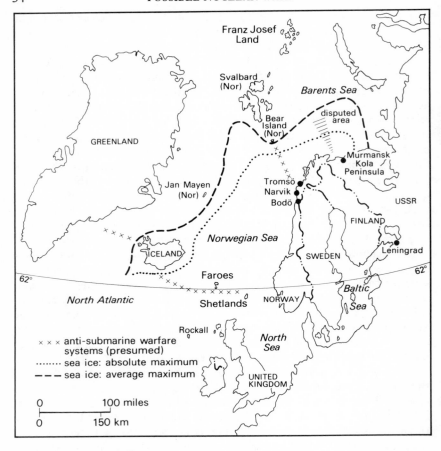

Figure 3.1 North Atlantic, Norwegian Sea and Barents Sea, showing presumed locations of anti-submarine warfare (ASW) detection systems.
Source: G. Kemp, 'The new strategic map', *Survival*, March/April 1977.

Attacks on Soviet naval command centres and aviation bases on the Kola Peninsula would probably be an integral part of the US Navy's operation. These may also destroy important early warning systems, reducing the Soviet Union's confidence that it could detect and respond to US nuclear attack and therefore encouraging it to place its missiles on 'hair-trigger' alert.

Even if the conflict does not immediately escalate to global nuclear war, the UK is bound to be subject to massive attack. Much of NATO's ASW and naval bases assigned to operations in the North Atlantic are based in Britain. In order to minimize the losses to Soviet aircraft, air defence bases and radar stations would also be attacked, along with other airfields to which aircraft may be dispersed. Naval bases such as Rosyth and the area around the Clyde would also be prime targets. Since the attack would necessarily be so large that total war with the UK was in any case inevitable, a wide range of other targets of significance to the British war effort would also be destroyed.

Further, because nuclear weapons would probably already have been used at sea, the strike on Britain is likely to be nuclear from the start. The early use of nuclear missiles would have the advantage, as far as the Soviet military was concerned, of avoiding the loss of many of the aircraft which might be required later. It would also be very much more effective.

WAR IN EUROPE

The equivalent of over $230,000 million is spent by the Warsaw Pact and NATO each year preparing for war in Europe.[20] Over 3,700,000 ground troops (plus a further nine million reserves), more than 42,000 battle tanks,[21] and, incredibly, about 12,000 nuclear warheads, are allocated specifically for such an eventuality.[22]

Clearly, political leaders of the NATO and Warsaw Pact countries believe war in Europe to be a real possibility. Since there are no active territorial disputes within Europe at present, it seems most likely, at least in the medium term, that such a war would be triggered by a conflict between the US and the USSR elsewhere in the world, which is then transferred in some way to Europe. Supposing war did break out, what might happen and how would the UK be affected?

It should be clear from chapter 2 that the Soviet Union is likely to opt for surprise attacks involving a massive use of force in an attempt to gain the initiative and achieve a quick victory. It has been said in the context of European war that 'if the victory is not achieved quickly the Russians believe no meaningful victory can be achieved at all.'[23]

Assuming that nuclear weapons are not used immediately, the Soviet divisions intend to concentrate their forces at a few points on the NATO front line along the East-West German border in a *blitzkrieg* attack. They hope to break through at two or three points so that powerful armoured columns can then race along a path of least resistance deep into West Germany in order to cut off or destroy communications, supply networks, and key command centres. They would be supported in this task by large numbers of fighter and bomber aircraft.

Since the war is likely to escalate suddenly into nuclear war at any time, the USSR plans to keep its forces dispersed until just before the offensive, in order to avoid presenting easy targets. It relies on delicate timing and rapid manoeuvres to concentrate its forces at the right time and place.[24]

Many experts are sceptical as to whether these complex Soviet plans are practicable. If it turned out that they were, the offensive might succeed. (Although many experts believe NATO's present defence to be sufficient to prevent any breakthroughs.)[25] The chances of Soviet forces penetrating deep into West Germany have been increased by the US Army's recently adopted 'Air Land Battle' strategy[26] which means, if it is adopted by the other NATO armies in Germany,[27] that the Soviet advance would not be met head-on at the East-West German border. Instead, it would initially meet little resistance as NATO forces concentrate on launching violent offensives upon critical vulnerable points as they become apparent. These may well be deep inside Eastern Europe.

Thus the battlefield will rapidly cover most of East and West Germany. As soon as the conflict extends beyond the immediate border area there will be no clear battle lines. Centres of resistance will be bypassed so that rapid ground and air attacks have a chance to destroy the other's aircraft, troop and tank concentrations, and stockpiles of arms and supplies before they can be dispersed or used.

The incentives for early strikes deep into enemy territory are enormous. For instance, most of NATO's arms and communication reserves are stockpiled at a few huge sites. (It is reported that half of the US army's 'theatre' ammunition reserves are stored at a single location.)[28] Most of NATO's 6,000 or so tactical nuclear weapons are stored at about 50 sites that would be well known to the Warsaw Pact.[29] Soviet nuclear short-range shells and missiles would probably also be concentrated at a few sites initially.

Since the early use of nuclear weapons can bring enormous military advantages there would be a strong temptation to use them, particularly since they might otherwise be overrun or destroyed by enemy forces. For instance some of NATO's nuclear weapons sites are only 60–100 miles away from the East German border. Soviet sites are also likely to be in danger of being overrun.

In addition, battlefield commanders will wish to use nuclear shells and missiles 'defensively' when their position is becoming impossible, or 'offensively' as the opportunity arises. It is almost certain that they will have been provided with the electronic codes required to release the weapons for use very early on in the conflict. Otherwise they may not have the opportunity to use them at all, since the authorization procedure takes about 24 hours.[30]

These factors, together with NATO's 'first use' policy, almost guarantee that the war will have 'gone nuclear' before the battle zone has extended far beyond Germany. Since it is inconceivable that medium-ranged aircraft or missiles such as NATO's Pershing 1A (range 700 km) and the Warsaw Pact's 'Scud' (range 300 km) and SS12 (range 900 km) will be deliberately excluded from the conflict, the war will extend rapidly to the whole 'European level'.

Many of NATO's fighter planes and bombers involved in the war would be operating from bases in Britain. American reinforcements would arrive through ports in the UK. Many key naval bases and command centres are located here. Massive nuclear attacks on these targets are therefore inevitable. Air defence facilities and bases for nuclear forces would be destroyed. Garrisons, fuel depots, energy supply industries, and other targets will be included, in order to prevent British reinforcements arriving, and to undermine the UK war effort. Military logic ensures the UK is attacked once a major European war starts.

Once nuclear weapons have been used, communications links and command centres, which may already have been damaged, are likely to collapse. Even if they are spared by the blast effect and the fires, electronic equipment and radio or radar facilities will be damaged by the electro-magnetic pulse (EMP). EMP is a very short and intense pulse of radio waves which is produced when a nuclear weapon detonates either many miles above the ground or at ground level. It produces damaging surges of current in all electrical conductors exposed to it.

This breakdown of command and control once a nuclear war has started means that, even in the unlikely event that the leaders of the Warsaw Pact decided before the war that the UK should be left unscathed, Britain would be attacked anyway. In the 'fog of war', with the enormous rate at which each side's forces would be destroyed, commanders are likely to ignore orders such as these, and attack all enemy bases which immediately threaten their survival.

Attacks on European Russia appear inevitable for the same reasons. Most of the Warsaw Pact's aircraft will operate from the USSR and reinforcements and supplies will come from there. US F111 nuclear bombers and other planes based in the UK and elsewhere can reach the Soviet Union. If they are installed, the Pershing II and Cruise missiles will also have sufficient range, though it is possible that these would be destroyed in pre-emptive attacks or used against targets in East Europe. British and French 'independent' missile forces might also be launched against the USSR.

Thus, a European war serious enough to extend significantly beyond the East-West German border will almost certainly escalate to strategic nuclear war, involving attacks on the territories of the superpowers. Even if the war is confined to Europe, the UK will inevitably be subjected to massive nuclear attack. The same conclusion has been reached by many distinguished experts, such as Lord Mountbatten,[31] Field Marshal Lord Carver,[32] three other Chiefs of UK defence staff[33] and the members of the authoritative Palme Commission.[34]

THE SPREAD OF NUCLEAR WEAPONS

The number of countries possessing nuclear weapons is steadily increasing. In addition to the five major nuclear weapon states – USA, USSR, UK, France and China – India has exploded a nuclear weapon and South Africa and Israel are widely thought to possess some. Pakistan, Argentina, Brazil, Libya, Iraq and several other countries are thought to be close to developing or acquiring such weapons.[35] Several of these states are in unstable regions of the world and may well become involved in a war in which their very existence is threatened. In this situation, they may well use their nuclear weapons.

Nuclear proliferation may itself provoke wars. States may feel forced to conduct pre-emptive attacks on their neighbours to prevent them from acquiring nuclear warheads. For example in 1981 Israel attacked the 'Osiraq' research reactor in order to slow down what it suspected to be Iraq's nuclear weapons programme. In the 1940s and 1950s some US military officials and others recommended such preventative strikes against the USSR and China.

It is not obvious that the use of nuclear weapons by South Africa or in a war between Brazil and Argentina, say, will necessarily result in a global war in which the UK is destroyed. However, in a region where NATO and Warsaw Pact forces are deployed or where the US and the USSR both have a strong interest, the risks are obviously extremely great. For instance, an Arab-Israeli war in 1990 might find each side with 30 to 40 Hiroshima-size nuclear warheads.[36] Each superpower would then have to intervene decisively, possibly with its own nuclear weapons, in order to protect its client.

If the US or USSR or their forces were attacked with nuclear weapons by a third nuclear weapons state, it might not be immediately clear who was responsible. In a period of international tension, this might trigger global war in which the UK would be destroyed.

THE INCENTIVE TO STRIKE FIRST

As the US and Soviet nuclear arsenals grow bigger and their missiles become more accurate, each side is able to destroy a larger proportion of the other's nuclear forces on the ground in a first strike. This creates a powerful incentive to strike first in any war.

Recent developments threaten to create a situation in which each superpower fears that the other can launch a successful 'disarming' first strike, in which a sufficiently high proportion of the victim's nuclear forces are destroyed that it cannot retaliate effectively. In this case, each state is likely to adopt policies which ensure that its missiles will not be caught in their silos. If this happens, the chances of nuclear war starting by accident or misjudgement will increase alarmingly. What are the developments which create these dangers?

The introduction of MIRV

During the 1960s, each missile could only attack a single target. MIRV technology was introduced by the US around 1970, followed about five years later by the USSR. This allows a single missile to carry several warheads into space, where they separate and proceed to different targets. A glance at figure 2.1 (p. 23) shows the effect this had on the arms race. The number of strategic warheads increased sharply as missiles carrying a single warhead were replaced with newer MIRVed ones. However, besides this quantitative effect, MIRV also shifted the advantage, in military terms, from the defender to the aggressor.

Consider the situation without MIRVed missiles. Suppose the US and the USSR both had 1,000 ICBMs (in reality the US has 1,053 and the USSR 1,398), each carrying a warhead with a 50 per cent chance of destroying an enemy missile in its silo. If one side launched all its missiles in a first strike, it would succeed in destroying about 500 of its opponent's missiles. This would leave the victim with a missile advantage in the aftermath, since it would have about 500 missiles while the aggressor would be left with none.

If each missile is MIRVed and carries six warheads, the situation is different. Then an aggressor could launch 800 missiles, with either 4 or 5 warheads targeted on each enemy silo. The victim would be left with only about 40 missiles carrying 240 warheads (still a formidable force), and the aggressor would have 200 missiles with 1,200 warheads; an advantage of 5:1.

This theoretical calculation, of course, takes no account of the existence of other targets or of the immense death and destruction both sides would in any case suffer. It is only presented to illustrate the destabilizing effect that MIRV technology has had.

Accuracy

As explained in chapter 2, the probability that a warhead will destroy a 'hardened' target such as a missile silo or underground command centre depends much more sensitively on its accuracy than on its yield (explosive power).

The accuracy of nuclear missiles has improved steadily over the last 20 years (see figure 2.3, p. 24). The most accurate ICBMs in the Soviet arsenal (i.e. the SS18s and SS19s) now have a 50 per cent chance of detonating within 300–450 metres of their intended targets (that is, a CEP of 300–450 metres). The Minuteman III missiles deployed in the US have a CEP of 200–300 metres. This means that a single warhead from any of these missiles has a good chance of destroying 'soft' targets such as bridges, radar installations and aircraft on runways. However, over eight of them from different missiles would be required to be reasonably certain of demolishing a 'hardened' target. At present neither superpower has, even theoretically, a good chance of completely disarming the other's land-based forces in a first strike, even after taking the effects of MIRV into account.[37]

The new generation of missiles which the US plans to install during the 1980s will change this situation dramatically. These missiles — the cruise missile, Pershing II, MX and Trident D5 — are expected to have accuracies of 40 to 100 metres (table 3.1). This makes it virtually certain (provided the missile works reliably) that a single warhead from any of these systems will destroy the 'hard' target it is directed towards.

Thousands of warheads are due to be deployed on these new missiles. If the plans go ahead, the USSR's land-based nuclear forces, together with its major command and communication centres, will (theoretically) be vulnerable to a US 'disarming' first strike by about 1990. If the arms race continues, the USSR can be expected to produce its own missiles with similar accuracies a few years later, making US land-based missile forces vulnerable in return.

Anti-submarine warfare

There is, of course, no advantage to be gained by destroying all of the adversary's land-based forces if thousands of nuclear warheads survive intact on submarines. At the end of 1982 the US had over 4,900 warheads on submarine-launched ballistic missiles (SLBMs) and the USSR had over 2,700. Since submerged submarines are mobile and difficult to locate, the SLBM forces have been regarded as invulnerable and, therefore, as a stabilizing factor.

However, the security of these forces is being eroded by enormous US investment in anti-submarine warfare. It has been reported that the US has now, or soon will have, the capability to detect and track continuously all of the 10 or 12 Soviet submarines carrying nuclear missiles which are at sea at any one time.[38] The USSR can no longer be entirely confident that its SLBM force can survive a US first strike.

Soviet inferiority in areas such as computer technology, and its enormous geographical disadvantages — Soviet submarines have to pass through a few narrow passages controlled by the US Navy whereas the US has open access to the Pacific and Atlantic — mean that the USSR presents no comparable threat to US ballistic missile-carrying submarines.

Table 3.1 US nuclear missiles planned for the 1980s

Type of missile	Number of missiles	Warheads/ missile	Total warheads planned	Yield/ warhead (kilotons)	Range (kilometres)	Accuracy (CEP) (metres)	Probability[a] that a single warhead from the missile would destroy a silo hardened to withstand 1,000 psi
Missile Experimental (MX)	100	10	1,000	475	13,000	50–100	99.9–100
Trident D5	up to 360	8 8 14	~3,600	475 335 150	12,000	50–100	99.9–100 99.7–100 99.7–100
Air-launched cruise missile (ALCM)	~4,300	1	~4,300	200	2,500	50	100
Sea-launched cruise missile (SLCM)	~600[b]	1	~600	200	2,500	50	100
Ground-launched cruise missile (GLCM)	464	1	464	200	2,500	50	100
Pershing II	~250[c]	1	~250	5–200	1,600–1,900	40	99.99–100

[a] Assuming the missile works reliably
[b] Plus thousands armed with conventional warheads
[c] At least 108 planned for deployment in West Germany. Sites for the remainder are not known

The vulnerability of command, control, communications and information systems

Command, control, communications and information systems (C^3I) consist of all those installations which enable decisions to be made on the basis of up-to-date information and then to be communicated quickly to the appropriate military forces. It is made up of a network of command centres, radio and radar installations, surveillance and communications satellites, ASW sonar arrays, and a large number of similar facilities.

Unless the C^3I system is effective, any military operation is likely to fail. If it works well, it allows the armed forces to be co-ordinated and directed so that their overall effectiveness is increased by two to four times (the so-called 'force multiplier effect'). For instance in World War II the RAF were able to defeat a much larger German airforce in the Battle of Britain by concentrating their forces swiftly where they were most telling. In a more modern context, if missiles can be retargeted quickly on the basis of up-to-date information, they will not be wasted on empty missile silos or abandoned command centres. When the US global positioning system, consisting of 18 NAVSTAR satellites, becomes operational after 1986 it will greatly increase the capabilities of aircraft, combat troops, ships and other users by enabling them to find their position to within 16 m and velocity to within a centimetre per second without referring to the ground or the stars.[39]

The importance of C^3I means that there is a powerful incentive to try to destroy the other side's systems as soon as war starts in order to break up and disorientate their attack and, possibly, temporarily prevent orders to launch from reaching ICBM launch-control centres and strategic missile submarines.

C^3I systems are inherently vulnerable to attack.[40] Most can easily be destroyed by blast, they are vulnerable to jamming, disturbance and to the effects of EMP. Only a few high-altitude bursts of nuclear weapons will disrupt high frequency communications and generate EMP over millions of square miles, damaging and destroying electrical equipment and radio and radar facilities. It would require only 50–100 warheads to destroy the US's national command system or the communication links between the National Command Authorities and US strategic forces. Since both the superpowers are investing enormous resources in anti-satellite weapons, satellites are also becoming vulnerable.

This vulnerability means that there is a strong temptation for each side to use as much of its forces as possible before the enemy has a chance to destroy its own C^3I facilities.

LAUNCH-ON-WARNING

The factors explained above combine to reduce substantially each superpower's confidence (particularly the USSR's) that it can absorb a first strike and still be able to retaliate. They encourage a massive nuclear attack early in a war since the costs of holding back and allowing the enemy the chance to strike first are so great.

The result will be that at some stage one or both of the superpowers will adopt a launch-on-warning (LOW) policy. We have noted in chapter 2 that the USSR, at least, has already considered this option. LOW would involve preparing to launch nuclear missiles as soon as radar and early warning satellites indicated that the opponent had initiated an attack. Since ICBMs only take 20–30 minutes to reach their targets, and SLBMs might take as little as 15 minutes, the nuclear forces would have to be placed on a hair-trigger alert. If the Pershing II missiles are deployed in Germany (and possibly in Alaska),[41] warning will be even shorter. They will be able to destroy targets deep inside the USSR about 10 minutes after launching.

For a LOW policy to work, a series of steps have to be taken in the few minutes available. The warning has to be checked and then the political leaders have to be found and informed. They have to be convinced that an attack is under way, and then the orders to launch have to be transmitted to the launch control centres. The launch procedure then has to be completed and the missiles launched.

The chances of all these steps being completed in time are slim. In the US, for instance, the launch procedures themselves take 15 minutes.[42] This will lead to increasing automation in order to reduce human involvement to a minimum. The urgency means that the political leaders will have little time to think or to make independent checks. They will have little choice other than to act in the way indicated by the computer. The shortage of time also provides a strong incentive to strike pre-emptively as soon as war seems inevitable. Thus the trend towards the adoption of launch-on-warning policies increases the danger of war by misjudgement or accident.

The existence of modern nuclear missiles might even generate the crisis in which they are ultimately used. An accident or false intelligence report might lead one superpower to suspect the other was preparing to attack, and so place its own forces on alert. The other, noting this move, might then take similar actions, thus creating a positive feedback loop which might lead to nuclear war.

NUCLEAR ACCIDENTS

There is a real danger that a technical malfunction or human error will trigger a nuclear war. The last comprehensive review of probable accidents and near misses involving nuclear weapons (in 1977) listed 113 accidents.[43] Since then there have been several more. We list a few examples below.

In November 1979, a 'war game' tape was accidentally inserted into the North American Air Defense (NORAD) computer, indicating a 'launch' of Soviet SLBMs and ICBMs. B52 bombers prepared for take-off and preliminary launch procedures were started for the ICBMs. The mistake was discovered after six minutes. In June 1980, another false warning occurred, which was later traced to an integrated circuit failure in a computer. False alerts occur at NORAD on an average three times a year.[44]

In September 1980 a US Titan II missile was blown out of its silo by an explosion caused by a technician dropping a wrench socket on a fuel tank. The explosion blew off the silo's 740 ton door and sent the re-entry vehicle with its nine megaton warhead 600 feet into the air. In the same year there were 20 other 'mishaps' at the Titan missile silos.[45]

In the US, about 5,000 people are transferred from nuclear weapons duty each year (about 4 per cent of the total), mostly because of irresponsible behaviour, drug abuse or psychiatric problems.[46] In Germany, US soldiers have sometimes been 'high' on drugs when connecting two pieces together to make nuclear missiles operational.[47] A man has been accused of 'going berserk with a loaded carbine' while assigned to nuclear weapons duty.[48] LSD, cocaine and amphetamines have been traded amongst US servicemen in the US Holy Loch Poseidon submarine base in Scotland.[49]

A member of a Minuteman missile launch crew has reported that another crew 'played a practical joke by recording a launch message and playing it when their friends came to relieve them'.[50]

On 18 October 1975, a US early warning satellite was 'dazzled' over Siberia. This was interpreted as being due to Soviet jamming, using an infrared laser beam. During a crisis this could have triggered war. It later became clear that the cause was heat from an accidental fire in a Siberian gas pipeline.[51]

These examples all concern US forces. This is a reflection of the US's greater openness, not of their being particularly prone to accidents. Indeed, since secrecy usually breeds carelessness and inefficiency, a greater risk of error or malfunction might be expected in the nuclear weapons forces of the UK, France, China and the USSR.

Most accidents are of course minor. Many others could only result in the release of radioactive materials, which would be serious but not catastrophic. However that may still leave a few accidents each year which might be sufficient to start a nuclear war. A number of safeguards have been incorporated into the management of nuclear weapons in an attempt to prevent such an eventuality. However these cannot be foolproof, particularly during a crisis when both sides are jittery. If the US or the USSR ever adopt a launch-on-warning policy, the danger of accidental nuclear war will become acute.

LIMITED NUCLEAR WAR

What then are the prospects for controlling a nuclear war once it has begun, and for finishing it before a high proportion of the available nuclear weapons have been used? We have already argued that any war between NATO and the Warsaw Pact in Europe or in the North Atlantic and Barents Sea which went beyond a few skirmishes would almost inevitably escalate to involve massive nuclear attacks on targets of military significance in the UK. In this case, then, the chances of subsequently limiting the war are of little practical importance to Britons and other Europeans, although people outside Europe still have an obvious vital interest.

Clearly, if the nuclear war started because one superpower believed (either correctly or mistakenly) that the other had launched, or was about to launch, a massive nuclear attack against it, the chances of limited war are slim. The resulting 'damage limiting' or 'disarming' strikes would be aimed at destroying as much of the opponent's nuclear forces, command centres, and communication and information-gathering facilities as possible before they could be used. Conventional military forces and the industries which support them would probably also be targets in order to prevent the forces from being used to invade in the aftermath. Given the immense devastation that would result from these attacks, both sides would know that the eventual 'victor' would be the state that recovered most rapidly in the years after the war. Therefore, each would target the opponent's key industries, administrative centres and those other facilities which would aid recovery. In this case, then, the war would be global and unlimited from the very beginning. 'Escalation control' can therefore only possibly apply to nuclear wars which are initially confined to some geographically limited area such as Europe or the Middle East.

However, since the leaders of all major nuclear powers are vividly aware of the dangers of a nuclear war, the fact that one has nevertheless started must surely indicate that control has already been lost. Factors we have already discussed, such as the 'fog of war' and the fine line between defensive and offensive military operations, or the actions of a third, minor, nuclear weapons state, could all have led to the escalation. Certainly the widespread use of nuclear weapons will have led to a breakdown of communications and control within the 'theatre' of war. If this 'theatre' was adjacent to the USSR (for instance the Barents Sea, Europe, the Near and Middle East, and SW Asia) then installations within the Soviet Union might also already have been subjected to nuclear attacks, making retaliation against US territory a virtual certainty. It is in this context that the military and political leaders must attempt to limit subsequent escalation. Will they be in any condition to cope with the complexities and stress involved?

From the beginning of the crisis, they will have been 'overwhelmed by floods of reports compounded of conjecture, knowledge, hope and worry', as Henry Kissinger, US Secretary of State during the 1973 Middle East crisis, has put it.[52] Much of the information will be partial, ambiguous or will appear to conflict with other pieces of intelligence.

Probably the decision makers will only partially understand their own country's war plans. In that case they will either make naive judgements or tend to rely on the advice of various 'experts' who may well be influenced by their own differing political or institutional interest. Sometimes the leaders themselves may be just as concerned with their political future as with avoiding war.

The threat of nuclear war will have transformed each minor decision into a potentially momentous one requiring the attention of one or several top leaders. These people will then have to supervise the implementation of the decision to ensure that it is carried out correctly and that no unknown standard operating procedure leads to an inadvertent escalation of the crisis.

Few people can withstand such stress for long. In the face of all this pressure, complexity and confusion, leaders will tend to rely on past prejudices and on interpretations formed early on in the crisis to guide their decisions. They are likely to neglect evidence which contradicts these interpretations and emphasize out of all proportion evidence that supports them. This tendency will increase as the crisis continues and as the leaders, generally elderly people, become exhausted and short of sleep. Their understanding of the situation could become less and less accurate at the same time as they become more and more committed to a particular analysis of events. Once nuclear war begins all these confusions and stresses intensify enormously. Each side knows that the other might launch a massive strike at any moment and that any accident or false move is likely to prove fatal. These are hardly the conditions under which sophisticated nuclear diplomacy is likely to work.

According to Western strategists, one of the earliest phases of a nuclear war might involve one side launching a 'warning shot' of one or more nuclear weapons for political effect. This could occur, for instance, if the leaders of one side decided that their opponent had coolly and deliberately provoked the crisis, in the belief that they would not risk 'strategic' nuclear war. The 'warning shot' is intended to convince the enemy that they have miscalculated and had better back down quickly.

Chapter 2 indicates that the Soviet Union regards such actions as foolish in the extreme: they signal the onset of strategic war while leaving the opponent the chance to launch the crucial first strike. It is however conceivable that as a crisis escalates, the stresses and misperceptions might be such that a 'warning shot' is launched. If that happens, further escalation seems almost inevitable. If it had proved impossible to end the war before such an action, a 'warning shot' would be likely to make it even harder to achieve agreement.

Wherever the warning shot was targeted, the prospect would be grim. If the warheads were detonated at sea they would hardly be a sign of much resolve unless they were near a battle zone, in which case they would probably trigger 'theatre' or 'strategic' nuclear war. If they exploded on land outside the USSR or US, then the original conflict would either be exacerbated or have been spread to another region of the world, all to no military advantage. A detonation high in the atmosphere over the adversary's territory would produce EMP over vast areas, damaging communications or early warning systems. It would probably be interpreted as the prelude to a disarming first strike and therefore trigger all-out war. In none of these cases, therefore, are the prospects of peace greater after the 'warning'.

On the other hand, the warning shot could be aimed at a target inside the US or the USSR. If so it would, at the very least, be regarded as an aggressive act requiring retaliation. A nuclear warhead exploding near a city would kill or injure several hundred thousand people by the effects of blast or fire. If it detonated near the ground, radioactive fallout would cover thousands of square kilometres down wind, resulting in a similar number of casualties. This would create pressure for revenge and retaliation. If the warning shot landed far from any town or industry it would not generate the same anger. However, by the same token, it would be a much less impressive signal of resolve. The leaders of the country subjected to the 'warning' might still decide that their opponents were bluffing and would be likely to back down rather than engage in actual nuclear war.

Neither the US or the USSR will agree to end a war in which its own territory has been attacked with nuclear weapons while the other's remains unscathed. The least that would result from such 'warning shots' is that they would be returned with interest, while the remainder of the forces would be placed on a LOW posture. Nothing would have been resolved.

We now go on to the possibility of fighting a carefully controlled strategic nuclear war, and of ending it before each side's cities and industries are obliterated.

All of the factors discussed so far in this chapter which push a conflict towards uncontrolled total war apply with extra force to limited strategic war. We have already noted that control must already have been lost for the conflict to have reached this stage, and 'theatre' nuclear war is probably already raging uncontrollably in one or more region of the world.

Although it is easy to speak, theoretically, of avoiding 'collateral' (unintentional) damage to cities and industry, in practice it would hardly be possible. As Ball points out in his highly regarded paper on the subject,

Soviet strategic forces are ill-based from the point of view of minimizing collateral damage. About half of the 26 Soviet ICBM fields are located west of the Ural Mountains and several of them are near some of the most densely populated areas of the USSR . . . . Prevailing wind patterns at any time of the year ensure that local fallout (the most lethal) would cover areas with the highest population density.[53]

Attacks on the Soviet ICBM forces would result directly in the deaths of between 6 and 28 million people.[54] The two strategic nuclear submarine bases at Vladivostock and Murmansk are located within urban areas. Similarly, millions of Americans would be killed or injured by the effects of radioactive fallout if the US ICBM force was attacked, and many important US aircraft and naval bases are close to population centres.

Thus 'precision' attacks against military targets will almost certainly result in millions of deaths and the long-term dislocation of the economy. To make matters worse, about 20 per cent of the nuclear missiles are likely to malfunction, with many of them detonating far from their intended targets.

The inherent vulnerability of the vital command, control, communication and information (C^3I) system was noted earlier. Even if they were not deliberately attacked, much of the system would be incapacitated by EMP and ionospheric disturbances and also by blast, heat and radiation from attacks on nearby targets.

Once the C^3I network is seriously damaged, controlled nuclear war becomes unworkable. Co-ordination and control breaks down and the information required for early warning, retargeting and for assessing damage is no longer available. In that situation there is little alternative other than to abandon 'controlled escalation' and to order most of the remaining forces to launch as soon as the message reaches them.

Even supposing the escalation could be controlled, this is of little use unless an agreement to end the war can be reached before everything is destroyed. However, it is hard to see how negotiations can hope to succeed in the middle of strategic nuclear war. The leaders of one or both sides may not survive, and if they do, they may not be able to contact each other or even their own forces.

If negotiations do start, neither side will accept defeat while it still has enough nuclear force to obliterate the other. So the objective must be to agree to a truce where both sides finish with approximately equal chances of recovery. However, neither side would have adequate information with which to compare the relative seriousness of the damage each had suffered. In any case the 'balance of devastation' could be dramatically different every half hour or so after each nuclear attack. Since the destruction in its own country would always be so much more apparent, each side would tend to refuse a truce until the 'balance was restored' after its own next attack. Even if a settlement was agreed, it is unlikely that this could be communicated to submarine and field commanders quickly enough to prevent further attacks which would trigger war once again.

CONCLUSION

Our conclusions from this chapter are clear. Wars and conflicts of interest which might bring the US and the USSR into a confrontation are bound to occur frequently. There are a number of factors which tend to escalate any crisis or war. As the number of nuclear weapons states increase and as tactical nuclear weapons are more widely deployed in the armed forces of the NATO and Warsaw Pact countries, the probability of 'crossing the nuclear threshold' grows.

Counterforce strategic nuclear weaponry has created an incentive to strike first rather than second in order to destroy a substantial proportion of the opponent's nuclear forces before they can be used. Today the victim can still be sure to be left with the capability to obliterate the aggressor in retaliation. However, once the next generation of missiles are installed this may no longer appear to be the case. This will increase the chances of nuclear war being triggered by accident or misjudgement and will make crises even harder to control than they are at present.

Any major war between NATO and the Warsaw Pact in Europe is almost bound by the logic of the conflict to become nuclear and to involve massive nuclear attacks on the UK. It will probably lead to global war.

If nuclear weapons are used far from Europe there is a chance that the conflict may be contained and the UK spared from any attacks. However, if the conflict spreads or triggers global war the UK would, once again, be bound to be subjected to early and massive nuclear attack.

A few nuclear weapons launched as a 'warning shot' will resolve nothing and will almost certainly be followed by larger-scale nuclear attacks. Scenarios in which the war ends after Birmingham, for instance, has been swapped for Minsk are based simply on wishful thinking.[55]

Limited strategic war is not feasible. Since control must surely already have been lost for the conflict to reach this stage, the chances of subsequently regaining control are extremely slim. It is impossible to conduct significant military attacks on targets such as silos, airfields or command centres without causing widespread death and destruction leading to powerful pressures for revenge and retaliation. The C^3I systems essential for fighting controlled wars are almost certain to collapse after the use of a substantial number of nuclear weapons. In any case, there are virtually no prospects of a truce being negotiated successfully before most of the nuclear arsenals of both sides have been used. In view of this, the Soviet strategy, outlined in chapter 2, of launching massive simultaneous nuclear strikes as soon as nuclear war starts has an undeniable coherence and realism. It therefore seems to be much more likely that the US will abandon 'controlled escalation' in favour of massive early nuclear strikes if nuclear war ever seems inevitable, than that the USSR will suddenly opt for limited attacks in that situation.

4

Soviet Weapons and their Targets

INTRODUCTION

The last two chapters have demonstrated that Soviet nuclear strategy and the realities of warfare put severe constraints upon the size of nuclear attack that the UK could expect and the types of target that would be destroyed. If any nuclear weapons are used on Britain, they will almost certainly be a part of an unrestrained, massive, sudden attack aimed at destroying many targets of military significance and also those which would be vital to our prospects for long-term recovery. This does not rule out the possibility that such a nuclear strike is preceded by conventional attacks, although we have shown that the location of tactical nuclear weapons and the realities of European war make this rather unlikely for the UK, if not for West Germany. There is also a remote chance that a nuclear war at sea or in some distant region of the world might not escalate to include attacks on the UK. Apart from the possibility of a terrorist group detonating a crude nuclear weapon in a British city, the UK is likely to be subjected either to all-out nuclear attack or to no attack at all.

In this chapter we assess the number of weapons in the Soviet arsenal that are likely to be assigned to targets in Western Europe, and estimate the proportion of these allocated to the UK. We then examine the categories of targets that are most likely to be attacked and the weapons that would be most appropriate for these tasks.

SOVIET NUCLEAR FORCES ALLOCATED TO WESTERN EUROPE

We begin by estimating which part of the Soviet nuclear forces with sufficient range to reach the UK is allocated to targets in Western Europe. This involves several serious uncertainties. There is some controversy about the numbers of certain types of weapon contained within the Soviet nuclear arsenal. There is even more uncertainty about the missions to which these have been allocated. For instance, people disagree about the capabilities and range of the USSR's medium-ranged bomber force. The proportion of these that are allocated to Europe and will carry nuclear rather than conventional weapons, and the fraction that are intended for use against shipping rather than targets on land is unknown in the West, and estimates are largely the product of educated guesswork. The ultimate source of most of the available data is the US intelligence services. The relatively closed nature of Soviet society makes corroboration difficult. We have chosen to base our discussion largely on data given in the *Yearbooks* of the Stockholm International Peace Research Institute (SIPRI),[1] *The Military Balance*[2] compiled by the International Institute of Strategic Studies (IISS), and on the testimony of officials to US Senate and Congressional committees.[3] These are widely regarded to be the most authoritative sources of information available.

Furthermore, weapons allocated to one mission could be re-allocated to another if the need arose. For instance aircraft assigned to missions against enemy shipping could attack land targets, and all modern Soviet (and US) ICBMs could be retargeted quite rapidly towards Europe if required.

Clearly, the way the weapons would actually be used, if nuclear war began, would depend upon the way in which the war started and on whether or not the war was still confined to Europe. In this section we make the conservative assumption that the USSR does not use any nuclear forces on Europe that would normally cover targets elsewhere. Several other uncertainties will emerge in the course of the discussion.

It will become clear that the number of nuclear weapons systems allocated to targets in Western Europe is fearsome. Of course, the US and other NATO countries have a similar number covering targets in Eastern Europe and European Russia. However, since our objective is to assess the scale of attack on the UK we discuss only Warsaw Pact forces.

Land-based intermediate/medium-ranged missiles

In March 1983 about 250 of the old SS4 and SS5 missiles are targeted on Western Europe.[4] They are inaccurate, carry a single warhead with a yield of at least 1 megaton, and are launched from their missile bases in European Russia (for instance, Yedrovo near Leningrad). The SS4 can reach all areas except the Iberian peninsula and the westernmost parts of France and Ireland. The SS5 can reach all targets in Western Europe. The missiles were first deployed in 1959 and 1961 respectively. They take up to eight hours to launch, are extremely vulnerable to attack (they are deployed in close groups of three or four and, until recently, two-thirds of them were on unprotected open pads), and they are now regarded as obsolete.[5] They are currently being replaced by the SS20 missile.

The SS20 missile has a range of 5,000 km and carries three independently targetable warheads, each with an explosive power of 150 kilotons. Unlike the SS4 and SS5 it can be launched reasonably quickly — about one hour[6] between the initial order and the launch — and it is mobile, although it must be launched from pre-prepared concrete sites. Each warhead has an accuracy of about 750 metres.[7] According to the US Department of Defense, about 350 SS20s had been installed by April 1983.[8] However about one third of these are installed in the Far East, out of range of Europe. The remaining two thirds are roughly equally divided between sites in central USSR and in missile fields west of the Ural mountains.[9] All these can threaten targets throughout Western Europe, although a small number may also cover targets in the Near and Middle East.

There are a number of shorter range missiles in the Soviet arsenal. In any plausible war in Europe, these missiles are likely to be launched from at least 70 km behind the East German border, out of range of most of NATO's battlefield nuclear forces. The distance between East Germany and East Anglia is about 600 km. The SS12 'Scaleboard' and its modern replacement, the SS22, have a range of 800–1,000 km, allowing them to reach most of England from East Germany. The 600 or so 'Scud' and SS23 missiles have a range of only 300–350 km, and will therefore be used against continental European countries, not the UK.

Intercontinental ballistic missiles

Between 180 and 360 Soviet ICBMs are specifically designated for the European theatre, including at least 120 SS11 and 60 SS19 missiles in the Derazhnya and Pervomaysk missile fields in European Russia.[10] However, as we have mentioned, all modern Soviet ICBMs can easily be retargeted against Western Europe. Although this is not taken into account here, a situation is presented in chapter 5 in which such retargeting is likely to occur.

Submarine-launched ballistic missiles

A number of different sea-launched missiles could be targeted on Europe. Six diesel-powered 'Golf-II' class ballistic missile submarines have been deployed in the Baltic since 1976 and a further four are in the Northern fleet in the Barents Sea and North Atlantic.[11] Each of these carry three SSN5 missiles which have a range of 1,200–1,400 km, in a single warhead with a yield of about 1 megaton, and an accuracy of 2,800 metres.

A further 18 SSN5 missiles are deployed on six 'Hotel-II' class nuclear submarines. These and the 400 SSN6 missiles on 'Yankee' class submarines are thought to be allocated to targets in the US. However, they are not of intercontinental range and may only be within range of Europe when nuclear war starts. Since the submarines may only be a few hundred miles away from western Britain, the missiles would have a short flight time (possibly less than ten minutes) and so there would be an advantage in using them against high priority targets once nuclear war broke out or appeared to be inevitable.

The 356 SSN3 'Shaddock' and 32 SSN12 'Sandbox' sea-launched cruise missiles are intended primarily for attacks on shipping but some of them may be used against land targets in Europe.

Aircraft

There are a number of aircraft which might be used to launch nuclear attacks on the UK and other European countries. The range quoted for an aircraft can vary according to how it is calculated. We shall quote the 'maximum combat radius' for an aircraft carrying its full payload (bombs, missiles, etc.) which flies at high altitude, approaches its target at high speed and low altitude and then returns to its base. The need for evasive action might reduce this range. On the other hand in-flight refuelling, reduced payloads, or returning to an airfield other than the starting point (or possibly taking a one-way trip) would extend the combat radius considerably.

About 150 Tu-22M 'Backfire' bombers have been deployed, 75 to 80 per cent of them allocated to Europe. Up to half of these are assigned to naval aviation, and are, therefore, most likely to be used against shipping, although they may also attack anti-submarine warfare, radar, and naval facilities on the coast of the UK, Norway and other NATO countries.[12] This leaves at least 60 Backfires specifically covering land targets in Europe. Each of these has a range of 3,000–4,000 km and carries four free-fall bombs[13] with yields of a few megatons. Alternatively, it could carry two AS6 'Kingfish' (or AS4 'Kitchen') missiles which have a range of about 700 km. These missiles are probably primarily intended for naval targets so we shall assume that nearly all of the bombers allocated to land targets carry free-fall bombs.

Almost 1,000 'Badger' (Tu-16), 'Blinder' (Tu-22) and 'Fencer' (Su-24) bombers are also deployed, with about the same proportion allocated to the European theatre as with the Backfire. The Blinder and Fencer have a range of about 1,200 km[14] and 1,700 km respectively which means that the UK is well within range from Eastern Europe, but is on the edge of their operational area if they take off from bases inside the Soviet Union. They all can carry one or two free-fall bombs with yields of a few megatons. The Badger or Blinder might instead carry a single AS6 or AS4 air-to-surface missile. These would effectively add another 700 km to their range.

There are two aircraft that have just the range required to attack the UK from East Europe and so should also be considered. About 550 MiG-27 'Flogger D' aircraft and 690 Su-17 'Fitter C/D' in the Soviet arsenal are probably assigned to nuclear missions. These types of aircraft have ranges of 720 km and 600 km respectively, and can carry a single nuclear bomb with a yield of a few megatons.

Due to the uncertainty about the yields of the free-fall bombs on all these bombers, in our calculations we have made the conservative assumption that each of these bombs has an explosive power of one megaton.

NUCLEAR FORCES TARGETED ON THE UK

The Soviet nuclear forces allocated to Europe must cover targets in Scandinavia, France, central and southern Europe, and Turkey as well as the UK. Any estimate of the proportion that cover targets in the UK is bound to be very approximate. However, the UK is second only to Germany in military importance to NATO in Europe and so the proportion is bound to be large.

Much of Germany would be devastated by short-range battlefield nuclear weapons, the 600 or so 'Scud/SS23' missiles and bombs from many of the 265 Su-7 and 100 MiG-21 nuclear-capable aircraft. Together with the Benelux countries, eastern France, north Italy and parts of Turkey, West Germany would attract attacks from most of the medium-ranged forces, such as many of the 550 strong MiG-27 aircraft force, and the 688 Su-17 nuclear-capable bombers. Many targets in Norway, Denmark and other Scandinavian countries would be allocated to Soviet naval aircraft and some of the SS12/SS22 missiles.

It therefore seems reasonable to suppose that at least one quarter (and possibly up to one third) of the remaining longer-ranged nuclear forces allocated to Western Europe are targeted on the UK.[15] This leaves about a quarter for remaining targets in France and Italy together with the small number of targets in Spain and Portugal, a quarter for further targets in Germany, the Benelux countries and Scandinavia, and between a sixth and a quarter to Greece, some targets in the Middle East and to remaining bases in Turkey.

This provides a rough estimate of the number of Soviet nuclear forces currently allocated to targets in Britain. The result is given in the final columns of table 4.1. Assuming that one quarter of the appropriate nuclear forces are targeted on the UK, the total yield of these nuclear weapons is between 510 and 590 megatons carried on 700 to 885 warheads. If the proportion is one third, the figures are between 620 and 720 megatons, carried on 870 to 1,020 warheads. Naturally, in an actual war, some of these are likely to be destroyed on the ground or intercepted before they reach the UK. Nevertheless it shows that the standard official Home Office figure of a 200 megaton attack on the UK is likely to be an underestimate.[16]

Table 4.1 Soviet weapons targeted on the UK[a]

Type of missile/bomber[b]	Range/combat radius (km)[c]	Total inventory	Number allocated to land targets in Europe[d]	% allocated to nuclear role[e]	Number in nuclear role allocated to targets in UK, assuming proportions of 1/4	1/3	Number of warheads/delivery vehicle	Yield/warhead (megatons)	Accuracy (CEP) (metres)	Total yield (megatons) of warheads allocated to UK, assuming proportions[f] of 1/4	1/3	Total number of warheads allocated to UK, assuming proportions of 1/4	1/3
SS20	5,000	350[i]	235[j]	100	58	78	3	0.15	750	26.1	35.1	174	234
SS4	1,800[g]–1,900[h]	250[j]	250	100	62	83	1	1.0[s]	2,300	62	83	62	83
SS5	3,500[g]–4,100[h]								1,100				
SS19 mod 2	10,000	360	60–120[k]	100	3–6[p]	4–8[p]	1	5.0	300	15–30	20–40	3–6	4–8
mod 3					12–24	16–32	6	0.5	300	36–72	48–96	72–144	96–192
SS11 mod 1	10,500	520[g]–570[h]	120–240[k]	100	24–48	32–64	1	1.0	1,400	24–48	32–64	24–48	32–64
mod 3	8,800	'some'[h]			6–12[p]	8–16[p]	3[r]	0.2	1,100	3.6–7.2	4.8–9.6	18–36	24–48
SSN5	1,300[g]–1,400[h]	57	30[l]	100	7	10	1	1.0	2,800	7	10	7	10
Tu-22M 'Backfire'	3,000[g]–4,000[h]	100[h]–150[g]	60[d,m]	100	15	20	4	1.0[s]	very good	60	80	60	80
Tu-22 'Blinder'	1,200[g]–3,100[h]	180	100[d,n]	75	19	19[q]	2	1.0[s]	moderate	38	38[q]	38	38[q]
Tu-16 'Badger'	2,000[g]–2,800[h]	650 approx.	225[d,o]	75	42	56	2	1.0[s]	moderate	84	112	84	112
Su-24 'Fencer'	1,600[g]–1,700[h]	550	412[d]	75	77	77[q]	2	1.0[s]	good	154	154[q]	154	154[q]
Totals										509.7 to 588.3	616.9 to 721.7	696 to 885	867 to 1,023

a Except where otherwise indicated, the figures come from the *SIPRI Yearbook 1982* (chapter 4, note 1) and *The Military Balance 1982–1983* (chapter 4, note 2). Where these disagree, both values are shown

b We include only the SS11 and SS19 intercontinental ballistic missiles known to be allocated to Europe, and those missiles and bombers that are usually classified as 'long-range theatre nuclear weapons'. Thus all SS12s, SS22s, SSN3s, SSN6s, and the SSN5s on 'Hotel-II' class submarines are omitted, as are the many hundreds of MiG-27 and Su-17 nuclear-capable aircraft. All of these could be used against targets in the UK, and in practice some of them probably would be. They are omitted because they are usually thought to be allocated to targets elsewhere, and also because of our policy of underestimating the severity of a possible attack wherever there is reasonable doubt. Of course, most of the Soviet intercontinental-range nuclear forces could be retargeted towards the UK if judged necessary

c Range for missiles or combat radius for bombers, assuming a full payload, high-altitude transit with a high-speed low-level approach to the target, and a return to base (see p. 54). No allowance is made for the range of the air-to-surface missiles that may be carried on some bombers

d An estimate of the number of missiles or bombs likely to be allocated to land targets in Europe. We assume that 75 per cent of the bombers are intended for use in Europe (see *SIPRI Yearbook 1982*, table 1.4, p. 18 and *The Military Balance 1982–1983*, p. 137). The numbers of aircraft thought to be assigned to Soviet naval aviation have been subtracted, although some of these may also be used against land targets (see m, n, o below)

e All the missiles will carry nuclear warheads, but a proportion of the bombers might carry conventional explosives instead. There is virtually no information available on this proportion. It has been assumed that all the modern 'Backfire' bombers intended for use against the UK are planned to carry nuclear weapons, while for the 'Badgers', 'Blinders' and 'Fencers' the proportion is 75 per cent. This assumption appears to be relatively conservative, especially since nuclear weapons would almost certainly have been used already in any war in Europe involving large-scale bomber attacks on Britain. The *SIPRI Yearbook 1982*, table 1.4, p. 13, takes the proportion to be 100 per cent, while *The Military Balance 1982–1983* assumes without any discussion that it is 50 per cent.

f It is assumed that between one quarter and one third of the missiles or bombers listed in this table, that are allocated to Europe, could be used to attack the UK (see p. 55 for discussion). The upper and lower limits on the numbers targeted on the UK are presented separately

g *SIPRI Yearbook 1982*

h *The Military Balance 1982–1983*

i See note 4 to this chapter. The USSR states that the figures are lower. To the authors' knowledge, however, the USSR has announced no figures more recently than November 1981, when Brezhnev declared a figure of 243 SS20s (as opposed to the US's estimate at that time of 250) and 253 SS4s and SS5s (compared to the 350 claimed then by the US). See *SIPRI Yearbook 1982*, p. 11

j Assuming one third of the SS20s are based in the Far East, out of range of Europe

k The total number of SS19 and SS11 missiles targeted on Europe is between 180 and 360 (note 10 to this chapter). We have no reliable information on what fraction of these are SS11s. Since the modern SS19s have been gradually replacing SS11s since about 1981, we assume that about one third of this programme has been completed.

l On the 'Golf I' class submarines in the Baltic and the North Atlantic fleet. For discussion see b above and p. 53 in the text

m Assuming that 50 per cent of the 'Backfires' assigned to Europe are allocated to Soviet naval aviation. We take the SIPRI figure since 30 'Backfires' are being produced each year, so that the IISS estimate would need some upward revision

n Subtracting the 50 'Blinders' assigned to Soviet naval aviation and then taking 75 per cent of the figure, as explained in d

o Subtracting the 250 'Badgers' assigned to Soviet naval aviation and the (approximately) 100 that are expected to operate in support roles; then as in d

p Assuming that one fifth of the SS19 missiles are model 2 and one fifth of the SS11s are model 3. These are the approximate proportions of these versions in the total inventory. In the absence of any evidence to the contrary, we assume that the same proportions apply to the missiles targeted on Europe

q Assuming, conservatively, that a higher proportion of 'Blinder' and 'Fencer' bombers are assigned to targets on the Continent, we take a maximum of one quarter of these aircraft to be allocated to the UK

r Three Multiple Re-entry Vehicles (MRV); but these are not independently targetable

s The free-fall nuclear bombs and the warheads on SS4 and SS5 missiles are usually quoted to have yields 'in the megaton range', meaning one megaton or more. We take the lower limit of one megaton in each case

TARGETS IN THE UK: PRIORITIES

A study commissioned by US Defense Secretary McNamara concluded that just 200 nuclear weapons, each with a yield of 1 megaton, would be sufficient to kill 52 million people in the Soviet Union and destroy 72 per cent of its industrial capacity.[17] It is clear, therefore, that the size of the Soviet arsenal estimated to be targeted on Britain is many times more than would be required to inflict similar levels of damage on this small island, if that was the Soviet Union's sole objective.

However, Soviet strategy for conducting a nuclear war in Europe, as described in chapter 2, involves launching nuclear attacks on the UK with three main objectives: to destroy or disable British and US nuclear forces, to weaken our ability to wage the prolonged war which the USSR's military expect to follow the initial nuclear attacks, and to do the utmost to slow down or prevent British post-war recovery. This makes every bridge, radio station, airfield, power station, army post or industrial plant into a potential target. Taking just airfields (of all kinds), there are over 900 of these in the UK.[18] The 700 to 1,020 or so nuclear warheads covering targets in the UK are insufficient to cover every potential target, particularly since many would be destroyed or intercepted before they reached their target.

Soviet military planners must, therefore, have decided upon targeting priorities. Naturally we cannot know their plans in detail. However, Soviet strategy and military writings such as those quoted in chapter 2 allow a reliable estimate to be made. We can also draw upon the priorities demonstrated in US targeting plans. The US also has a counterforce policy and thus is likely to have decided upon similar priorities for its 'major attack options' (MAOs).

In the following sections each of the various categories of potential target is examined and its relative priority estimated. Examples of particular targets are given in order to illustrate the discussion. A more complete list of targets is provided in chapter 5, where a number of detailed attack scenarios are presented.

Nuclear forces

It will be no surprise that nuclear forces and their associated facilities are high priority targets. The US Navy base at Holy Loch near the Firth of Clyde normally serves up to ten Poseidon missile submarines.[19] The UK's four 'independent' Polaris missile submarines operate from the Royal Navy's Faslane base nearby. These would be extremely urgent targets and might be attacked using SSN5 or SSN6 missiles from nearby Soviet submarines (within a few hundred miles), where the short flight times would allow a surprise attack. The Polaris refit dockyard at Rosyth in the Firth of Forth, and the hunter-killer submarine base at Devonport (Plymouth) would also be very important targets.

There are 25 to 30 USAF and RAF bases in Britain from which nuclear-capable medium-ranged bombers and shorter range strike aircraft operate regularly. For instance, US F111 nuclear bombers operate from bases in Lakenheath in Suffolk and Upper Heyford in Oxfordshire amongst others. The new Tornado strike aircraft operate from bases such as Cottesmore (Leicestershire) and Honnington (near Bury St Edmunds). Harriers are based at, for example, Yeovilton (Somerset) and Wittering (near Peterborough). Vulcans are at Waddington (Lincolnshire) and Scampton (Lincolnshire) and Lightnings and Phantoms are at Leuchars (Fife) and Binbrook (Lincolnshire). Nimrod Airborne Early Warning aircraft operate from St Mawgen (Cornwall), Kinloss (Grampian) and a number of other airfields, and Orion P3s are planned for Stornoway. All these airfields, and several others, would be high priority targets since they could be used for attacks on Europe, the Soviet Union, the Soviet navy or incoming Soviet aircraft.

Nuclear weapons are stored at many of these airfields. They are also probably stored at sites such as Coulport, Machrihanish and Beith in Strathclyde, and Chilmark in Wiltshire. All such stores would be urgent targets, since it would be important to destroy them before their contents were dispersed or used in military action.

If they are installed in the US bases at Greenham Common near Newbury and Molesworth in Cambridgeshire, ground-launched cruise missiles will be extremely high priority targets. If possible, the USSR would prefer to destroy them before they are dispersed from their bases since then they would be most vulnerable and only a few warheads would be required. Even if they were dispersed, however, the Cruise missiles' great nuclear warfighting ability make them an urgent target.

The British nuclear warhead factories at Cardiff and at Burghfield near Reading would be important targets in case they contained finished or almost finished warheads. They would also be targeted, together with the Atomic Weapons Research Establishment at Aldermaston, in order to prevent the production of new nuclear weapons in the medium and long term.

Strategic command centres

We have already noted the importance that the Soviet Union attaches to attacks which disrupt the co-ordination of the adversary's war effort. The destruction of British national leaders and British and NATO command posts will at least delay orders to attack and may paralyse some sections of our armed forces for a long period. Campbell has published evidence to show that the top British political and military leaders intend to leave London in favour of a massive underground command centre at Hawthorn near Bath.[20] If this is correct then Hawthorn would be subject to massive attack, as would Whitehall, the NATO and Polaris Head-quarters at Northwood (West London), the RAF and USAF command centres at High Wycombe, the Royal Navy and NATO headquarters at Pitreavie Castle (Dunfermline), Portsmouth and Plymouth and a number of other centres.

Communications and intelligence centres

Effective command and control cannot be maintained without timely intelligence and good communications. The Ballistic Missile Early Warn-ing Station at Fylingdales in North Yorkshire is one of the highest priority targets in the UK, and may well be attacked by submarine-launched SSN5 missiles in order to ensure its early destruction. The very low frequency (VLF) radio communication centres at Rugby, Anthorn and Criggion used to contact Polaris and other submarines would also be prime targets. Communications and intelligence centres such as those at Cheltenham, Edzell in East Scotland, Menwith Hill near Harrogate, and Chicksands in Bedforshire are all likely to be given high priority. There are a large number of potential targets in this category, and many more than have been mentioned above are of the highest priority.

Besides military installations, civilian air-traffic-control radars and long-range radio facilities are also likely to be targeted. It is impossible to predict the point on the list where these facilities would be no longer deemed worthy of attack. The string of US microwave link stations running from Browncarrick Hill to Thurso and Swingate near Dover to Alconbury, would probably only be hit at two or three points: if the links are broken it does not matter if the majority of stations survive. Regional radio stations and transmitters are likely to be low priority.

Conventional forces

Soviet strategy operates on the assumption that a war involving conven-tional forces will follow the initial nuclear exchanges. This war may be prolonged over weeks or months. Thus the Soviets will aim to destroy at the outset the facilities upon which the British and NATO war effort would be based. These will include many economic targets as well as strictly military ones.

Aircraft will probably be dispersed away from the 25 to 30 most impor-tant military airfields already mentioned to a large number of other bases. The list of important targets in this category would at least include those air-fields with hard surfaced runways longer than about 1,700–1,800 metres.

Besides military airfields such as Yeovilton, St Athan near Cardiff, Valley in Anglesey and Farnborough, civilian airfields such as those at Heathrow, Liverpool, Coventry and Exeter would probably be destroyed. Nuclear weapons are now small enough to be carried by most types of aircraft and many of these are capable of operating from small airfields, or even sections of motorway. Since the other sites would lack important maintenance and refuelling facilities it is unlikely that aircraft would be dispersed to them until the war was well under way. The USSR is, therefore, under pressure to attack all these larger dispersal airfields as quickly as possible, before the aircraft are too widely dispersed.

Air defence forces such as the operations centre at West Drayton, the missile base at Bawdsey in Suffolk and the fighter/interceptor base at Leuchars in Scotland are likely to be attacked along with the radar and communications centres mentioned above.

District Army Headquarters and large troop garrisons such as at Catterick, Aldershot and Bulford would probably be destroyed during the initial exchanges, as would the ports and docks on the south and east coast that could be used to transport the troops to the continent. Stores of ammunition, vehicles, tanks and spares such as those at Burtonwood near Liverpool, Glen Douglas (north of the Firth of Clyde), Donnington and Poole are obvious targets, as are petrol, oil and lubricant (POL) depots at bases such as Invergordon and Immingham Dock near Grimsby.

Naval bases would be used to support NATO operations in the North Atlantic and elsewhere and so many of them would be destroyed. In order to prevent US reinforcements and supplies from arriving, docks at Liverpool, Barry Island or Southampton, for instance, would be quite high on the Soviet target list.

Economic targeting

During the 1960s the declared objective of US economic targeting was simply to destroy one-half to two-thirds of Soviet industrial capacity. According to this criterion, it did not matter whether the targets were biscuit factories, underwear manufacturers or chemical plants. Since 1974 the US has abandoned this approach. Soviet writings indicate that Soviet targeting policy was always based on more specific objectives. One Soviet objective is to attack economic facilities crucial to the enemy's war effort. As Colonel Shirikov has written 'the economic structure, and industry in particular is the basis of a state's military power.'[21]

The other objective is to ensure that the adversaries, and even potential adversaries, are crippled sufficiently severely to ensure that they cannot recover in the years following the war, to come to dominate the USSR. Since Soviet planners assume that the USSR would be devastated in any nuclear war, this implies very heavy attacks on the UK.

Before going on to discuss various categories of target, there is a general point to be made. Since the sectors of a modern economy are so inter-dependent, the destruction of one element will have ramifications throughout the whole system. This raises the possibility that critical interdependencies may be identified, so that attacks on a few 'bottlenecks' — for instance ball-bearing factories — would have immediate and dis-proportionate effects on the rest of the economy.[22] The idea has led to a great deal of activity in the US targeting community over the last decade, and it is probable that Soviet planners have engaged in similar studies. For instance, in SIOP-5 — the US targeting plan authorized in 1976 — fertilizer plants became a favoured targeting option because of the critical role that analysts thought these would play in Soviet agricultural recovery.[23]

The 'bottleneck' approach is appealing to targeting staff because it promises to increase the effectiveness of their nuclear forces. However, it is unlikely that Soviet target plans involve too sophisticated a use of this approach; the results of economic analysis and input-output models are too dependent upon the initial assumptions. It is likely that the Soviets have adopted a few of the basic elements of the bottleneck approach,[24] but that in general they simply aim at massive destruction.

Transport

Besides docks and ports, there is advantage in destroying important road systems, rail junctions and bridges. This would hamper the movement of troops and supplies and would hinder long-term recovery. However, these targets are generally very resistant to blast damage and there are a large number throughout the country, so only a few key transport links are likely to be destroyed. These would probably include bridges such as those over the Severn, the Tay and the Forth; motorway inter-sections such as the M5/M6 interchange near Birmingham or the M61/M62/M63 near Bolton; and rail centres such as those at Crewe, Watford or Doncaster.

Military industry and research

Military research establishments, such as Portland on the south coast, are likely to be targeted to prevent Britain rebuilding its military power. The chemical warfare and biological research station at Porton Down might be destroyed for the same reason, and also to prevent any existing stores being used.

The same rationale would encourage the destruction of military-industrial plants. These include the 13 Royal Ordnance Factories[25] and centres operated by companies such as British Aerospace, Rolls Royce,

Westland Ltd, British Shipbuilding, Plessey and GEC. A map in the 1981 *Defence Estimates*[26] showing the location of the large number of plants of major defence contractors in the UK reveals them — not surprisingly — to be located in most of the highly populated areas of the country. The aircraft and shipbuilding industries often have runways or docks associated with them which increases their importance as targets. The remainder of military industry would be of lower priority than other, more basic, economic facilities.

Energy

The importance of the energy industry is repeatedly emphasized in Soviet writings. For instance, 'Especially effective could be attacks against the electric power and oil refining industries, since electric power is required in large amounts by all branches of the national economy, including the defence industries.'[27] Without electricity, many machines and industries cannot work, communications fail, pumps for water and sewage remain idle. Without oil, there is no fuel for transport or machinery. There are, however, many hundreds of possible targets associated with energy resources, and Soviet planners must choose between them.

A high proportion of our electrical power comes from coal (82 per cent in 1981/82).[28] One approach would be to destroy coal mines and coal stocks. These are, however, too dispersed and too resistant to blast to present attractive targets. Therefore, although a few of the major coal mines might conceivably be attacked, Soviet nuclear forces are likely to be concentrated on the power stations instead. There are about 200 power stations generating over 20 megawatts of electrical power in the UK. In view of all of the other targets of equal or higher priority, this is still too large a number for all of them to be covered. However, many of these are very small and over half the supply is produced by the 30 or so largest stations[29] (with over 900 megawatts capacity). These larger power stations would therefore be high priority targets. Grid control points, such as those at Pitlochry and Kirkintilloch, might also be targeted.

There are 14 nuclear power stations controlled by the Central Electricity Generating Board, producing about 11 per cent of the UK's electrical power between them.[30] Since these, and the other reactors controlled by the UK Atomic Energy Authority and by British Nuclear Fuels Ltd, can also be used to produce radioactive materials for nuclear weapons — indeed some already are so used — they are unlikely to be ignored in any Soviet attack. The uranium enrichment plant at Capenhurst in Cheshire, the fuel manufacturing plant at Springfields in Lancashire and the reprocessing and waste storage installations at Sellafield (Windscale) are also priority targets. As described in chapter 8, nuclear attacks on nuclear reactors have the added 'bonus' (in the jargon of targeting staff) of dispersing large quantities of long-lived radioactive materials over the UK, hindering its post-war recovery.

Oil refineries and oil storage depots at ports are very vulnerable to the blast and heat effects of nuclear explosions. These and oil terminals from the North Sea oil fields are likely to be high up the targeting priorities list — alongside nuclear power stations and above transport links and military industry. Without them military operations will grind to a halt and long-term recovery will be doubtful and slow. Gas stores at Canvey Island in the Thames estuary and the four North Sea gas terminals would also be attacked. It is possible that the oil rigs in the North Sea themselves would be destroyed, though this would require high blast pressures. Pipelines and smaller fuel stores within the UK are too resistant to blast and too dispersed to be worthwhile targets.

'Bottleneck' industry

The chemical industry is often singled out as a particularly significant 'bottleneck' in modern economies. Without inorganic and organic industrial chemicals, plastics, drugs or fertilizers, much of the economy would collapse.

Iron and steel works, aluminium, copper, magnesium and other non-ferrous metal plants, electronic component manufacturers, cement works, ballbearing factories, and heavy machinery production, are also vital to many other sectors of the economy.[31] Apart from electrical component factories (which are smaller and more dispersed), these industries are generally concentrated in a relatively small number of large plants. Also since many of these will be located in the same areas, possibly close to power stations, oil refineries and docks, a single warhead will often suffice to destroy several such plants at once. Thus a number of these industrial areas would be attacked in any war with the USSR.

Financial centres

Even a small nuclear attack, consisting of only a few tens of missiles, would cause sufficient damage for the marketing, financial and monetary structure of the UK to collapse.[32] There is, therefore, no need for systematic attacks on financial institutions and banks. Nevertheless a single nuclear warhead exploding on the Bank of England in the City of London might be expected. This would vaporize the gold stocks and destroy the government's financial centre, the Stock Exchange, and the head offices of many of Britain's largest firms and merchant banks, making the identification of existing resources and any future international trade much more difficult.

Government and administrative centres

The national government centres such as Whitehall and Hawthorn would be destroyed as prime military targets, as already described. Second level administrative centres such as Cardiff, Edinburgh, Manchester, Newcastle and Birmingham are unlikely to be attacked in themselves since the effect this would have on Britain's recovery would probably be marginal. They are, in any case, likely to be destroyed in attacks intended to destroy higher priority targets in or near to these centres.

As described later in chapter 10, according to British government plans, after a nuclear war the UK will be governed from a hierarchy of levels. At the top there would be ten Regional Seats of Government in England and Wales and a further three in Scotland, which would govern from specially prepared bunkers each containing senior civil servants, army and police officers, and at least one cabinet minister. Lower down the hierarchy at the county and district level, civil servants would govern from more rudimentary centres. In the first days and weeks after the war, the Home Office expects only the lower levels of government to be in a position to operate.

It is possible that the higher levels of this hierarchy might be explicitly attacked in order to ensure that the government was ineffective and unable to co-ordinate post-war recovery. However, the bunkers are likely to be of low priority — possibly below that of population centres — since many of them would be destroyed by attacks on nearby targets of greater importance, and because it is doubtful that they would be effective even if they did survive intact. Civilian communications systems such as telephone exchanges and regional radio and TV transmitters might be more tempting targets. Again, however, much of these will have been damaged by the effects of EMP or blast from other explosions.

Population centres

Population centres might be attacked in order to lower the morale of the nation during the war and to reduce the labour power available to rebuild afterwards. They are, however, low priority targets. In fact a high proportion of the targets that have already been discussed are in or close to population centres. For instance, there are several top priority NATO and UK military command centres in London and other large towns. Faslane and Holy Loch submarine bases are near Glasgow. Many important airfields, weapons stores, and communications centres are near towns. In fact, targets of military significance tend if anything to be concentrated in the areas of the country with high levels of population. This is even more true of the economic targets.

METHODS OF ATTACKING TARGETS

Having decided upon the target list, the Soviet military planner must choose the weapon within the Soviet arsenal most appropriate to each target and also choose the precise location at which it should explode. This section discusses briefly some of the considerations behind such a choice.

Soviet planners must identify a 'desired ground zero' (DGZ) for each installation on the target list (and presumably have done so), on the basis of photographs and other intelligence data. The DGZ is the point on the ground at or above which the warhead should explode in order to disable or destroy the intended target most effectively. For instance, at an airfield, it might be the place where two or three runways cross. For an extended target such as an oil refinery complex it might be simply a central point.

Certain targets are damaged by the effects of heat, initial neutron and gamma radiation, radioactive fallout or EMP. In most cases, however, it is primarily the blast effects of the explosion that are used to destroy the target, with the other effects being counted as a 'bonus'.

Different targets have to be subjected to different levels of blast pressure before they are destroyed. For instance, a 'hardened' underground bunker may survive overpressures of several hundreds of pounds per square inch, whereas an oil refinery would be destroyed by blast pressures of five pounds per square inch. The nuclear warhead allocated to a given target should have sufficient explosive power (yield) and accuracy to ensure that the target is subjected to a level of blast pressure that is sufficient to demolish or disable it.

It has already been explained in chapter 2 that the accuracy of a warhead is much more critical to its ability to destroy a 'hard target' than is its yield: a twofold improvement in accuracy is as effective as an eightfold increase in explosive power. Thus a lower yield warhead from the relatively accurate SS20 or SS19 missile is most appropriate for an attack on an underground bunker or store, rather than an inaccurate SS4 missile with its higher yield 1 megaton warhead. Many targets are sufficiently resistant to blast to warrant a 'groundburst' attack. This means that the warhead is detonated at surface level or at a low enough altitude for the resulting fireball to touch the ground. In that case, blast overpressures in the immediate vicinity of ground zero (the actual point at or above which the warhead detonates) range from hundreds to many thousands of pounds per square inch (psi). A groundburst also produces a vast cloud of radioactive dust, much of which falls back to the ground in the following minutes and hours. Winds may carry this radioactive fallout many miles downwind.

Many targets, however, are less resistant to blast and an airburst —

where the warhead explodes high enough for the fireball not to touch the ground — would be more appropriate. The blast pressure wave reaching a ground structure following an airburst is composed of two parts — a wave coming direct from the detonation point and a wave that has been reflected from the ground. These combine in a so-called 'Mach stem' to form a pressure wave that is more intense than the one that would be produced by a groundburst of the same yield. The phenomenon is complex, but the end result is that it is possible to maximize the area of ground subjected to more than a given blast overpressure by choosing to detonate the warhead at a particular altitude.[33] Naturally, this 'optimum' height varies according to the yield of the warhead.

Soviet targeting staff must choose the altitude at which each warhead detonates in order to optimize the area that would be subjected to sufficient blast pressure to destroy the desired target. In this way, they can hedge against possible inaccuracies in the missile or bomber. For instance, in a leaked 1962 US Air Force manual *Nuclear Yield Requirements* — still highly classified but described by Campbell[34] — the heights of burst that the US had selected for various targets in the USSR, Western and Eastern Europe and North Africa, appear to be chosen to optimize 6 psi, 15 psi, and 40 psi — 6 psi to destroy aircraft, 15 psi for industrial storage and sites, and 40 psi for more blast-resistant structures such as bridges.

Major targets will probably be targeted by two or more warheads, preferably carried on different missiles or bombers. There are several reasons for this. First the target may consist of several different components, each requiring a different ground zero and height of burst. For instance, a nuclear bomber air base would probably be attacked with an airburst and at least one groundburst. The airburst would be detonated at the height which optimized the volume of space within which aircraft at the base or those which had just taken off would be destroyed. The groundburst would be primarily designed to crater the runway and to cause levels of radiation in the immediate surroundings such that the base was unusable for days and weeks after the attack. Another groundburst with a different ground zero might be used to destroy a nuclear weapons store near the base.[35]

These bombs should either be timed to detonate within about micro-second of each other — well within the capability of modern day technology — or with several minutes between them[36] (about 20 minutes if the first bomb is a groundburst, five or ten minutes if it is an airburst). This is because the effects of the first bomb might otherwise knock the second off course or damage its detonation mechanism. This effect is known as 'fratricide'. Its effects are most severe for attacks on missile silos, where inaccuracies of 100 metres or so can make all the difference. For the majority of targets in the UK, fratricide is a little less serious, since such inaccuracies are not so critical.

The second reason for multiple targeting is that the CEPs (accuracies) of the missiles presently allocated to the UK are such that they may detonate far enough from their desired ground zeros for the target to survive. For instance, an SS5 missile has a CEP of about 1,100 metres. Thus, some of these missiles will land over 1.5 km from their targets — too far away, for instance, to damage or destroy a runway. So the cautious military planner would allocate at least one extra warhead to increase the chances of at least one operating as hoped.

A third reason is that the missile or warhead may malfunction, or possibly fail altogether. For instance, the International Institute of Strategic Studies estimate that there is only a 65 per cent chance that an old SS4 missile will function as planned after launch. Modern missiles such as the SS19 or SS20 are estimated to be approximately 80 per cent reliable, as are the nuclear bombers.[37] To guard against such failures, cross-targeting of major military bases is required.

The final reason why major targets are covered by more warheads than appear strictly necessary is that some of the bombers and missiles may be destroyed before they can be launched or, in the case of bombers, are intercepted by air defence systems.

Timing is another very important consideration for any military planner. Attacks on cruise missiles deployed in Britain, for instance, would be carried out using missiles which could reach the target in 15 minutes or so, rather than bombers which would take an hour or two to arrive. Similarly, attacks on the Holy Loch and Faslane submarine bases, on Fylingdales Early Warning System, or the VLF radio transmitter near Rugby (used to communicate with Polaris submarines) would be carried out with modern land-based missiles or with SSN5 or SSN6 missiles launched from nearby submarines. On the other hand an oil refinery or nuclear power station can be allocated to a nuclear bomber since in this case the extra hour's flight time is unimportant.

SUMMARY

By examining the Soviet nuclear forces which are now probably targeted on Europe we can make a rough estimate of the proportion of these that are likely to be allocated to the UK. Making conservative assumptions throughout, we arrive at an approximate number for each weapon's system. About 700 to 1,020 warheads are likely to be targeted against Britain, with a total explosive power of 510 to 720 megatons.

On the basis of Soviet strategy, and making reasonable assumptions, we have assigned rough priorities to the categories of potential targets within the UK. Nuclear forces and their associated command and communications centres are top priority. In order to destroy the UK's capability to fight the prolonged war which the USSR envisages would follow the initial nuclear exchange, a wide range of conventional military forces, air defence systems, logistic centres such as ports and transport centres, airfields, oil refineries, nuclear and conventional power stations, military industrial plants and heavy industry would be attacked. Other industrial targets would be destroyed in order further to reduce Britain's prospects for long-term recovery. Various administrative and population centres might also be attacked, though these would have a low priority and would in any case be largely destroyed as a consequence of attacks on nearby targets of higher priority.

With a knowledge of the targets and of the available weapons systems it is possible to make good estimates of which missiles the Soviet Union would allocate to the various types of target, and how they would probably be destroyed if nuclear war broke out.

Chapters 2, 3 and 4 have therefore enabled us to place rather reliable limits on the size and nature of the nuclear attack that the UK would be subjected to in a nuclear war.

5

Patterns of Nuclear Attack

Now that a framework has been established which provides rather strict constraints on the context, size and characteristics of a probable nuclear attack on the UK, we go on to construct a number of detailed nuclear attack scenarios. In this chapter, four or five scenarios are presented that we regard as realistic. In order to allow a more systematic study to be made of the effects of nuclear attack on Britain, a series of smaller, much less probable, attack patterns are also presented. In addition, we have prepared an attack against economic and population centres in the UK that might occur after a 'successful' massive first strike by NATO on the Soviet Union, so that only 5 to 8 per cent of the Soviet arsenal is available for a retaliatory attack. Lastly, we suppose that ground-launched cruise missiles have been dispersed into the countryside, and examine the consequences of an attack aimed at destroying them.

At the end of the chapter we review a number of scenarios produced since 1957 by the Home Office and other official and quasi-official sources. We examine the rationale behind them and their plausibility. But first we consider briefly the likely timing of an attack and the warning we are likely to receive.

TIMING OF AN ATTACK

The development of missiles and modern bombers and their support systems means that nuclear military operations no longer depend 'on the time of year, day, or weather conditions' for their success — as Colonel A. A. Sidorenko puts it in his text *The Offensive: Characteristic Features of the Offensive in a Nuclear War*.[1] However, there may be times at which NATO is least prepared and when, therefore, the USSR might be most tempted to attack. This has led to some interesting discussions as to whether it is to the Soviets' advantage to attack on a Sunday during the height of the tourist season when the roads would be clogged up, NATO staff would be on leave, and the harvest is still to be collected in. Alternatively there may be greater advantage to an attack on Christmas morning, about 3 to 4 a.m. Washington time, when the US would be least prepared and the frozen ground conditions would be most suitable for a large-scale use of vehicles.

Such discussions are, however, inconclusive. They also tend to assume that the USSR might attack completely out of the blue without any preceding period of international tension or crisis (even of a few hours) during which the US and NATO leadership — and probably the forces as well — would be placed on alert. As we argued in chapter 3, this is unlikely. Nuclear war will be the result of escalation, misperception, panic, or accident rather than of a Soviet cost-benefit analysis, especially since the leaders of the USSR accept that their country would be inevitably devastated in such a war.

Thus the timing of the attack would be primarily determined by unpredictable factors such as a malfunction in the early warning systems or the way the period to crisis developed. The most that can be said is that, within these constraints, the Soviet Union will aim to gain the maximum possible advantage from surprise. This might mean attacking without warning as soon as nuclear war appears to the Soviets to be inevitable, for instance after nuclear weapons have been used in a naval battle or a war far from Europe, or before cruise missiles, Pershing II missiles, tactical nuclear weapons or aircraft are dispersed in a conventional war in Europe. All other things being equal, greatest surprise would probably be gained by attacking the UK sometime between 7.00 a.m. and 11.00 a.m. — a time when political leaders in Washington are most likely to be asleep or least alert (2.00 a.m. to 6.00 a.m.).[2] Other factors contingent to the crisis are likely, however, to be more decisive.

WARNING TIME

Home Office circulars[3] suggest that up to two weeks warning may be given of the possibility of impending attack, though we are advised that the warning could only be a matter of a day or so. As chapter 3 shows, it is very possible that warning times could be much shorter even than that. A nuclear war resulting from a combination of misperception and accident might be preceded by a crisis only a few hours long. Members of the general public might remain ignorant of their peril until a few minutes before the first missile arrived.

A conventional war in Central Europe might continue for several days before the nuclear threshold was crossed. However, the present military postures of NATO and the Warsaw Pact provide a strong incentive to either side to launch an early pre-emptive nuclear attack before the enemy can disperse or use their forces. This incentive, together with all the other escalatory pressures discussed in chapter 3 mean that the period between the outbreak of conventional war in Central Europe and the nuclear attack could be anything from a few minutes to several days. Longer periods would be less likely.

The government would probably delay making public preparations for war and issuing official warnings for as long as possible. The chaos, absenteeism and congestion that such a warning would provoke would interfere with official preparations. The government might also fear that public preparations might be perceived by the adversary as an indication that war was inevitable and thereby trigger a nuclear attack. During the Cuban missile crisis for instance, the British government refrained from instituting its evacuation plans even though war seemed imminent.[4]

A missile launched from European Russia would take 10 to 20 minutes to reach a target in the UK. A submarine-launched missile might take less than 10 minutes if the submarine was within a few hundred miles of the British coast. Surveillance satellites make it possible to detect missile launches almost immediately — within a minute or so. However, after the warning has been confirmed, political leaders have been informed, and decisions taken, it appears unlikely that most people would receive even the proverbial four-minute warning of impending nuclear attack.

THE INITIAL ATTACK

Soviet strategy and the realities of nuclear war have already been discussed in chapters 2 and 3, where it was shown that the initial attack on the UK will probably be nuclear and that this will almost certainly be a massive, simultaneous missile attack on a wide range of targets lasting perhaps only an hour or so.

The initial attack might begin with the detonation of a high-yield nuclear warhead (one megaton or more) at an altitude of about 100 miles over the south of Britain. This would generate an electro-magnetic pulse (EMP) which would damage or destroy radio and radar stations and electronic equipment over the whole of the UK and much of the rest of northern Europe. The first missile wave is likely to be followed an hour or two later by a second wave, consisting of more missiles and of nuclear bombers.

It is *after* these attacks that the UK is most likely to be attacked with conventional forces supplemented by further isolated nuclear attacks. Both the US and the USSR have stockpiles of chemical weapons and so Britain may also be attacked with these. Biological weapons have been banned by international treaty since 1975 following the 1972 Biological and Toxic Weapons Convention.[5] Nevertheless, it is often rumoured that stores of these exist and so survivors of the initial attacks may also be in danger of exposure to cholera, rabbit fever, anthrax, or a selection of other deadly diseases.

DETAILED ATTACK SCENARIOS

Target identification

Having identified the categories of target that the Soviet Union plans to attack it is a straightforward, if time-consuming task to prepare a list of actual targets in the UK. Certainly, there is a problem in that most military activities in Britain are covered by a veil of official secrecy. When Clarke was researching his book on *The Nuclear Destruction of Britain* for example, the Ministry of Defence declined to supply him with a list of RAF bases in the UK. As Clarke comments,

There is something of the absurd in a situation where the British public is denied information which is — beyond doubt — known to the enemy and which represents the only basis on which the quality of the defence effort can be judged. Defence, it may be concluded, is an area outside public accountability in the opinion of successive British governments.[6]

More recently, it has taken repeated parliamentary questions to get anything like a complete list of major US military bases in Britain out of the Ministry of Defence.[7]

In the last two or three years however a great deal of information about military bases and installation in Britain has been compiled in unofficial publications. Much of this has been brought together by Campbell, in articles in the *New Statesman* and subsequently in his book *War Plan UK*.[8] Other useful sources are the *UK Airfield Register*,[9] such magazines as *Flight International*, and the work of Laurie[10] and Rogers.[11, 12] Often more information is available about American and even British military sites in the UK, in publications of the US government, than is officially published in Britain itself.

As for industrial targets, there are obviously fewer problems with secrecy here. We have worked largely from official reports such as the *Defence Estimates* for 1981 and 1982,[13] reports from bodies such as the Central Electricity Generating Board and United Kingdom Atomic Energy Authority (UKAEA), and standard maps and references on chemical, oil, steel and other industrial plants in the UK.

It is possible, because of the problem of secrecy, that the target list which is presented in appendix 1, omits a number of important military targets. It may also contain a few inaccuracies in relation to the targets which are included; although care has been taken, as far as possible, to double-check the information.

Attacks A to K

Using the target list and the priorities discussed in chapter 4, a series of attack scenarios have been prepared which are labelled A to K. They range from an attack of 42½ megatons, on only the nuclear forces and the most important of their associated command and communication facilities, to an attack using weapons with yields totalling almost 350 megatons aimed not only at the targets of military significance (including facilities such as oil refineries, ports and Royal Ordnance factories) but also at a large number of industries and other facilities which could help in any long-term recovery.

Table 5.1 Types of target included in Attacks A to K

Attack A	Strategic command and control centres; ballistic missile early warning systems; submarine and nuclear-capable aircraft bases; prospective cruise missile bases; peacetime and probable wartime nuclear weapons stores
Attack B	Plus major aircraft dispersal bases; very important command, control, communication and information centres; major air defence and anti-submarine warfare bases not targeted in A (because they are considered unlikely nuclear weapons stores); second-level nuclear targets (Rosyth, Cardiff Royal Ordnance Factory)
Attack C	Plus all major conventional military facilities, i.e. barracks, naval bases, additional airfields (so that all with runways longer than 1,800 metres are included); ports of prime military significance; additional radar, intelligence, communications and command centres so that every one of major military importance is included; Sellafield (Windscale), Capenhurst and Springfield nuclear plants, and the Calder Hall military reactor
Attack D	Plus minor military bases and communications centres, airfields with hard-surfaced runways of lengths between 1,000 and 1,800 metres. These targets are omitted from all subsequent attacks (i.e. E to K)
Attack E	As in C, plus large oil and gas refineries and terminals; nuclear power stations; additional ports; the Bank of England
Attack F	Plus large conventional power stations (greater than 900 megawatt capacity); a few important transport links; two electricity grid control centres
Attack G	Plus Royal Ordnance Factories and a few major military industries
Attack H	Plus a few major chemical and other heavy industrial plants
Attacks I to K	Include an increasing number of major plants in 'bottleneck' industries, and some more transport links. Attack K includes a few general urban–industrial targets

The attacks are built up incrementally by adding new categories of targets at each stage (see table 5.1). As we will argue shortly (on the basis of the earlier chapters), we do not believe that any attack smaller than Attack H is plausible. We include the smaller attacks only to allow us to study the effects of nuclear war systematically in the later chapters.

The targets which have been included in each attack are given in the target list (appendix 1). To illustrate the location of the targets more vividly a series of maps (figures 5.1–5.11) have been prepared which show the rings within which the blast pressure from each bomb used reaches at least one pound per square inch. As explained in chapter 6, these indicate the area over which people would be injured by the effects of blast. A pressure of one pound per square inch blows out doors, smashes windows and causes light damage to roofs. The consequences of these attacks are discussed in chapters 7 and 8.

Attack A   The smallest scenario involves attacks on nuclear forces and the most important command and information centres associated with them. Airfields from which aircraft carrying nuclear weapons are expected to operate regularly, or where nuclear weapons are likely to be stored, are mostly attacked with a groundburst and an airburst using warheads from accurate missiles (mostly the SS20 and SS19 mod(1)) for reasons explained in the previous chapter.

Fylingdales and Boulmer (another less important early warning facility) are destroyed with airbursts from SS11 missiles. Like all radar and radio installations, these are vulnerable to low levels of blast. An airburst is therefore used, so that as large an area as possible is subjected to blast pressures sufficient to destroy them. They are destroyed by the winds associated with the blast wave for pressures of 7 psi or more. These would be generated up to about 5.5 km from a one megaton airburst, so the inaccuracy of 1 km or so of the SS11 is unimportant. Any of the other land based missiles, except perhaps for the old slow-reacting and unreliable SS4, might have been used instead, as might a submarine launched SSN5 missile.

Nuclear weapons stores such as the USAF stores at Burtonwood near Liverpool, Chilmark near Salisbury and Coulport near the Firth of Clyde are attacked with groundbursts from modern missiles.

In order to destroy missile submarines in Holy Loch or Faslane, these bases were attacked with ground or waterbursts from SS19 mod(1) warheads. Any escaping submarines are destroyed by similar explosions at the entrance to Holy Loch and Gare Loch. This area could easily have been subjected to a much larger attack, involving pattern bombing of the whole Firth. Alternatively a single, very large, warhead might have been detonated in the centre of the Firth. We have switched to this latter option from Attack C onwards with a waterburst in the middle of the estuary from a single five megaton SS19 mod(2). Any one of these alternatives would result in a surge of water travelling up the estuary, flooding parts of Glasgow and other towns on the Clyde.

Nine major command centres such as Whitehall, High Wycombe and Pitreavie Castle near Dunfermline are attacked with groundbursts. Two of them — the probable wartime centre of government at Hawthorn and the Northwood NATO and UK naval command centre in west London — are attacked with five MT warheads on the SS19 mod(2) missiles.

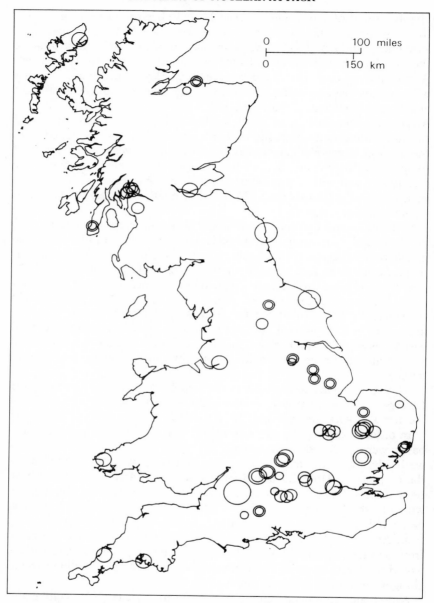

Figure 5.1 Attack A. This map and subsequent maps in figures 5.2–5.11 show targets in Attacks A to K. The circles represent the extent of blast damage at 1 pound per square inch (psi) and above. Outside these areas serious injuries would not be caused by blast effects and there would be little damage to buildings other than windows broken, tiles removed etc.

Stornoway US anti-submarine warfare base is targeted on the assumption that the present development plans have been completed. Similarly we have assumed that ground-launched cruise missiles have been deployed at Greenham Common and Molesworth but that they have not been dispersed away from their bases.

Fifty-four targets are attacked in A, using 75 warheads with a total explosive power of 42.5 megatons (see table 5.2). Seventy-seven per cent of the explosions are groundbursts; a reflection of the blast resistant nature of most of the targets. Because of the importance of destroying the targets in this attack quickly only missiles are used — most of them modern, accurate, ones.

Table 5.2 Numbers of warheads used and total yield (megatons) in Attacks A to K, attack on dispersed cruise missiles, and minimum retaliatory 'MAD' attack. These numbers and yields are also shown as percentages of the totals available for use against the UK

Attack	Number of warheads used	Total yield (megatons)	Number of warheads used as % of total available, assuming proportion allocated to UK is		Yield of warheads used as % of total available, assuming proportion allocated to UK is	
			1/4	1/3	1/4	1/3
A	75	42.5	8–11	7–9	7–8	6–7
B	160	87.0	18–23	16–18	15–17	12–14
C	242	116.9	27–35	24–28	20–23	16–19
D	286	129.45	32–41	30–33	22–25	18–21
E	293	163.75	33–42	29–34	28–32	23–27
F	315	185.75	36–45	31–36	32–36	26–30
G	348	213.65	39–50	34–40	36–42	30–35
H	342	219.2	39–49	33–39	37–43	30–35
I	392	257.65	44–56	38–45	44–51	36–42
J	441	306.65	50–63	43–51	52–60	42–50
K	485	347.65	55–70	47–56	59–68	48–56
'MAD'	117	37.95	13–17	11–13	6–7	5–6
Dispersed cruise missiles	366	699.2[a]	—	—	—	—

[a] Includes 24 SS18 intercontinental ballistic missiles

As in all the following scenarios, the fact that many of the missiles are MIRVed imposes additional constraints. We assume, conservatively, that warheads from the same missile cannot cover targets more than 100 km apart. Obviously, the number of SS20 warheads used in each attack (from A to K) must be a multiple of three, and the number of SS19 mod(1) warheads a multiple of six, since these missiles have MIRVs of three and six respectively

Attack B   In this scenario, an additional 71 targets are attacked. Large military and civilian airfields, such as Valley in Anglesey, Manston in

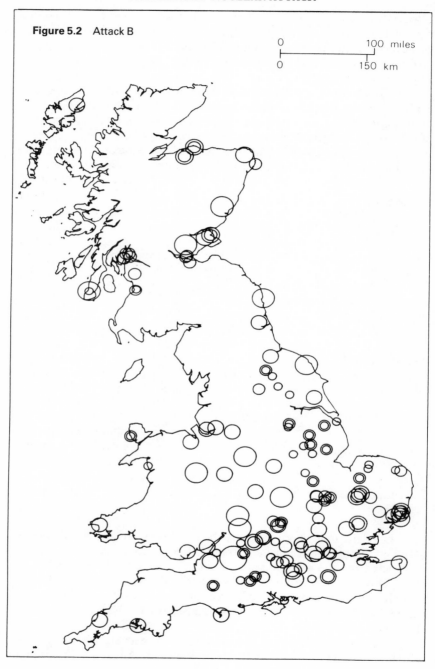

Figure 5.2   Attack B

Kent, Heathrow and Luton, are now included since they are almost certain to be used as dispersal bases for nuclear capable aircraft.

Air defence bases and very important signals intelligence and military radar stations are now targeted. Rosyth Polaris refit yard, the Cardiff nuclear weapons factory, the very low frequency radio communications centres at Criggion and near Rugby, the reserve government centre at Rhydymwyn in North Wales and the (peacetime) headquarters of the UK land forces at Wilton near Salisbury, are added to the list, along with several similar targets.

Once again, the attack consists mainly of groundbursts (about 71 per cent) using warheads from modern missiles, although a very few bombers are used against, for instance, Stansted airport and Martlesham Heath in Suffolk, the switching centre for AUTOVON — the US military's world-wide telephone network. A total of 160 warheads are used in Attack B, with a total yield of 87 megatons.

Attack C   Attack C is expanded so that all major nuclear and conventional military bases are included. Thus all airfields with hard surfaced runways long enough for major military aircraft to use (i.e. longer than about 1,800 metres) are targeted, as are army command centres, barracks, naval bases, conventional weapons dumps, and second level communications, radar and intelligence centres.

Barracks, such as Fulwood barracks at Preston and Imphal barracks in York, would be almost entirely demolished, and their occupants killed, with overpressures of 10 psi or less. Therefore, most of them are attacked with airbursts. Some key army and navy command centres, however, are attacked with groundbursts to ensure their destruction.

It is a general principle, which applies to all the attack scenarios, that any target which can be destroyed by moderate overpressures (a few tens of psi or less) may nevertheless be attacked with a groundburst provided the warhead used is accurate enough to ensure its destruction. A groundburst creates radioactive fallout which will contaminate areas of thousands of square miles as a 'bonus' to the demolition of the target, killing people and hindering recovery.

In addition to Royal Navy and US Navy bases, a few civilian ports are also targeted in C. These are Liverpool/Birkenhead, Marchwood (near Southampton), and Barry Island docks, which NATO probably plans to use as landing points for reinforcements and supplies from the US, and Felixstowe, Harwich, Shoreham, Folkestone and Dover which are the most important ports for transporting armies to the Continent. The submarine construction and refit docks at Barrow-in-Furness, where the British government intends to make the Trident submarines, are also attacked.

Ports and docks are resistant to blast effects (although the shipping itself would be more easily damaged) and, therefore, groundburst or water-

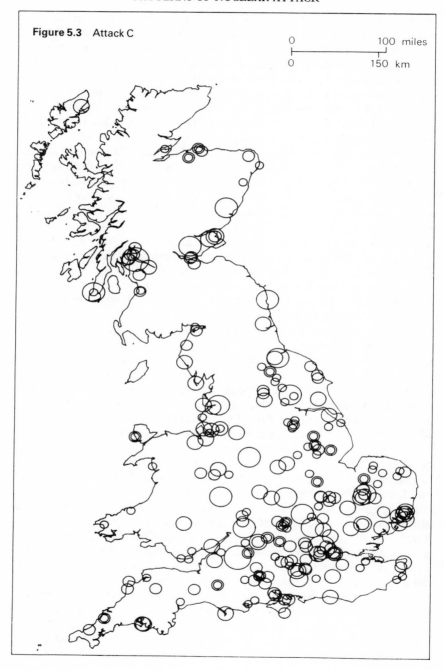

Figure 5.3 Attack C

burst attacks on them are to be expected. Even if the missile was off target, the radioactive fallout would render the port unusable for days. If the bomb is detonated in (or just above) water, vast quantities of water vapour are carried high into the atmosphere, where it is likely to condense and fall back to the ground as rain, carrying much of the radioactive debris from the explosion with it. This creates even higher radiation levels in the vicinity of the explosion than a simple groundburst.

It appears that the meteorological conditions over Britain for much of the year are such that the water vapour in the cloud from even a ground-burst or airburst may well condense to form rain, carrying radioactive material to the ground,[14] as occurred in Hiroshima. Waterbursts may also cause flooding, as we have already noted in relation to the Clyde in the section on Attack A.

The nuclear reprocessing plant at Sellafield (Windscale) is attacked in C, together with the Springfields nuclear fuel manufacture plant, the Capenhurst uranium enrichment plant, and the BNFL reactors at Calder Hall and Chapelcross. These are destroyed with groundbursts, so the radioactive material they contain is dispersed over wide areas of the UK.

The chemical warfare and biological research station at Porton Down could well have been targeted. However, we chose not to do so, since there are several important military targets nearby, such as Boscombe Down USAF base, Bulford army base, and the headquarters of the UK land forces at Wilton. Blast from bombs on these would badly damage Porton Down, possibly releasing some of its deadly contents into the environment.

Altogether 208 targets are attacked in C, using 242 warheads with a total yield of 116.9 megatons. It is still overwhelmingly a missile attack, but bombs from a Backfire, a Fencer and two Badger aircraft are used on ten less 'time urgent' targets. As figure 5.3 shows, much of the country, including many of the most highly populated areas, is affected even by this scale of attack.

Attack D   In Attack D, many of the small airfields (runways of over 1,000 m) and less important military bases and communications centres are included to increase the size of attack to 129.45 megatons.

Although these are all perfectly plausible targets which might indeed be attacked in an actual nuclear war, they are of less military significance and of lower priority than most of the economic targets included in Attacks E to K. Therefore, the targets added on in D are not included in any of the subsequent attacks.

Attack E   Attack E consists of the targets attacked in C plus oil refineries and terminals, North Sea gas terminals, remaining ports, nuclear power stations and also the Bank of England. The oil and gas installations are very vulnerable to the effects of blast — 5 psi would probably be sufficient to destroy them — and so airbursts are assumed. Often a single warhead is used to destroy several facilities, as in the Teesside area.

Figure 5.4   Attack D

Figure 5.5 Attack E

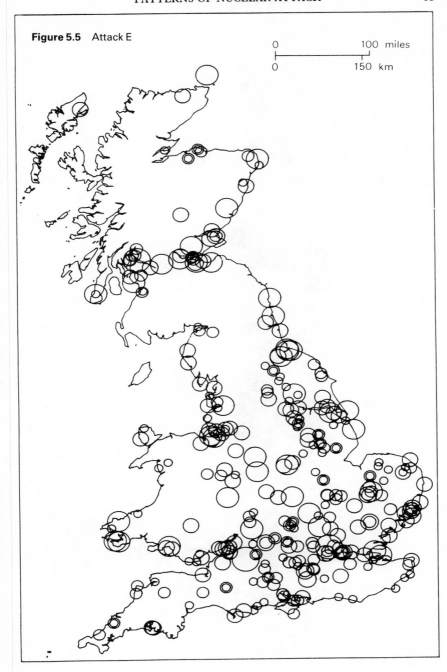

Figure 5.6   Attack F

We have assumed that the nuclear power stations are attacked with groundbursts – overpressures of about 200 psi are required to breach their containment vessels so that their radioactive contents are entrained by the rising fireball and dispersed over the country. If the objective was simply to disable the plant an airburst would be sufficient, since blast pressures of as little as 5–10 psi would probably be sufficient to cause a 'meltdown'.[15] This would result in serious but comparatively limited releases of radioactivity.

These additions bring the total number of targets attacked to 258 involving 293 warheads with a total yield of 163.75 megatons.

Attack F   Attack F is a 185.75 megaton attack, in which large conventional power stations with over 900 megawatt capacity are included, together with a couple of electricity grid control points and a few important transport links such as those listed in chapter 4. Since bridges, motorway intersections and railway junctions are resistant to high blast pressures, groundbursts are used to destroy them.

Attack G   Attack G adds 32 targets to the total, by including Royal Ordnance factories and a number of the large commercial plants making military equipment. Since there are many such plants in the UK, we have only included a selection of the more important ones, such as the Rolls-Royce factories at Filton (Bristol) and Derby, Westland aircraft and Vickers near Weston-super-Mare, and Plessey and British Aerospace plants such as those in Weybridge, south west of London. Most of these are attacked with airbursts so that the proportion of groundbursts is now reduced to about 64 per cent of all weapons. The total explosive power of the warheads used in Attack G is 213.65 megatons.

Attack H   With the inclusion of a very few major chemical and other industrial targets, for the first time the attack becomes realistic and plausible. The realities of nuclear war, Soviet strategy and targeting priorities, and the size and character of the Soviet arsenal (as discussed in the earlier chapters) all indicate that Attack H is the minimum scale of attack that the UK can reasonably expect in a nuclear war. Almost all the targets attacked are of short-term military importance, with only a few warheads aimed explicitly to hinder long-term recovery, even though the importance of such targets is frequently emphasized in Soviet strategic writings.

Assuming that only one quarter of the Soviet long range theatre nuclear forces are targeted on the UK, at 219.2 megatons, Attack H involves 37 to 43 per cent (30 to 35 per cent if the proportion is one third) of the total yield of the warheads available. The 342 warheads used amount to 39 to 49 per cent of the number available (33 to 39 per cent if the proportion is one third). Therefore, the attack is feasible even if NATO nuclear forces succeed in destroying over half of the Soviet nuclear arsenal before it can be used. It consists mainly of attacks with missiles and the modern

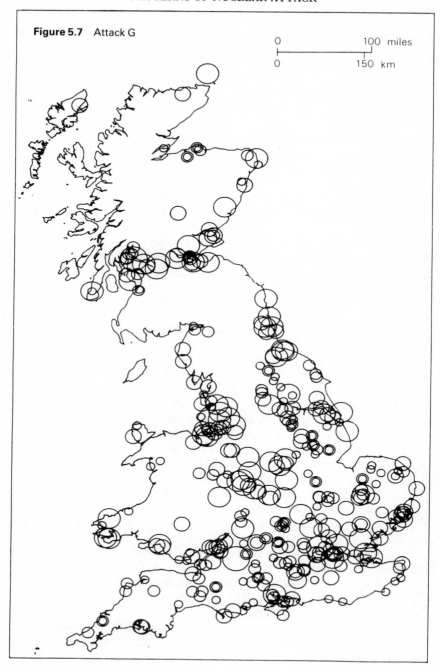

Figure 5.7 Attack G

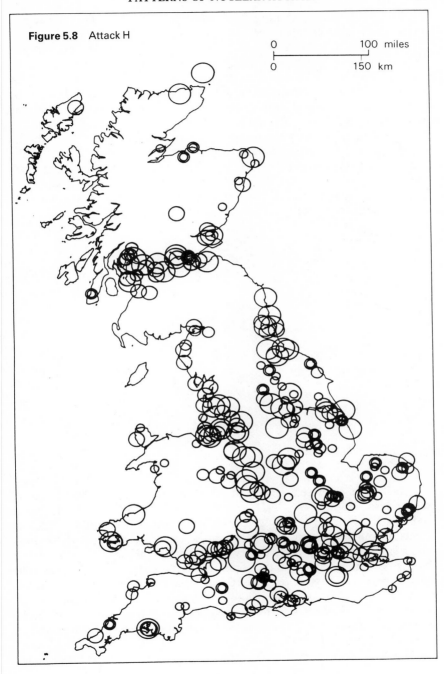

Figure 5.8   Attack H

0   100 miles
0   150 km

Backfire bomber using only a very small proportion of the Fencer and more easily intercepted, older, Badger and Blinder bombers.

Since it includes so few industrial targets and excludes the military targets added in Attack D, Attack H is if anything an underestimate of the most probable scale of attack on the UK. However, we base much of our discussion in later chapters upon it, in order to ensure that we cannot be accused of exaggerating the effects of nuclear war. The details of the weapons used in the attack are included in appendix 1.

The numbers of the various types of missiles and bombers used in this attack are shown in table 5.3. Figure 5.8 demonstrates the extent of the areas in Attack H where there are blast casualties and damage to, at least, doors, windows and roofs. They cover much of the most highly populated areas, even though population centres in themselves are not targeted. The effects of this and other attacks are detailed in chapter 7.

Table 5.3 Numbers of missiles and bombers used in Attack H

Type of missile/bomber	Number of missiles/ bombers used	Number allocated to targets in the UK, assuming a proportion allocated of	
		¼	⅓
SS20	44	58	78
SS4	39 ⎫	62	83
SS5	12 ⎭		
SS19 mod (2)	3	3–6	4–8
SS19 mod (3)	7	12–24	16–32
SS11 mod (1)	29	24–48	32–64
SS11 mod (3)	0	6–12	8–16
SSN5	3	7	10
Backfire	14[a]	15	20
Blinder	3	19	19
Badger	6	42	56
Fencer	5	77	77

[a] One Backfire carries two Kingfish air-to-surface missiles instead of four free-fall bombs

Attack H is a revised version of the scenario mentioned in chapter 1, which was adopted by CND in their 'Hard Luck' exercise and was publicized by peace groups and members of Scientists against Nuclear Arms throughout Britain in September 1982.[16] The British Medical Association presented the casualty estimates for this scenario (calculated by the present authors with the computer model described in chapter 6) in their report on *The Medical Effects of Nuclear War*,[17] as representing the best estimates then available of the outcome of attack on Britain.

Attacks I–K   In Attacks I to K the numbers of heavy and 'bottleneck' industrial targets is steadily increased, and some transport links such as Watford and Clapham railway junctions are also added to the list. Finally, in Attack K, a few population centres are also targeted in their own right.

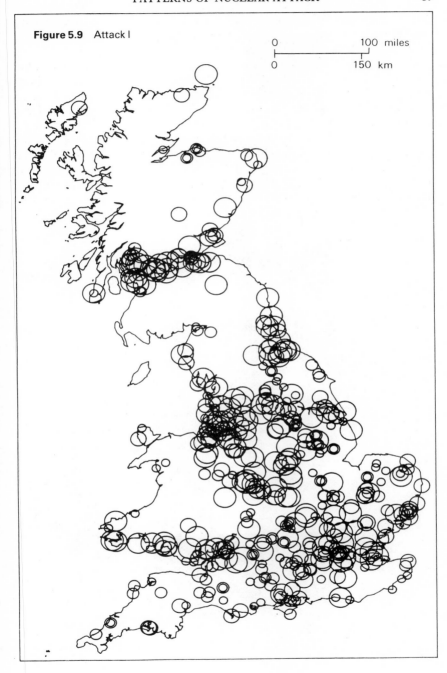

Figure 5.9 Attack I

0   100 miles

0   150 km

Figure 5.10   Attack J

Figure 5.11 Attack K

Nearly all of the additional warheads are carried on old SS4 missiles or Badger, Blinder and Fencer bombers. Most are airbursts, since most industrial targets are destroyed by overpressures of 5 to 10 psi.

The total yields of the weapons used in Attacks I, J and K are 257.65 megatons, 306.65 megatons and 347.65 megatons respectively. Thus, even in K the total yield is only 59 to 68 per cent (48 to 56 per cent if the proportion is one third) of the explosive power of the weapons available, and only 47 to 70 per cent of the warheads allocated to the UK are used.

There would be little problem constructing larger attacks than K. The weapons are available to include more industrial plants; the military targets included in D, and other ones of lower priority; administrative centres, regional and sub-regional seats of government, major coal mines, population centres; and lower priority targets in categories such as transport, energy or docks. However, we decided to finish at K and a glance at figures 5.9–5.11 shows why.

The areas that are still relatively free from blast effects, such as the Scottish Highlands, the border country and central and northern Wales, contain few targets and few people. In the rest of the country the devastation is so great, even for Attacks I and J, that a sizeable increment in the megatonnage of the attack increases the extent of the damage and the number of deaths by only a relatively small amount. Attacks of greater than 350 megatons, though certainly feasible, would represent a complete overkill, as chapters 7 and 8 will show.

DISCUSSION

These, then, are our scenarios. We believe that Attacks H to K are realistic estimates of the sort of nuclear attack that the UK might be subjected to if nuclear war began.

Naturally, an actual attack would be different from any of these in detail. Some targets which we have omitted might be destroyed instead of those we have included. It is difficult to decide upon relative priorities for targets towards the lower end of the list within each category.[18] Some warheads will explode further from their targets than we allow. A number of them will detonate tens or hundreds of kilometres away from their intended target because of malfunctions or bombing errors. Assuming a reliability of 65 to 80 per cent for missiles and bombers, in Attack H over 40 of such 'errant' warheads are likely to detonate in the UK (assuming that a similar number malfunction so badly that they either do not reach the UK or do not detonate). Our attacks are, therefore, likely to be an underestimate, since the USSR is perfectly aware of these unreliabilities and is likely to have allocated many of the 'spare' weapons that we assume not to be used in order to double or triple target important bases.

Even if we take the extreme situation where all the Soviet weapons not used in Attack H have been destroyed by NATO forces, where none of the malfunctioning missiles or misplaced bombs detonate over the UK and where the accuracies of the warheads that do arrive are much less than expected, the total numbers of casualties are not greatly reduced. We have shown this by randomly removing 20 per cent of the warheads in H and assuming that the actual ground zeros of the remainder are distributed normally around the intended target with a standard deviation of 2 km. We have then calculated the casualties according to the model described in chapter 6. Fifty such modifications were constructed using a random number generator.

The casualties ranged from 86 to 95 per cent of the total number of casualties in Attack H, with an average of 91 per cent. This relatively small reduction after the removal of 20 per cent of the warheads is due to the double-targeting in H of many of the important military bases. In these cases, the removal of one of the warheads does not mean that the target is removed. The introduction of 2 km inaccuracies (CEPs) is also not of any great consequence for total casualties, because the damage from any single weapon extends much further than the scale of the targeting errors. Also, since the intended targets are not located in any constant relation with the population centres, the errors will lead to more casualties in some cases and less in others.

Minimum retaliatory (MAD) attack

There is one possible scenario in which the size of attack on the UK is significantly smaller than Attack H. In the event that NATO succeeds in destroying the overwhelming majority of the Soviet nuclear forces in a first strike then only a few of the quickest reacting or least vulnerable bombers and missiles will be left for the USSR to use against the West.

We have assumed that the surviving SS19 and SS11 missiles which are allocated to Europe are retargeted on to the US and that all the old SS4 and SS5 missiles and Badger, Blinder and Fencer bombers have been destroyed before launch or take off. Less than half of the modern Backfire bombers and SS20 missiles allocated to targets in the UK are assumed to have been launched before they are destroyed and a few of these malfunction or are intercepted en route. Most of the SSN5 missiles survive since submarines are less vulnerable to attack and only a small proportion of them are assumed to be destroyed. Thus, our minimum retaliatory strike consists of 8 SSN5 missiles, 4 Backfire bombers and 31 SS20s, carrying between them 117 warheads with a total yield of 37.95 megatons. This represents 11 to 17 per cent of the warheads presently targeted on the UK and 5 to 7 per cent of the total yield.

Since NATO has, in this scenario, already used its nuclear forces and

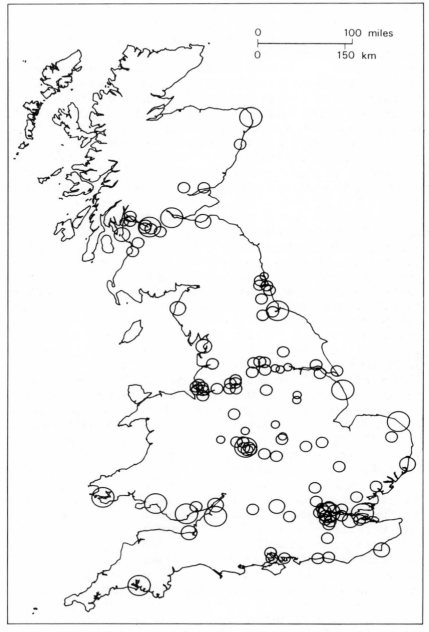

Figure 5.12   Targets in minimum retaliatory 'MAD' attack. The circles represent the extent of blast damage at 1 psi and above.

the USSR can do little with its few remaining forces to limit any further damage that may be inflicted upon it in the immediate future, we assume that the Soviet Union chooses to attack energy resources and urban/industrial areas in an attempt to destroy the NATO countries' economies and societies. Thus, a number of nuclear and conventional power stations, large oil refineries, and oil and gas terminals are attacked, together with the major cities and industrial areas.

This attack is presented (figure 5.12) to demonstrate that even under the most favourable military conditions, the effects of nuclear war would devastate the UK. In fact, it is doubtful that a NATO first strike, whether intended 'offensively' to disarm the USSR or 'defensively' to limit the damage of an attack that it suspected the USSR was about to launch, would be as 'successful' as we have assumed here.

Dispersed cruise missiles

Following a NATO 'modernization' decision in December 1979, the US intends to deploy 96 ground-launched cruise missiles (GLCMs) in Greenham Common base near Newbury starting at the end of 1983, and a further 64 at Molesworth near Huntingdon two or three years later. The extraordinary accuracy of these missiles means that they could be used with great effectiveness to destroy missile silos, command bunkers or airfields in European Russia as well as military targets in Eastern Europe. The Soviet Union will therefore regard it as of the highest priority to destroy them before they are launched, if at all possible.

In Attacks A to K we assumed that the GLCMs were deployed but remained stationed in their bunkers at Greenham Common and Molesworth. However, in times of international tension, the US plans to disperse them up to 100 miles from base to make them less vulnerable to attack. They may be sited anywhere from the Peak District to the New Forest or from Devon to Norwich. In this case, if the USSR does not know where the GLCMs are it will be obliged to launch a blanket attack on every possible dispersal area to be sure of destroying them. The Secretary of State for Defence (Air Force), G. Pattie, has stated in reply to a parliamentary question, that in these circumstances 'more than 1,000 megatons would be needed to destroy the ground launched cruise missiles once they were dispersed'.[19]

It is, however, likely that the Soviet Union would be able to track the GLCMs as they are dispersed from their bases. They travel in huge convoys consisting of 22 vehicles, six of them weighing over 35 tons. Sixteen missiles are carried by each convoy. They would be easily spotted by satellite and, in any case, would probably be followed by spies within the UK. In our scenario, therefore, we assume that the USSR knows the location of the ten convoys to within about 30 km. In order to destroy

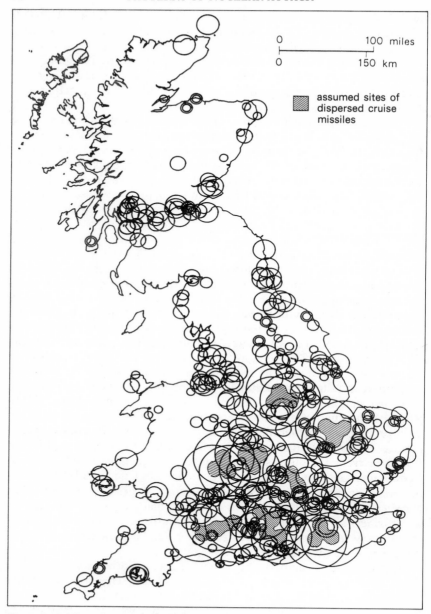

Figure 5.13   Targets in attack on dispersed cruise missiles. The circles represent the extent of blast damage at 1 psi and above. The areas to which the cruise missiles are assumed to have been dispersed are shaded. They are subjected to 10 psi or more.

them, 24 SS18 missiles, out of a total of 308, are diverted from what would otherwise be their targets on the US mainland. We have chosen these to be the model (1) and model (3) versions which carry single 20 megaton warheads.[20] This choice allows a greater economy in the number of missiles that need to be used. Clearly, a wide range of targets other than the GCLMs would also be attacked. We have added the SS18 missile attacks to Attack H, our minimum realistic attack.

Obviously, the US are not going to disperse the cruise missiles to areas near bases that are likely to be attacked in their own right. Neither are they likely to disperse them to built up areas where they will cause an obstruction and be spotted. The most likely dispersal sites are in areas of the countryside well away from other prime targets.

On the assumption that two of the flights of cruise missiles are undergoing maintenance, and therefore cannot be dispersed, we have chosen eight such areas and then pattern bombed them in a way which ensures that they are all subjected to at least 10 psi (the overpressure that we assume to cause damage to the GLCMs and their launchers sufficient to prevent their launch). The resulting attack pattern is shown in fig 5.13. Of course, we could have assumed that they were dispersed in different areas (for example, south-east Norfolk, between Leicester and Northampton, or in Kent) but we believe the scenario we have chosen to be plausible. The total megatonnage of the warheads used is 699.2 (219.2 megatons in Attack H plus 480 megatons on the 24 SS18 warheads).

HISTORICAL ATTACK SCENARIOS

We finish this chapter by introducing five historical attack scenarios. Four were produced by government ministries as a basis for civil or home defence exercises. (The important distinction between home and civil defence exercises is discussed in chapter 10.) The fifth comes from an article published in the Home Office journal *Fission Fragments* which is circulated amongst the volunteer scientific advisers within the civil defence organization.[21]

For all but one of the government scenarios, the targets lists are still not officially released and so we have had to rely upon unofficial sources for our information. We have also had to make some assumptions about the weapons used and whether or not they are airbursts or groundbursts.

'Dutch Treat'

The first example comes from a civil defence exercise, code named 'Dutch Treat', conducted in 1957 (figure 5.14). It involved eight 1 megaton groundbursts, mainly on city targets — London, Liverpool, Sheffield,

Figure 5.14   Targets in the 'Dutch Treat' civil defence exercise of 1957. The circles
represent the extent of blast damage at 1 psi and above.

East Kilbride and Glasgow. Aldermaston Atomic Weapons Research Establishment was hit, together with Aberporth and Brawdy airforce bases in South West Wales.

1960 civil defence exercise

A civil defence exercise dating from 1960 has the unique distinction of being the only one for which the targets have been officially published — in a Ministry of Health circular.[22] (See figure 5.15.) It is described as a 'minimum retaliatory attack'. Four 10 megaton bombs were detonated over London, Birmingham, Manchester and Leeds, and eleven 1.5 megaton weapons over cities such as Newcastle, Middlesbrough, Liverpool, Southampton and Bristol. The circular did not specify which of these were airbursts and which groundbursts, so we have assumed that all the 10 megaton bombs were groundbursts and the remainder airbursts. This has the effect of maximizing the number of casualties.

The 1957 and 1960 exercises took place at a time when the nuclear arsenals of the superpowers were relatively small. It is estimated that the USSR had a total of 1,034 medium and intermediate range missiles and nuclear capable bombers in 1960.[23] About 250 inaccurate SS3s and SS4s had been deployed, but otherwise the warheads would have been delivered to their targets in Britain by Badger bombers. The small numbers of weapons, the megaton yields, and the attacks on city targets assumed in these exercises were, therefore, reasonably realistic even though both attack scenarios appear to underestimate the scale of attack and to be slightly quirky. In 'Dutch Treat' Aberporth and Brawdy RAF bases appear to have been selected for destruction for no apparent reason. In the 1960 exercise, Scotland escapes unscathed.

From the mid-1960s until the mid-1970s civil defence against nuclear war was largely neglected by governments amid a growing consensus that it was a futile activity. In the mid-1970s, however, it was revived. A civil defence exercise was conducted in 1975 code named 'Inside Right', and another in 1978 ('Scrum Half'), but few details of them are available.

Fission Fragments (1978)

In November 1978, however, a talk given by a scientific adviser called E.J. Grove to the South West Region Scientific Advisers' Conference was published in *Fission Fragments*, the Home Office Scientific Advisers' journal. It included a sketch map (figure 5.16) showing the targets of a 'possible counterforce attack pattern on Britain'. They are not labelled, but in almost every case the intended target is easily identified. The overwhelming majority of them are major RAF or USAF bases, but the Fylingdales ballistic missile early warning station and five other important

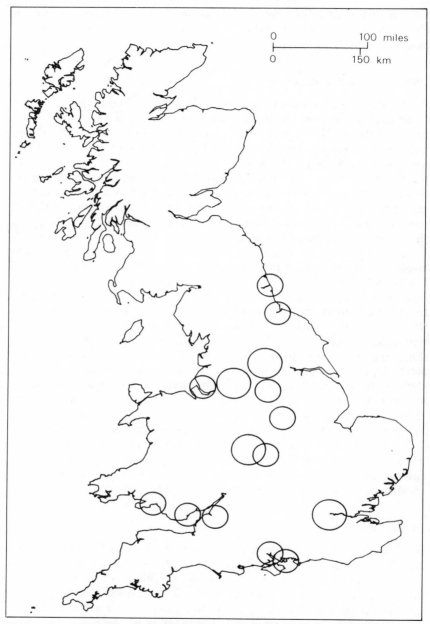

Figure 5.15   Targets in a civil defence exercise of 1960. The circles represent the extent of blast damage at 1 psi and above.
Source: Ministry of Health Circular No. 9/1960.

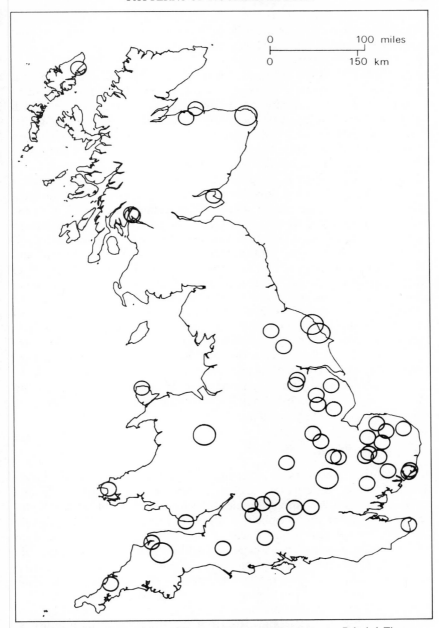

Figure 5.16   Targets in a 'possible counterforce attack pattern on Britain'. The circles represent the extent of blast damage at 1 psi and above.

Source: E. J. Grove, *Fission Fragments* 23, November 1978.

communication or radar centres are also included, together with the Faslane Polaris base, Greenham Common, and the US and UK command centres at High Wycombe. Holy Loch submarine base and several other major centres are omitted.

Altogether 52 targets are shown. We have assumed that each of these is destroyed with a single 1 megaton groundburst on all the targets, except Fylingdales and the other five communication and radar centres for which we judged an airburst to be more appropriate. Thus we assume a total yield of 52 megatons. Even this yield could be an overestimate of Grove's intentions, since in many cases he might have preferred to assume that smaller yield SS20 warheads would be used.

This scenario supposes, as does US and NATO policy, that a nuclear attack could be limited to attacks on nuclear forces and a few of the most vital of their associated radar and communications centres. Any prime targets near population centres — such as the Northwood command centre and several other targets in London, Burtonwood (near Liverpool) and other nuclear stores, and airports, such as Heathrow, Luton, and Manchester — are omitted on the ground that the USSR would prefer to leave them intact, despite their great military importance, rather than to provoke an attack on Soviet cities with the UK's Polaris missiles. We have argued earlier that this view is inconsistent with Soviet nuclear policy and with the realities and objectives of nuclear war. Grove's scenario is therefore unrealistic because it omits all of the other categories of military and economic target, beside the nuclear forces, that would almost certainly be destroyed in a nuclear attack.

Although we have shown that such limited nuclear attacks are highly improbable, Grove's scenario is in line with modern trends in the beliefs of many US and NATO strategists.

'Square Leg' (1980)

In September 1980 various government departments conducted a home defence exercise code named 'Operation Square Leg' (figure 5.17). The target list has not been officially released. However most of the bomb plot has been revealed by Campbell in the *New Statesman*.[24] He reports 62 airbursts and 69 groundbursts with a total yield of 205 megatons — an average of 1.5 megatons per weapon. It is likely that these figures exclude many of the airbursts that were supposed, in the exercise, to have occurred more than one hour after the attack started.[25] So the total yield of the attack may well have been between 260 and 350 megatons.

Although government officials have emphasized that 'Square Leg' was just an exercise, the scale and pattern of the attack, with its mixture of military and civilian targets, is actually rather plausible. Many of the most important military targets, such as High Wycombe, Brawdy anti-

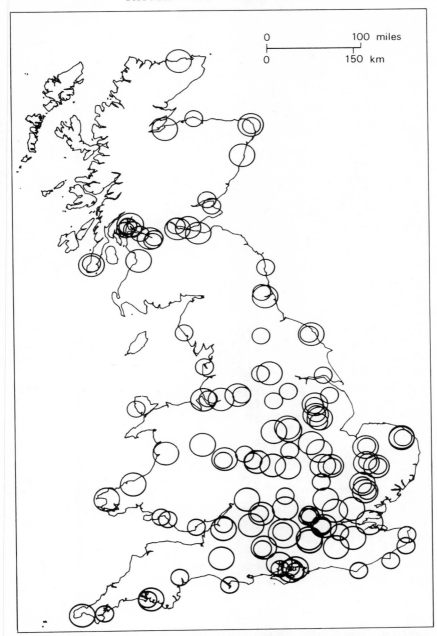

Figure 5.17 Targets in the 'Square Leg' home defence exercise of 1980. The circles represent the extent of blast damage at 1 psi and above.

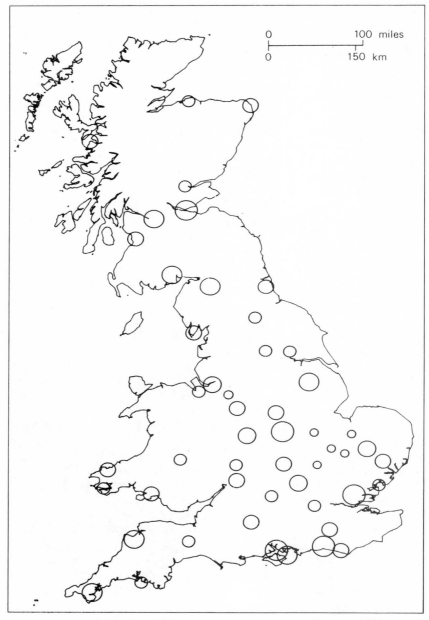

Figure 5.18   Targets in the 'Hard Rock' home defence exercise which was to have been held in 1982. The circles represent the extent of blast damage at 1 psi and above.

submarine warfare base, Catterick army barracks, Greenham Common, Heathrow airport, and a number of US and RAF bases are attacked. Several ports, Canvey Island liquefied gas plant, Sellafield (Windscale) nuclear reprocessing plant, Birmingham and Manchester are also included, amongst a number of other military/economic targets.

The 'Square Leg' scenario also has a few surprising features. No targets in inner London are attacked, for example Whitehall, the US 6th Fleet command centre and the intelligence centre at Grosvenor Square, or Northwood. Penzance, Eastbourne and Machynlleth are targeted for no obvious reason. However, the main unrealistic feature is the use of only high yield (megaton range) bombs. As we showed in chapter 4, many warheads, particularly those on the modern missiles, have yields of only a fraction of a megaton.

'Hard Rock' (1982)

The home defence exercise planned for September 1982, code-named 'Hard Rock' (figure 5.18), was to have been the largest since the Civil Defence Corps disbanded in 1968. Widespread opposition to such exercises, particularly amongst many local authorities, led to 'Hard Rock' being postponed and subsequently cancelled. However, the details of 'Hard Rock' were published by Campbell[26] later in 1982.

The 'Hard Rock' scenario assumed a few weeks of international tension followed by six days of conventional bombing before the initial nuclear attack. Many of the highest priority nuclear bases, including Holy Loch submarine base and the NATO command centres at Pitreavie Castle and Northwood are attacked in the conventional raids (even though, for instance, Northwood is buried 200 feet underground in a reinforced bunker!). This assumption reflects the increasing influence within NATO of the belief that extended periods of conventional war over all of Europe are possible. However, the growth of this belief is not the result of any changes in Warsaw Pact or NATO military posture. If anything, these postures have tended to make it increasingly likely that any war extending beyond the 'Central European battlefield' would involve nuclear weapons.

The nuclear attack is assumed to continue for 6½ hours, during which time 54 nuclear warheads, with a total yield of 48.4 megatons, are detonated over the UK. No major strategic forces are hit and 6 of the 11 bombs aimed at military targets miss. Some 20 cities are apparently targeted, but only Plymouth, Hastings, Leicester and Glasgow are actually hit. In all the other cases the bombs 'miss' and detonate several miles away in less populated areas. The closest explosion to London is a near miss aimed at Heathrow Airport. A few major economic and industrial targets are hit, such as the St Fergus gas terminal and the oil refineries at Fawley and Milford Haven. A number of bombs land on tiny towns of no military or economic significance.

The warning given in Home Office civil defence exercises that the scenarios should not be taken to be realistic is scarcely necessary in this case. It is hard to imagine how a scenario as unrealistic as this would be of any value for testing the feasibility of civil defence plans against nuclear war.

6

Estimating the Effects
of Attack

This chapter describes methods for predicting the casualties and damage which would be caused by nuclear weapons. These methods are incorporated into a computer 'model' — that is, an interconnected series of computer programs. We deal here just with the immediate effects of heat, blast and fallout. Longer-term consequences are covered in chapter 8.

A CAUTIONARY NOTE

It is important to state at the beginning that a great degree of uncertainty is involved in these calculations. Predictions of what the effects of blast and heat would do to people and buildings rest in part on the evidence of the two bombs dropped on Japan in 1945. But these were low-yield weapons by modern standards (12.5 kilotons at Hiroshima, 22 kilotons at Nagasaki), much smaller than any of the weapons which the Soviets would use in an attack on Britain today. There are reasons why the difference in explosive yield itself would result in weapons in the megaton range having qualitatively different effects from the Japanese bombs — quite apart from their greatly magnified explosive power — as we will explain. The houses in Nagasaki and Hiroshima were mostly of traditional Japanese wooden construction, and allowances must also be made for the differences from modern western building methods.

What is more, the bombs on both Japanese cities were airbursts, and although they produced some radioactive fallout in the form of 'black rain' (blackened by ash and dust), this was not as great as it would have been for groundbursts. The behaviour of fallout clouds has to be predicted largely on the basis of the atmospheric tests conducted over the Pacific Ocean, in the Nevada desert and elsewhere, in the 1950s and early 1960s prior to the Test Ban Treaty of 1963.

There have also been a large number of experiments with test buildings, other structures, vehicles and animals — including exposing all of these to actual nuclear explosions. And there have been many theoretical studies, using computers. But it is fair to say that many uncertainties and difficulties of calculation remain unresolved.

The problems are emphasized by Glasstone and Dolan in the preface of their book *The Effects of Nuclear Weapons*, which is produced jointly by the United States Departments of Defense and Energy, has gone into three editions since 1957, and is widely regarded as the standard work on the subject.[1] This chapter relies heavily on the book for data and techniques of calculation. They say:

We should emphasize . . . that numerical values given in this book are not — and cannot be — exact. They must inevitably include a substantial margin of error. Apart from the difficulties in making measurements of weapons effects, the results are often dependent upon circumstances which could not be predicted in the event of a nuclear attack. Furthermore, two weapons of different design may have the same explosive energy yield, but the effects could be markedly different.[2]

The problems are illustrated by the examples of Hiroshima and Nagasaki where the larger bomb, on Nagasaki, is thought to have killed only about half as many people as were killed at Hiroshima.[3] A large part of this difference can be explained by differences in the density and distribution of population in the two cities and by differences in topography; but the comparison still indicates some of the difficulties of extrapolating to other, hypothetical attacks.

There is a lack of precise knowledge about the likely impact of certain of the effects of nuclear weapons on the human body, especially the effects of radiation. And as Glasstone and Dolan mention, there may be significantly altered effects arising from the particular circumstances of an attack. These would include, obviously, the types and numbers of targets hit, and the sizes of weapons used, whether airbursts or groundbursts; but also the weather conditions at the time, since these can influence the effects of heat, and determine the pattern in which fallout is distributed. Another important consideration is whether any warning is given of attack, and if people as a result have taken any sheltering precautions.

Where difficulties arise in prediction because of lack of knowledge of the physical and biological processes involved, or because of their complexity, our approach has been to summarize the issues involved as fairly as we can, and to argue for the plausibility of our own assumptions or simplifications, given all the uncertainties. For those factors which are likely to change with the circumstances of an attack, and others over which there is particular controversy, our approach has been to show the consequences, in predicting casualties and levels of damage, of a whole series of varying assumptions. These include different weather patterns, different assumptions about sheltering, and different assumptions about the biological effects of radiation. In chapter 7, we describe how sensitive our computer results were to alterations in certain key assumptions.

In general, however, we are confident that, where there are uncertainties in the calculations, they will tend to be in the direction of producing underestimates of the number of casualties and the extent of the destruction. This is for three reasons. First, where a value for an important variable has had to be chosen from within a range of uncertainty, we have tended towards the conservative end of that range. Second, we rely as described on data and methods which originate almost exclusively from the US Department of Defense; and this is an institution which would tend also to err if at all in the conservative direction. Lastly, there are some direct, and many indirect, effects of nuclear weapons which are left out of account altogether in these calculations of numbers of casualties, because it is almost impossible to make precise predictions about them. Such effects would nevertheless certainly occur, and some of them are described in later chapters. Meanwhile it cannot be emphasized too strongly that in this chapter we are concerned to estimate just the immediate consequences of the most significant and readily predictable features of a nuclear attack, from the point of view of damage and casualties.

NUCLEAR EXPLOSIONS: A SUMMARY

Conventional high explosive weapons derive their energy from chemical reactions. In nuclear explosions two very different processes are responsible. In an atomic or *fission* weapon each atom of uranium or plutonium splits into two parts, giving off neutrons which cause other atoms to split, and so on, in an uncontrolled chain reaction. Each fission gives off energy mainly in the form of heat. In a hydrogen or *fusion* weapon certain types of hydrogen atoms fuse together at temperatures comparable to those at the centre of the sun. In order to achieve these temperatures, a fission device is generally used as an initiator. For this reason this is sometimes termed a fission-fusion or *thermonuclear* weapon.

It is further possible to surround the entire arrangement in a casing of uranium. The high-speed neutrons produced in the fusion reactions create fission processes in this casing material, so that the result is the sequence fission-fusion-fission. In such weapons perhaps half the explosive power or *yield* will come from fission.

The time-scale involved is absolutely minute, typically less than one millionth of a second. Yet on a weight-for-weight basis the energy produced by a nuclear explosive is millions of times greater than that produced by a chemical explosive. The temperatures reached in a nuclear explosion are much higher, tens of millions of degrees, compared with a few thousand in a conventional explosion. As a result of this immense temperature difference the distribution of explosion energy is very different. In a chemical explosion most of the energy appears as kinetic energy which is almost entirely converted into a blast or shock wave, with relatively little thermal radiation. By contrast, thermal radiation is an important component of a nuclear explosion.

In the instant after the detonation of a nuclear weapon the small mass of weapon materials will have been vaporized and the nuclear chain reactions will have ceased. But the highly excited atoms of the weapon debris continue to emit large quantities of neutrons, gamma rays and 'soft' or lower energy X-rays. The X-rays are absorbed by, and heat, the surrounding air. This produces a luminous fireball which expands rapidly. The fireball re-radiates its heat, and this can cause burns and start fires at long distances from the point of detonation. Much of the thermal energy however is absorbed by the air, which expands and creates a fast-moving shock wave. It is this shock wave, and the high-speed winds associated with it, which cause damage to buildings and casualties from blast effects. At the same time the fireball is rising quickly, since on expansion it becomes lighter than the surrounding air. As it shoots upwards and cools, it forms the classic mushroom cloud and stem.

As well as the heat given off in the explosion, there is also a very brilliant flash of light. This could cause temporary blindness. If people were looking directly at the fireball, the radiant heat could be focused on to their retinas, and they could be permanently blinded. (This effect was very rare in Hiroshima and Nagasaki however.) It is conceivable that people might suffer other injuries as a consequence — for example if they were driving cars at the time — but such possibilities are ignored in our calculations.

The neutrons and gamma rays emitted in and immediately following the explosion are referred to as *initial nuclear radiation* (INR). INR is defined, rather arbitrarily, as lasting until one minute after the detonation. It is assumed that after this time most of the materials which are the source of the neutrons will have been carried up in the mushroom cloud to a sufficient height, that the radiation no longer reaches the earth's surface.

INR was the principal cause of the radiation sickness deaths and injuries which occurred in Japan. However, this was a consequence of the relatively low yields of the weapons. The range of lethal INR is greater, for small yields, than are the ranges of lethal burns and blast effects. (The 'neutron bomb', which is a low-yield weapon, is specifically designed to enhance these effects of INR.) As the explosive yield gets larger, the range to which dangerous INR extends is less than that at which practically the entire population present would in any case be killed by blast and burns. The present study is concerned entirely with high-yield strategic weapons, and therefore the effects of INR are ignored.

Nevertheless, it is possible that some cases of radiation sickness could be caused by INR from weapons with yields of the order of hundreds of kilotons (as for example the SS20s). Those affected would have been relatively close to ground zero, either out of doors but shielded from the fireball, or else in buildings or shelters offering rather little protection against radiation, but who somehow managed to escape death from blast effects.

Radioactive *fallout* is constituted from the materials which have been carried up into the mushroom cloud. When the explosion takes place at or near the earth's surface then large quantities of soil and surface material can be drawn into the rising fireball. As the fireball cools the radioactive weapon debris, and the products of fission reactions, condense with and on to dust particles. The fission products are a very complex mixture of more than 300 isotopes (different radioactive species) of some 36 elements. The highly radioactive particles return to earth, either falling under their own weight or brought down with rain or snow, as fallout. The larger particles might measure between one-fiftieth of a millimetre and half a millimetre. They would be deposited around the crater and then drop more slowly in a complex pattern over a wide area which might extend several hundred kilometres downwind. This is referred to as 'early' or 'local' fallout.

Very small particles could be carried up into the stratosphere. This would also be the case with the vaporized weapon debris from airbursts. Such particles could circle the globe a few times before slowly returning to earth. This is 'delayed' or 'worldwide' fallout. We are concerned here just with local fallout.

For an airburst nuclear weapon detonated at about 12,000 metres or lower, the total energy released in the explosion is divided approximately in the proportions 50 per cent in the blast or shock wave, 35 per cent in the form of thermal radiation, 5 per cent as initial nuclear radiation, and 10 per cent as the 'residual' nuclear radiation emitted by fallout.

COMPUTER MODELS FOR CASUALTY PREDICTION

This is a broad overview of how estimates of casualties are obtained. It may be that non-specialist readers will wish then to skip the detailed discussions of the methods of calculation which follow and go straight to the results in chapter 7. This more detailed account is, however, presented in a relatively non-technical way. The mathematical aspects are covered in appendices 2–4.

The first requirement is some means for representing the land area of Britain and the distribution of population throughout the country. We divide the country up into a grid of 1 km squares. These squares are shown on most large-scale Ordnance Survey maps, for example on the 1:50,000 Series. To cover the whole of England, Scotland and Wales, about ¼ million squares are needed. (Northern Ireland and the Channel

Islands are left out of the calculations.) The actual land area is approximately 227,500 km^2. The total area of grid-squares is greater, because of squares overlapping the coast-line.

The 1971 census was used for population data, since census results are available in a form which gives the total number of persons living in each 1 km grid square.[4] Only some 152,400 grid-squares are recorded as containing any population; the remainder are uninhabited. Every grid-square can be referred to uniquely by an Ordnance Survey National Grid reference. Thus the targets for bombs, and the extent of their effects, can all be recorded in relation to the referencing system used on all OS maps.

The use of 1971 census data requires some explanation. A new census was taken in 1981, but the results are not as yet converted to 1 km grid-squares (and may never be). The advantages of using grid-squares are their uniform size and shape, and the fact that the population count in each gives a direct measure of population density (persons per square kilometre). It will be possible in due course to use 1981 population data by enumeration districts. There are about 130,000 enumeration districts in Britain. They are of varying shapes and sizes, which causes difficulties; and these data were not available at the time of writing. Data for larger units such as wards, parishes and local authority areas are available, but these units are too large for representing the effects of weapons with any accuracy.

The problem with the 1971 census is, of course, that it is out of date. However, there have not been large enough changes in population numbers, or movements of population since 1971, to cause substantial inaccuracies in the results at the national level; although predictions for a few local areas will be seriously in error. What is more, the Home Office computer model described in chapter 9 also uses the 1971 data, and this makes possible direct comparison of their results with ours.

Because the number of grid-squares to be considered is so great, it is not practical to carry out the calculations involved at the national scale by hand, and computers are needed. Some local studies for small areas have been made manually, for example, that of *London after the Bomb*.[5] Sufficient information is given in this chapter to allow readers to make their own calculations for small areas, given local population data. Not only can calculations be carried out, however, much more quickly and accurately by computer; but it is possible to experiment with many different sets of targets and with a number of varying assumptions.

The programming language used is FORTRAN and the programs run on a large main-frame computer (IBM 370/168) at the University of Newcastle. They are much too large to fit on a micro-computer; but they have been run on a mini-computer (VAX 11/780). Computer run-times for each of the attack scenarios vary according to the numbers of weapons involved, but generally range from 200 to 3,600 seconds of central processing (CPU) time. Since the 370/168 machine is capable of half a million arithmetic operations per second, this gives an indication of the huge computational task involved.

The process of estimating casualties in an attack starts with two sets of data inputs: the population distribution for Britain, and a set of targets with weapons of specified yield, groundburst or airburst, assigned to each. Deaths and injuries are then calculated from the three effects, heat, blast and fallout. Figure 6.1 gives a simplified flowchart for the structure of the computer programs.[6]

The census records in principle where people are at midnight on the night in question in 1971. One implication of using census data is therefore, that the distribution of population at the time of attack is as it would be at night, with most people 'at home'. If an attack were launched during a normal working day, or at a weekend, the distribution of population could be very different. However, there are no suitable sources of national data that could be used to represent either of these situations. There are questions in the census relating to people's places of work; but it would be difficult, if not impossible, to predict the locations of those at school, out shopping or involved in leisure activities away from home. Also the workplace data are not available either by 1 km grid-squares or for the entire country in 1971 below the local authority level.

The question of where people are at the time of an attack could also be affected by whether warnings were given, and by possible civil defence measures. The Home Office currently has a 'stay-put' policy whereby people are advised, in the *Protect and Survive* leaflet, to go home and stay at home.[7] It is of course quite conceivable that they might not follow this advice, and would try to get out of the larger urban areas and away from the obvious targets. Official evacuation schemes have been considered in the past (see chapter 10). But in the absence of detailed plans the resulting distribution of the evacuated population is again difficult to predict. One very crude assumption might be to take a uniform average population density over the whole country, as representing the optimum result of an evacuation policy. But this is hardly realistic, since many areas could not provide any accommodation for the evacuees.

Besides the question of how the population is distributed geographically, there is another important consideration, and that is how many people are in buildings and how many out of doors. This could have consequences for the numbers of people killed and injured by burns, as we shall see. A surprise attack during the day would be likely to catch more people outdoors than one during the night. Such was the case at Hiroshima, where the air-raid warning seemed to be a false alarm — there was only one plane in the sky — and it was also a fine sunny day. More people might be caught in the open if an attack occurred during an attempt at evacuation.

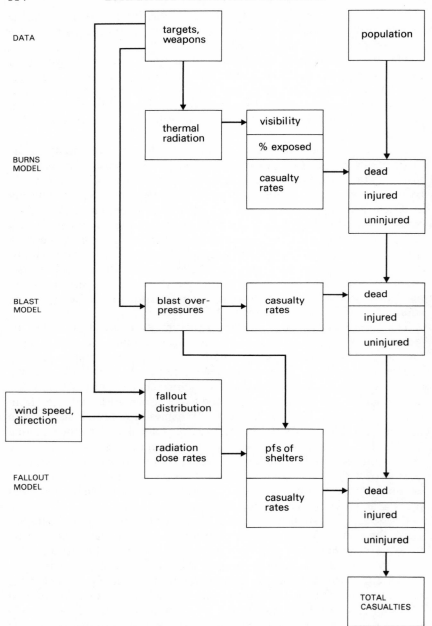

Figure 6.1   Flowchart showing the structure of the computer programs or 'models' used to calculate short-term casualties from burns, blast and fallout. (pf = protection factor)

However, the only distribution of the population which the available data really allow, is an assumed night-time distribution. This probably leads to underestimates of the numbers of casualties. A surprise attack during working hours on a weekday would in general find many more people in the city centres or nearer to potential industrial targets than would be the case at night-time. As for the proportion of the population out of doors, we examine the consequences of a range of different assumptions.

Given the two data inputs of population distribution, and attack pattern, the first part of the computer model calculates numbers of burns, deaths and injuries from the direct effects of thermal radiation (see figure 6.1). The population data are modified after each bomb is considered, by removing those counted as dead, and recording separately the remaining numbers of injured or uninjured people. The next part of the model calculates deaths and injuries from blast. Again the numbers of uninjured and injured survivors are recorded. The last part of the model calculates fallout casualties. The end-product is a set of totals of deaths and injuries from all causes, and a number of uninjured 'survivors' after all three effects.

The process of estimating casualties is therefore sequential. The burns casualties are estimated first for all weapons; then the blast casualties; finally the fallout casualties. It is as though all the bombs were detonated simultaneously. In reality they would not be. Here we assume a single concentrated attack in each case: but the attack could still be spread in several waves, perhaps over a period of hours or even days. The Soviet Union might see what damage was caused by the first weapons and re-target others accordingly. Later weapons might be directed against less critical targets such as remaining dispersal airfields, or troop concentrations. Even in a sudden attack, all weapons would not detonate precisely simultaneously.

For weapons separated by only a few miles, a second bomb might well find a higher proportion of survivors from the effects of the first bomb out in the open. The sequential nature of the model as set out in figure 6.1, means that these effects of interaction between different weapons are not properly considered. For example in assessing thermal radiation effects, we assume always that a constant proportion of the population (say 5 per cent) is outdoors or at windows, and so exposed to the fireball. This proportion would in reality be likely to increase as successive weapons in the same area caused increasing blast damage to buildings, or the resulting fires forced people to flee outside.

Similarly, in assessing blast damage, we assume that the blast pressure needed to demolish a typical house remains constant; where presumably a much lower level of pressure would be needed to destroy an already damaged house. The calculation of radiation doses in areas of overlapping fallout effects from several bombs is also dependent on the assumption of simultaneity.

We do not take account of the possibility of these particular interaction effects. To allow for the non-simultaneity of explosions would introduce excessive complications, and probably would not be justified by any increase in accuracy of prediction. In any case there would be no reliable means of determining the likely relative timing of weapons in an attack; nor any experimental data on which to base predictions of the resulting interactions.

However, there are other types of interaction which we *do* allow for. For example many people will be counted as injured once, and then counted as injured again by a different cause from the same weapon, or by other nearby weapons. For example burns victims might also subsequently be injured by blast or by fallout. Or people might be injured by burns from more than one bomb.

The simple assumption is made that people who are injured from more than one cause will die. This is regarded as plausible especially as some of the injuries will be 'synergistic'; that is to say, in combination their consequences are more serious than the sum of the separate injuries would suggest. For example one effect of radiation sickness is to lower the body's resistance to infection. In these circumstances burns, for example, would be much more serious than otherwise. It also seems unlikely that many people will receive prompt medical treatment, or even any treatment at all, in the conditions following a nuclear attack (see chapter 8). All the predicted injuries are 'serious' ones. There would be numerous other minor injuries not accounted for.

Again, the level of protection offered by buildings against the effects of radiation will obviously depend in part on the extent to which they suffer blast damage. This becomes an extremely significant factor in the heavier weights of attack. It is allowed for by varying the assumed levels of radiation protection in an area, in proportion to the seriousness of the blast damage experienced there.

THERMAL RADIATION EFFECTS

Somewhere between 18 and 35 per cent of the energy from a nuclear explosion is released in the form of an intense burst of radiant heat. The lower value is for a groundburst weapon. People who are exposed in direct line of sight to the fireball, either in the open air, or at windows facing the explosion, may suffer burns of varying severity depending on the distance. People indoors and away from windows, or in the shadow of buildings, will generally be protected (although it is possible for some of the radiation to be reflected).

The amount of thermal radiation or 'radiant exposure' to which people or buildings are exposed is usually measured in calories per square centimetre (cal/cm^2). The range at which a certain level of thermal radiant exposure will be produced varies with the yield of the bomb, the height of detonation, and the conditions of the atmosphere. If the air is clear, the effects will extend further; if it is misty or smoggy, the range will be reduced. There are other ways in which the weather can have an influence. If the bomb explodes below a layer of cloud, then the heat flash will be reflected off the underside of the clouds, and this will increase the range for a given level of radiant exposure. The same can happen with a layer of snow on the ground.

A second cause of death or injury would be from burns caused *indirectly* through fires, as distinct from the burns caused by direct exposure to the fireball itself. Fires would be started by the thermal radiation from the explosion setting light to materials on the outside of buildings, or to furniture, upholstery and bedding exposed near windows. Trees and shrubs could also be set alight, as could such materials as fallen leaves, newspapers and other rubbish. However, fires started inside buildings would be more likely to take hold and spread than those started outdoors. In buildings damaged by blast there could be fires started by electrical short-circuits; where central heating boilers were damaged; where gas pipes were fractured; or where petrol, oil or other inflammable liquids were spilled.

Chapter 7 examines the possible extent and nature of fires throughout the country. There would undoubtedly be many people killed and injured in these fires, which could spread over vast areas. However, in common with other studies of nuclear war, we have omitted such casualties from direct burns in fires from our calculations; not because they would not happen, but because of the difficulties of prediction. As the Office of Technology Assessment (OTA) say '. . . the extent of fire damage depends on factors such as weather and details of building construction that makes it much more difficult to predict than blast damage.'[8]

In order to calculate the number of burns cases caused by direct exposure to the heat of the fireball, it is necessary first of all to determine the amounts of heat falling on surfaces at different distances from the explosion. The relevant equations, taken from Glasstone and Dolan, are given in appendix 2. We assume clear visibility (19 km) throughout, and no cloud or snow cover.

Once the level of thermal radiation is found for a given location, it is possible to estimate the resulting burns casualties. What is needed is a figure for the proportion of the population exposed to the fireball; and some assumed relationship of the levels of heat to the seriousness of the burns injuries caused. The proportion exposed is obviously very difficult to predict with any certainty and could easily vary from place to place.

Some of the factors which might affect this have already been discussed: time of day or night, time of year (and hence the weather), warning time, and the possibility that earlier bomb damage might leave more people exposed to weapons following later. It is only really possible to pick some average figure more or less arbitrarily. In general the standard assumption is made that five per cent of the population is exposed. In chapter 7, however, we examine the consequences of varying assumptions between 0 per cent and 30 per cent exposed. Five per cent seems to be a conservative figure. The OTA study takes a range of values from 1 to 25 per cent exposed.[9]

For the relationship of radiant exposure values to seriousness of injury, we have again experimented with a variety of possibilities, since not all authorities are in agreement. The simplest approach is that of the OTA who assume that all those receiving a radiant exposure of 6.7 calories per square centimetre and above, suffer fatal burns; those receiving between 3.4 and 6.7 cals/cm^2 suffer serious burns injuries that would require extensive medical treatment for survival; and those receiving less than 3.4 cals/cm^2 would either be uninjured or only slightly injured.[10] As a guide, 6.7 cals/cm^2 is sufficient to set light to newspapers or synthetic fabrics. Table 6.1 shows the distances in kilometres at which the critical values of 3.4 and 6.7 cals/cm^2 would be reached, from weapons of eight different yields, assuming a clear day with visibility of 19 km. For example, for a one megaton airburst, people would be killed at a distance of 14.7 km, and seriously injured at 19.1 km.

One problem here is that the prognosis attached to different levels of burns injuries is strongly dependent on the level of available medical

Table 6.1 Distances from ground zero (in kilometres) at which the level of thermal radiant exposure would be 3.4 and 6.7 calories per square centimetre. These are the levels at which people exposed to the fireball would be seriously injured or killed by burns, respectively, on the assumptions of the Office of Technology Assessment (*Effects of Nuclear War*, p. 32)

Explosive yield (megatons)	Groundburst		Airburst	
	Injured (3.4 cal/cm^2)	Killed (6.7 cal/cm^2)	Injured (3.4 cal/cm^2)	Killed (6.7 cal/cm^2)
0.15	6.1	4.6	8.4	6.4
0.5	9.6	7.5	13.2	10.3
1.0	12.2	9.7	19.1	14.7
1.5	13.9	11.2	22.2	17.2
2.0	15.2	12.3	24.5	19.2
3.0	17.1	14.0	29.8	23.5
5.0	19.8	16.3	35.3	28.1
10.0	23.6	19.8	47.7	38.2

Assumes 19 km visibility, and no cloud or snow cover
Height of airbursts taken to maximize 10 psi blast damage area
Source: Compiled from data in Glasstone and Dolan, *Effects of Nuclear Weapons*, pp. 316–22

services. In chapter 8 we show that even after a small-scale attack there is no possibility that more than a minute fraction of the likely number of burns victims could receive treatment to modern peacetime standards.

Glasstone and Dolan offer a more sophisticated approach.[11] They give probabilities that differing percentages of an exposed population will suffer burns of varying degrees of seriousness, for given levels of radiant exposure and for different weapon yields. The seriousness of the burns is expressed in terms of the accepted medical classification into first, second and third degree, which are largely distinguished by the depth to which the skin is burned in each case. Another important factor is the percentage of the total body surface which is affected.

The burns probabilities vary, at a given level of radiant exposure, for different explosive yields; since with a higher-yield bomb, the same quantity of thermal radiation is received over a longer period, and the effects on the body are slightly less serious. The figures assume that people take no evasive action. This would in theory be possible for higher-yield bombs, where the radiation would last for sufficient time that people would feel the pain and could possibly cover themselves quickly.

It still remains to decide what the chances of survival are for those suffering different degrees of burning. Glasstone and Dolan are not explicit on this question, but on the basis of their discussion it is possible to suppose that in the conditions of nuclear war, third degree burns would be fatal, second degree burns would constitute a 'serious injury' (perhaps fatal if untreated), and that first degree burns would constitute mild injuries from which people could recover without medical aid.[12]

In chapter 7 we show the consequences for total predicted burns casualties of taking both these latter assumptions, and the OTA assumptions. Of these the OTA's are the more pessimistic. For the standard version of our model however, we take a third set of figures which lie somewhere between the previous two. We use Glasstone and Dolan's data for skin burn probabilities, and then assume that all those with third degree burns are killed; that half those with second degree burns die and half are 'seriously injured'; and that of those with first degree burns, a quarter are 'seriously injured'. On these assumptions, table 6.2 shows the resulting percentages of the exposed population who are killed or seriously injured, at varying distances from weapons of eight different yields, either airburst or groundburst.

The consequences for *total* casualties of these differing burns models are not very great, partly because the area in which burns are caused is also that in which most blast casualties occur; and so where fewer are counted as killed by burns, the injured and uninjured 'survivors' of burns are more liable to become casualties of blast effects.

The burns model is applied to the bomb and population data in the following fashion. Each weapon is examined in turn. The yield of explosion and height of burst determine the size of the circular areas affected. The population data are retrieved for all relevant 1 km grid-squares, using a special automatic search technique.[13] The distance from ground zero to the mid-point of a particular grid-square is computed, and the equations given in appendix 2 are used to estimate the corresponding

Table 6.2 Distances from ground zero (in kilometres) at which different percentages of that fraction of the population which is exposed to the fireball would be killed or seriously injured by burns (authors' model)

Height of burst	Explosive yield (megatons)	% killed: % seriously injured:	100 0	91 9	59 41	41 45	9 29	0 2
Groundburst	0.15		3.9	4.2	4.6	5.0	5.6	7.4
Airburst			5.3	5.7	6.3	6.8	7.7	10.1
Groundburst	0.5		6.2	6.6	7.2	7.8	8.7	11.0
Airburst			8.5	9.0	9.9	10.7	11.9	15.0
Groundburst	1.0		8.0	8.5	9.2	9.9	10.9	13.5
Airburst			11.9	12.7	14.0	15.1	16.9	21.5
Groundburst	1.5		9.2	9.8	10.6	11.3	12.4	15.2
Airburst			13.8	14.8	16.2	17.6	19.5	24.5
Groundburst	2.0		10.1	10.7	11.6	12.4	13.6	16.5
Airburst			15.4	16.5	18.0	19.4	21.5	26.9
Groundburst	3.0		11.6	12.2	13.2	14.0	15.3	18.4
Airburst			18.7	20.0	21.8	23.5	26.0	32.4
Groundburst	5.0		13.5	14.3	15.3	16.3	17.6	20.9
Airburst			22.5	23.9	26.1	28.0	30.8	37.7
Groundburst	10.0		16.5	17.4	18.6	19.6	21.1	24.6
Airburst			30.4	32.3	35.1	37.6	41.2	50.1

Assumes 19 km visibility, and no cloud or snow cover
Height of airbursts taken to maximize 10 psi blast damage area

Sources: Estimates of skin burn probabilities (first, second and third degree) from Glasstone, and Dolan, *Effects of Nuclear Weapons*, fig. 12.65, p. 565. Authors' assumptions that all third degree burns cases die; 50 per cent of second degree burns cases die and 50 per cent are 'serious injuries'; 25 per cent of first degree burns cases are 'serious injuries'

thermal radiation level. This value is converted into estimates of the percentages of deaths and serious injuries among the exposed population. These percentages are then used to amend the population data, so as to remove those counted as dead, and to record numbers of uninjured and injured 'survivors' of burns effects in each grid-square. All 152,400 inhabited grid-squares are processed in this way.

BLAST EFFECTS

Most of the immediate material damage caused by a nuclear explosion comes from the enormous resulting shock or blast wave. The pressure created by this blast wave is measured, usually in pounds per square inch (psi), as an amount by which it exceeds normal atmospheric pressure. This is referred to as an 'overpressure'. Many structures will suffer some damage from blast at overpressures greater than 0.5 psi. As a guide, 5 psi is sufficient to demolish the average brick-built house completely. The distances to which different overpressure levels extend, depend on the yield of the explosion and on the height of the detonation.

There is an important difference, as discussed in chapter 5, between ground and airbursts in this respect. The range of blast effects is greater for an airburst than for an equivalent yield groundburst, because the shock wave is reflected from the ground and combines with the direct wave, to produce a merged or Mach wave. Also, with an airburst, none of the energy of the explosion is spent excavating a crater.

The human body, being an elastic structure, is surprisingly resistant to the direct forces of blast pressure in themselves; although very high overpressures could cause such injuries as burst eardrums, haemorrhage of the lungs, and rupture of the walls of the chest and stomach. None of these would happen in general at pressures less than 12 psi, which are powerful enough to demolish almost all buildings. For this reason the majority of blast deaths and injuries will be from indirect effects. The great pressures and high-speed winds will cause buildings to collapse or explode, people to be blown out of buildings or against obstacles, or people to be hit by smaller projectiles. Very many injuries will be caused by flying glass, bricks and other fragmented debris.

It is possible to represent the extent of blast effects quite simply by a series of circular rings, centred on ground zero. Each circle corresponds to the distance at which some given maximum level of blast overpressure will be experienced. These distances have been determined theoretically and from measurements on actual nuclear explosions. Glasstone and Dolan provide figures for a 1 kiloton explosion, at different heights of detonation, which can be scaled up or down to give values for other yields.[14]

The figures assume an initial atmospheric pressure equal to that at sea-level, and a perfectly flat ground surface. In practice the blast wave would be channelled and deflected by uneven or hilly topography. This happened at Nagasaki, which lies in a valley, and where the blast-damaged area was elongated in shape; rather than roughly circular as at Hiroshima where the ground is flat. There are, however, no simple means of taking this factor into account in our computer model, and so the predictions for hilly areas will be correspondingly approximate. In other respects, however, it is thought that blast effects can be predicted with reasonable accuracy.

Table 6.3 gives an indication of the range in kilometres for four different levels of maximum overpressure, for eight different weapon yields. Thus for example at 2.9 km for a 1 megaton groundburst, the maximum overpressure will be 12 psi. Above 12 psi practically all buildings will be destroyed including those with concrete or steel-frame

Table 6.3 Distances from ground zero (in kilometres) at which maximum overpressures would be experienced from blast, of 1, 2, 5, and 12 pounds per square inch (psi)

Explosive yield (megatons)	Groundburst				Airburst			
	12 psi	5 psi	2 psi	1 psi	12 psi	5 psi	2 psi	1 psi
0.15	1.5	2.4	4.1	6.2	2.0	3.5	6.3	9.4
0.5	2.3	3.6	6.2	9.3	3.0	5.2	9.5	14.0
1.0	2.9	4.5	7.8	11.8	3.8	6.6	12.0	17.7
1.5	3.3	5.2	8.9	13.5	4.4	7.5	13.7	20.2
2.0	3.7	5.7	9.8	14.8	4.8	8.3	15.1	22.2
3.0	4.2	6.5	11.3	17.0	5.5	9.5	17.3	25.5
5.0	5.0	7.8	13.4	20.1	6.5	11.2	20.5	30.2
10.0	6.3	9.8	16.8	25.4	8.2	14.2	25.8	38.1

Height of airbursts taken to maximize 10 psi blast damage area

Source: Glasstone and Dolan, *Effects of Nuclear Weapons*, fig. 3.73c, p. 115

structures. At about 5 psi brick houses will be demolished. In the range 2 to 5 psi, houses will suffer serious damage, with roofs off and walls cracked. And between the 1 and 2 psi levels, houses will be slightly damaged, with roof-tiles removed, windows smashed and external doors blown out. Even 1 psi is not the lower limit of damage; indeed glass could be broken by overpressures of a fraction of a pound per square inch. At Hiroshima for example, where the explosive yield was only 12.5 kilotons (0.0125 megatons), windows were broken generally to a distance of 15 km, and in some cases as far away as 27 km (compare these distances with those for much higher yields in table 6.3).

The ranges of blast damage for airbursts will vary as mentioned with the height of detonation. An attacker would want to adjust the height of explosion deliberately, in such a way as to subject the largest possible area to blast damage at some chosen overpressure level or greater. The height is then said to be 'optimized' for the given overpressure. In table 6.3, and in our model generally, the heights of detonation of airbursts are optimized for the 10 psi level. This is a middle-range value: attacks on cities might be optimized for lower levels of blast damage, those on 'harder' industrial or military targets perhaps for higher levels.

Given the predicted maximum overpressures at different points on the ground, the next step is to relate these values to the percentages of the population killed or seriously injured as a result. The evidence on which to base such relationships comes principally from the effects of the Hiroshima and Nagasaki bombs, from experimental studies with animal cadavers and from experiments with dummies in buildings exposed to actual nuclear weapons tests. We have adopted the assumptions made by the Office of Technology Assessment, which they in turn derived from the US Department of Defense.[15] These give percentages killed and injured in the four overpressure ranges 1–2 psi, 2–5 psi, 5–12 psi and above 12 psi, as illustrated in table 6.4.

Table 6.4 Percentages of population killed or seriously injured by blast, in different overpressure ranges

Overpressure range (pounds per square inch)	% killed	% seriously injured
greater than 12 psi	98	2
5–12 psi	50	40
2– 5 psi	5	45
1– 2 psi	0	25

Source: Office of Technology Assessment, *Effects of Nuclear War*, p. 19

The OTA describe these figures as 'relatively conservative'. They assume 'a mean lethal overpressure of 5 to 6 psi for people in residences, meaning that more than half of those whose houses are blown down on top of them [by overpressures of 5 psi] will nevertheless survive.'[16] The figures relate to the entire population present in the relevant zone, whether indoors or outdoors. Where people are inside buildings, these are assumed to be of normal construction, and not specially blast-proofed.

Other American studies have used an even simpler method of estimating blast deaths. They assume that the numbers who survive at overpressures greater then 5 psi, will equal the numbers who are killed at overpressures less than 5 psi. Thus the number of predicted deaths is found by counting the population inside the 5 psi circle. Where the population is uniformly distributed, this model gives slightly more predicted deaths than do the OTA assumptions.

It might be asked, how well do the Office of Technology Assessment assumptions fit the actual pattern of casualties which occurred at Hiroshima and Nagasaki? There are several problems in answering this question, not the least of which is that considerable controversy exists about how many people actually *were* killed and injured by the bombs in Japan. This controversy arises, however, not because different authorities — Japanese, American and British — disagree very greatly about the *rates* at which casualties occurred at varying distances. It arises because of large uncertainties about how many people were present in the two cities at the time of attack.

The most recent and comprehensive study of *Hiroshima and Nagasaki* does however give some detailed data, collected by the Hiroshima City Survey Section in 1946, for the distribution of the population in that city, by 1 km rings from ground zero outwards.[17] When the OTA casualty rates are applied, they give 99,000 'predicted' deaths, against an actual figure (as quoted by the City Survey) of 119,000. 'Predicted' total casualties according to the OTA are 199,000, against an actual figure of 198,000. The distribution of these casualties by distance is also fairly well 'predicted', with the worst fit being where the break falls between the 2–5 and 5–12 psi overpressure ranges.

At first sight, therefore, the OTA assumptions give remarkably good 'predictions' for Hiroshima. (It is even possible that the data in question from Hiroshima provide one of the sources on which the OTA rates are in turn based — although we have no information on this.) However, these comparisons must be qualified in several ways. First, the Japanese data relate to all causes of death and injury, while the OTA rates refer only to blast. American studies have indicated that, of those who survived injury at Hiroshima, around 70 per cent suffered blast injuries; and that among those who died, the percentage would probably have been higher.[18] However, this still means that the OTA rates are giving overestimates. There is the further point that many of the houses at Hiroshima were of traditional wooden construction and collapsed, it is thought, at about 3 psi. Modern western houses would be stronger (although some of the more recently-erected masonry and concrete buildings at Hiroshima were of earthquake-proof construction).

On the other hand there is the most important consideration that the Hiroshima bomb was of very low yield by present-day standards. The OTA rates are intended to apply by contrast to weapons in the megaton range. The blast pressures and wind forces for these high-yield weapons last much longer, and this results in more damage and more casualties at equivalent overpressure levels. All in all, it seems that the OTA assumptions are broadly compatible, allowing for all of these factors, with the actual patterns of casualties which occurred in Japan.

As we have already mentioned, no allowance is made in our model for the possibility that where the same area is subjected to blast effects from successive explosions, the effects of the later bombs might be to cause greater damage and more casualties at an equivalent overpressure level.

In making the calculations of blast casualties, the same technique is used to retrieve the population data for the circular areas affected by each weapon, as was used in the burns model. As before, each weapon is processed in turn. The yield of weapon together with the height of detonation allow the radii of the four overpressure rings to be calculated. For each 1 km grid-square in the affected area the numbers of uninjured and injured survivors of thermal radiation are retrieved. Where the boundary between two rings cuts across grid-squares, the populations of those squares are divided approximately between the rings in proportion to area.

The numbers killed and injured by blast are then determined by applying the percentage casualty rates in table 6.4 to these populations. The population data base is then amended once more, by removing those counted as dead, and recording the numbers of injured and uninjured 'survivors' of both burns and blast. Those who were previously injured by burns, and are now injured by blast, are assumed to die. Those who are injured by blast effects from more than one bomb are also counted as dead. This process is repeated for all weapons.

FALLOUT EFFECTS

The third major direct cause of casualties is radioactive fallout. The estimation of fallout casualties is far more complex than for either thermal radiation or blast effects, because many different factors affect the radiation dose which an individual may receive from fallout. This section is divided into three separate parts. First a means is described of estimating radiation doses in the open. Second, corrections have to be made for the protection offered by buildings. Third, radiation doses have to be related to the resulting numbers of casualties.

Predicting radiation doses in the open

For a groundburst, the amount of local fallout is related to the explosive yield, to the fraction of that yield which is obtained from fission reactions, and to the nature and materials of the ground surface. Since the radioactive cloud is moved by the wind, and since the fallout will descend during a period of many hours, even days, the pattern in which it is deposited is strongly affected by the weather. The direction and speed of the wind are important, and these can be different at varying heights above ground, and can of course change with time. Fallout can as mentioned be brought down locally by the rain. Local topography and wind turbulence (including the winds from nearby explosions) will also affect the distribution of the fallout.

The consequence is that the pattern of radioactive contamination on the ground can be highly irregular. This was illustrated in the monitoring of the nuclear weapons tests in Nevada and in the Pacific (figure 6.2). The spread of radioactivity was not even, and there were local areas of especially high contamination ('hot spots'), compensated by other less heavily affected areas. Fallout particles once on the ground could be carried along and redistributed by rainwater.

There are many difficulties in using the evidence of the atmospheric tests to predict what might happen from, say, a groundburst on a city. Because most of the test explosions in the megaton range were conducted over the Pacific Ocean, the patterns of fallout had to be inferred from relatively few measurements.[19] There is also the problem that it is impossible to predict — except perhaps a few hours in advance — the detailed weather pattern for the day of an attack. What is more, any prevailing weather conditions may be changed locally in the short term by the detonation of multiple nuclear weapons and by mass fires. The best we can do is to assume average or seasonal weather conditions. In chapter 7 we show the result of making different assumptions, with wind speeds varied between 16 and 40 km/hr, and wind directions in all four points of the compass.

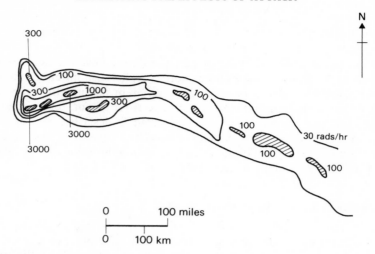

Figure 6.2   Pattern of fallout from a 10 megaton groundburst. The contours show dose-rates in rads per hour. Shaded areas are 'hot spots'. This is a hypothetical example but illustrates the irregular pattern typical of actual atmospheric tests.
Source: Glasstone and Dolan, *Effects of Nuclear Weapons*, fig. 9.100b, p. 434.

So far as the shape of the fallout distribution pattern goes, most studies simplify the situation radically, by assuming that the direction and speed of the wind are constant for the whole time that the cloud is moving. The 'effective' speed of the wind is taken as the average of speeds at different altitudes. A certain allowance is made for cross-winds, or 'wind shear', in widening the cloud as it drifts away from ground zero. The result is for the predicted pattern to approximate to an ellipse or cigar shape, whose long axis lies in the direction of the wind (figure 6.3). Home Office scientists believe that these elliptical patterns 'may be regarded as a reasonable approximation for average UK winds which are, in any case, of such speed as to be conducive to a roughly elliptical pattern.'[20]

Other studies have used much more elaborate atmospheric models, which take detailed account of observed wind patterns, in order to predict the wandering movements of the fallout clouds.[21] But it is doubtful whether the additional sophistication is accompanied by any increased accuracy in estimating total radiation casualties. There still remains the difficulty that actual wind characteristics vary from day to day.

The idealized elliptical plumes may not give an accurate prediction of the resulting levels of radioactivity from fallout at *particular* points on the ground. But they *will* give a tolerably good estimate of the total quantity of fallout, and the total area in which this comes down. As Glasstone and Dolan say, 'Although they [the idealized patterns] will undoubtedly underestimate the fallout in some locations and overestimate it in others, the evaluation of the gross fallout problem over the whole area affected should not be greatly in error.'[22] In the heavier attacks on Britain, as we shall see, the fallout plumes from many groundbursts overlap, to carpet most of the country. The consequence is that predictions of fallout casualties on a regional basis should be reasonably reliable, if not those in some local areas.

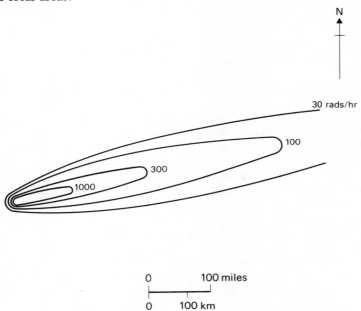

Figure 6.3   Idealized pattern of fallout from a 10 megaton groundburst with a 48 km/hr 'effective' wind speed (compare figure 6.2). The elliptical contours show 'unit-time reference dose-rates', that is theoretical dose-rates at one hour after the explosion, in rads per hour. The 'fission fraction' is 0.5.
Source: Glasstone and Dolan, *Effects of Nuclear Weapons*, fig 9.100a, p. 434.

Detailed methods for deriving the shapes and sizes of the idealized plumes are given in appendix 3. In outline the physical processes involved are these: when the mushroom cloud from the explosion of a weapon of yield greater than about 100 kilotons stops rising, it begins to spread horizontally to form a large circular disc. Its final radius is referred to as the 'stabilized cloud radius' and this can be quite large. Table 6.5 gives some figures: for example, the cloud for a 1 megaton groundburst will be nearly 9 km in radius. This cloud is then driven along by the wind.

Imagine a point on the ground, downwind of ground zero. At some time after the explosion, depending on the distance and the wind speed, the front edge of the cloud will arrive over that point. This is the 'time of arrival'. (The time involved is not precisely the distance from ground zero divided by wind speed, since the size of the cloud itself must also be taken into account.) Fallout particles begin to drop on to the ground, and accumulate as the cloud goes overhead, until the trailing edge of the cloud passes and the fallout stops. This is the 'time of completion'.

Table 6.5 Radius (kilometres) of 'stabilized' mushroom cloud for groundbursts or low airbursts

	Explosive yield (megatons)							
	0.15	0.5	1.0	1.5	2.0	3.0	5.0	10.0
Cloud radius	3.5	6.3	8.9	10.8	12.6	15.9	21.6	34.9

Source: Glasstone and Dolan, *Effects of Nuclear Weapons*, fig. 2.16, p. 34

All the while, and continuing after the time of completion, the level of radioactivity of the fallout is decaying. This rate of decay can be expressed as $(time)^{-1.2}$. This is sometimes expressed by the 'seven-tenths rule', which states that the intensity of the activity reduces approximately by a factor of ten, as the time lengthens by a factor of 7. Radiation doses are often measured in rads. If the dose-rate is say 100 rads per hour at one hour after the explosion, it will, according to the seven-tenths rule, be 10 rads per hour after seven hours, 1 rad per hour at $7 \times 7 = 49$ hours, and so on. As a guide, radiation workers in peacetime are usually limited to a maximum exposure of 5 rads in a *year*. Cumulative doses of approximately 300 rads and greater could prove fatal. It is clear from these facts about the rate of decay that the most extreme risks from fallout are in the days immediately following an attack; and that the greater part of the total dose which people will eventually receive is likely to be absorbed in these first few days.

The actual radiation dose-rate at the point on the ground will therefore *rise* as the fallout particles accumulate, up to some maximum level; but then the radioactive decay processes will overtake the effects of the increase in the quantity of fallout, and the dose-rate will *fall* again. The time at which the maximum dose-rate is reached, is the 'time of maximum'. This is shown diagrammatically in appendix 4.

A loose analogy may help to make this clear. Imagine instead of fallout, snow falling on to a warm surface. As the snow cloud passes, the amount of snow on the surface increases. However, at the same time the snow is melting (analogous to radioactive decay). So the resulting level of snow rises to a maximum, and then decreases again as the effects of melting come to predominate. The snow will continue to melt after the snow shower has stopped, just as the radioactivity will continue to decay after fallout is completed.

To find the *total* radiation dose (in rads) which would be received at the given point on the ground, up to some specified limit of time, it is necessary therefore, to allow for these continuously changing dose-rates. Mathematically this is a matter of integrating over the time-period in question.

The way that the calculations are made in practice (following Glasstone and Dolan) is by means of the somewhat artificial concept of the 'unit-time reference dose-rate'. This is the theoretical dose-rate (in rads per hour) at one hour after the explosion (the 'unit time'). The concept is artificial because over most of the areas eventually affected, fallout will not have actually arrived one hour after the explosion. Its usefulness lies in the fact that real dose-rates at times later than this can be determined by allowing for radioactive decay in the intervening period. In the idealized patterns illustrated in figure 6.3 each ellipse represents some value for the dose-rate at one hour. The smaller ellipses represent high dose-rates, the larger ellipses lower rates at greater distances from ground zero. Glasstone and Dolan give data for the lengths and widths of these ellipses, for specified weapon yields.[23] The standard effective wind speed is taken to be 24 km/hr. Corrections can then be made to the lengths of the ellipses for higher or lower wind speeds.

It is also necessary to make corrections for two other factors. The first is the fraction of the explosive yield which is obtained from fission reactions. This is usually taken for high-yield thermonuclear weapons to be 0.5. This reduces all the reference dose-rate values by one half.

The second factor is what is called a 'ground roughness' or 'terrain shielding' factor. Radiation from fallout lands on the ground over a circular area. If the ground is perfectly flat, a person will receive a varying amount of radiation depending on how near he or she was to the centre of the circle. This is the effective assumption on which the theoretical dose-rates are calculated. But if the ground is rough, as it would usually be in practice, the dose-rate will be reduced, because some of the radiation will need to pass through the ground or other obstacles to reach the person and will be attenuated in the process. We take a value for this factor of 0.7, which implies a 'relatively level terrain'.[24] That is to say, the one-hour reference dose-rates are further reduced to seven-tenths of their value.

Table 6.6 gives the dimensions for the one-hour reference dose-rates for weapons of a range of yields, assuming a 24 km/hr wind-speed. The values are corrected for both the fission fraction and for ground roughness. It will be immediately apparent from this table how very large are the areas affected by fallout from a single weapon. For a 1 megaton ground-burst, the 1 rad/hour contour is nearly 1,100 km long and over 100 km wide. (The whole of Britain can be fitted into a rectangle 656 by 1,050 km.) The one-hour dose-rates can be in excess of 1000 rads/hour at distances of tens of kilometres from ground zero.

In our model each groundburst weapon is taken in turn. A wind direction and an effective wind speed are chosen. In principle these could be different for each bomb. In practice we have assumed the same speed and direction for all weapons in an attack. Unless otherwise stated, the wind speed is taken as 24 km/hr, and the wind direction south-south-westerly. The idealized dose-rate ellipses (corrected for fission fraction and ground roughness) are positioned in relation to ground zero, with their long axes oriented correctly to the chosen wind direction, in relation to the National Grid. Then for every grid-square affected, the one-hour reference dose-rate can be found.

Table 6.6 Dimensions (in kilometres) of ellipses representing idealized fallout patterns, for groundbursts of different yields. Each ellipse corresponds to a different 'unit-time reference dose-rate'. This is the theoretical dose-rate (in rads per hour) one hour after the explosion. The effective wind speed is 24 km/hr, the fission fraction 0.5 and the ground roughness factor 0.7

Unit-time reference dose-rate (rads/hr)	Yield (megatons)							
	0.15	0.5	1.0	1.5	2.0	3.0	5.0	10.0
	Length of ellipse (km)							
1	463	797	1,089	1,307	1,488	1,787	2,251	3,080
3.5	371	639	873	1,048	1,193	1,433	1,805	2,471
10.5	248	428	585	702	799	960	1,210	1,659
35	140	240	329	395	450	541	683	938
105	72	124	171	205	234	281	356	491
350	31	53	73	88	101	122	155	217
1,050	18	31	43	51	59	72	92	131
1,750	13	22	31	38	43	53	68	98
2,450	11	19	26	31	36	44	57	84
3,150	9	16	23	27	32	39	51	75
	Maximum width of ellipse (km)							
1	43	79	111	137	158	193	250	353
3.5	32	60	87	108	126	156	205	296
10.5	20	39	58	73	86	108	144	212
35	12	25	38	49	58	74	101	153
105	5	12	19	26	31	41	57	91
350	2	6	11	15	18	25	37	63
1,050	0.9	2	4	6	8	11	18	33
1,750	0.5	1.6	3	4	6	8	13	26
2,450	0.4	1.2	2	3	4	6	11	21
3,150	0.3	1	2	2	3	5	9	19

Source: Calculated from data in Glasstone and Dolan, *Effects of Nuclear Weapons,* table 9.93, p. 430

For each grid-square the 'time of arrival' of fallout is calculated, taking into account the wind-speed and allowing for the radius of the fallout cloud. The dose-rate can then be found for this time of arrival. The 'time of maximum' dose-rate and 'time of completion' of fallout are determined from the time of arrival by an approximate method due to Bentley[25] and described in appendix 4. The resulting total accumulated radiation dose for the grid-square is then calculated, up to some chosen limit of time. We take 14 days. The patterns of these values for accumulated doses can themselves be plotted as a series of contours, as illustrated in figure 6.4. This shows doses up to two weeks from a 1 megaton explosion, with a 24 km/hr wind speed. The resulting shapes are not now elliptical.

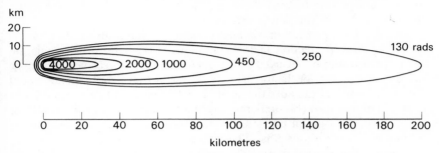

Figure 6.4 Total open-air radiation doses in rads, accumulated during the two weeks after the explosion, from a 1 megaton groundburst. The 'effective' wind speed is 24 km/hr, the 'fission fraction' is 0·5, and the ground roughness factor is 0·7.

Since the fallout plumes from different bombs will overlap in many places, this accumulated dose has to be calculated in turn for each weapon affecting the grid-square in question. All the doses are then added together. This is done for all the 'inhabited' grid-squares in the country. The fact of overlap of plumes is one reason why it would be even more complicated to have weapons whose detonations were not assumed to be more or less simultaneous, as discussed at the beginning of this chapter — since the periods of radiation dose from two or more weapons affecting a single grid-square could then become staggered in time.

The composition and rate of decay of fallout would be seriously altered where nuclear power stations or reprocessing and storage facilities were hit, as they are in all of our attack scenarios from E onwards. We do not allow for this eventuality here, but discuss the question separately in chapter 8.

Protection factors of buildings and shelters

The next step is to derive, from the levels of fallout radiation dose which people would receive in the open air, the levels of dose which they would receive should they be sheltering in buildings. Most studies assume that all people still alive after an attack will be indoors rather than outdoors. This is a somewhat dubious assumption. The effects of blast and fire will be to destroy or seriously damage buildings over very large areas, and in these zones the protection available against the effects of radiation will be minimal.

Away from the main blast-affected areas, however, there will be buildings only partly damaged (perhaps just with windows broken), or even completely unscathed. Assuming that people are sheltering inside, they would certainly obtain a substantial degree of protection against the effects of radiation. In areas which are some distance downwind of the nearest groundbursts, people may have an hour or two to take sheltering precautions before the fallout arrives.

The level of protection against radiation offered by a building is expressed as a 'protection factor' (pf). This is the ratio of the radiation dose which would be received in the open, to the dose received inside the building. A protection factor of 5 would mean that people inside would receive one-fifth of the dose they would receive outdoors. It is possible for ordinary unmodified (but undamaged) buildings to have pf values of 10 or more, and for special-purpose fallout shelters to have pf values of hundreds or even thousands. The values assumed for pfs are thus very significant, since they can radically reduce the calculated radiation doses, and so have a marked effect on the resulting number of predicted fallout casualties.

The nominal protection factors of buildings or shelters can vary widely depending on their materials of construction, and on their geometrical relation to adjacent buildings. The denser the material, the more effect it has in attenuating the radiation; so that steel and concrete would offer more protection than wood. The greater the thickness of a given material, the greater the protection. To measure the protection factor for a complete building it is thus necessary to allow for the relative areas, and thicknesses, of solid walls, windows, doors and roof. In Home Office calculations the assumption is made (see chapter 9) that people will block the more vulnerable door and window openings with bricks, concrete blocks or furniture, as recommended in the *Protect and Survive* leaflet, so as to raise the pf. The Home Office also assume that people build 'internal refuges' with doors, sandbags and furniture, in order further to increase the radiation protection.

One building can gain protection from other adjoining structures. Thus a terrace house is shielded by its neighbours, and offers better protection than does a semi-detached house, which in its turn is better than a detached house or bungalow. Fallout particles will accumulate on any flat surface — on the ground but also on flat or gently sloping roofs. In multi-storey buildings the best fallout protection would be in the centre of the middle storeys, away from both roof and ground. Some studies fix a single average pf value to cover all conditions. Others, such as those of the Home Office, take a range or 'spectrum' of values, to allow for different types of house and flat (see chapter 9).

The protection factor value which is applied in calculations of casualties must take account not just of the materials and shape of the building. Estimates of the total accumulated radiation dose are made for an extended period, in our case two weeks. Only if people stay inside for that whole time, will the nominal pf calculated for the building apply. If they spend any time outside, the effective pf value must be lowered.

This is a difficult matter to predict. But it is reasonable to imagine that after an attack people might be obliged to go outdoors, although aware of the hazards, to seek food, water or fuel, or simply driven out by intolerable conditions inside the shelter. Others might be ignorant or heedless of the dangers, and be looking for friends or relatives, seeking medical help, attempting rescue work, or merely wandering in a zombie-like state, as were many of the survivors at Hiroshima and Nagasaki. Plans exist for giving warnings of fallout danger (see chapter 10) but these might fail in the event.

In everyday life the effective pf offered by (unmodified) buildings, allowing for the average amounts of time people spend in and out of doors, might be around three. On this basis some American studies have taken values of between three and six for houses and flats.[26] Katz in a massive study of *Life after Nuclear War*[27] in the United States, takes an average value for the *basements* of American houses, of ten. However, only a small proportion of the British population have access to basements suitable for sheltering; around 3½ per cent in London for example.[28] Rotblat suggests a value of five for the effects of radiation in the period immediately following an attack, and three in the longer term.[29]

With these kinds of consideration in mind, we use a single average pf value for buildings in areas suffering less than 1 psi of blast overpressure, of eight. Some buildings in these zones will be completely undamaged, but many will have windows broken and other light damage. The shelterers could perhaps block the holes again if they acted quickly and could find suitable materials. We believe this pf of eight to be a reasonable figure. However, in chapter 7 we show the effect of taking much higher values, of 16 and 24, as well as a lower value of five.

In areas suffering more severe blast damage, the average pf is reduced in proportion to the seriousness of the damage. Here we use four different pf values to correspond to the four ranges of blast overpressure used for the blast casualty calculations. A pf value of one is used for the two highest overpressure ranges, in excess of 12 psi, and 5 to 12 psi, since most buildings and practically all houses will have been demolished here. A value of two is taken where overpressures are between 2 and 5 psi, since here roofs would probably be missing and walls cracked or severely damaged. A value of five is taken for areas suffering overpressures between 1 and 2 psi, where doors would be blown out and roofs damaged.

These assumptions are admittedly fairly crude. They do however rest on some calculations made by the authors of the *London after the Bomb* study.[30] The effects of blast damage could be to reduce protection factors in two ways. First, there is the radiation from fallout which is lying on the ground *outside* the building. If there are holes in walls, windows broken and so on, more of this radiation will penetrate through the holes than would through the intact structure, to reach the shelterers inside. Second, fallout particles themselves are likely to enter *inside* the building, just as ordinary dust in the atmosphere comes in through open windows. People will then receive radiation from both inside and outside sources.

The *London after the Bomb* group allow only for this second effect. They assume that the ratio of the dose-rate from fallout in the building, to the open air unshielded dose-rate, is proportional to the ratio of apertures in the building to the total outside wall and roof area. The resulting protection factor can be worked out by combining the contributions coming from inside and outside.

These blast-related protection factor values we consider to be plausible, especially bearing in mind that the first of the two factors mentioned above is not allowed for; and that any magnified damage in areas of overlapping blast effects from multiple weapons is also ignored.

Nevertheless, the effects on total fallout casualties of some different sets of values, both higher and lower than these, are shown in chapter 7. The question of the possible radiation protection offered by the Home Office designs of 'inner refuge' and temporary do-it-yourself shelters are further examined in chapter 10. More substantial, permanent designs of fallout shelter are also discussed in chapter 10.

Injury and death related to radiation dose

The final stage in estimating casualties from fallout, is to relate the radiation doses received inside buildings — allowing for their protection factors — to the numbers of resulting cases of radiation sickness, either serious or fatal. This is once again an uncertain, even controversial question.

The effects of radiation on the human body can vary considerably between individuals. In particular they vary with age and body size, so that children and old people are especially at risk. For these reasons the effects are usually expressed statistically, in terms of a percentage of persons, out of a large number exposed to a given dose, who would be likely to die or fall ill as a result. A figure often referred to is the 'LD-50' (lethal dose 50 per cent), which is that level of dose which results in half the exposed population dying. The effects also vary according to the period over which the total dose is received. The body has a certain capacity for repairing the harmful effects of radiation, and so a given dose spread over weeks or months will not have consequences as serious as the same dose received in days or hours.

Table 6.7 describes some of the symptoms of radiation sickness at different levels of dose (in rads). Radiation has the effect of damaging or destroying the internal structure of the cells of the body. The rate of production of blood cells, especially the white cells, drops. This in turn lowers the body's resistance to infection. At doses much above 100 rads the symptoms can include fatigue, vomiting, nausea, diarrhoea and loss of hair. At higher doses, women as well as men may be made temporarily sterile. If pregnant women are exposed to radiation, the children may be born deformed or mentally retarded.

Table 6.7   Medical effects of radiation

Dose (rads)	Symptoms	Deaths (average)
0–100	Men become temporarily sterile in 20–50 rads range	0
100–200	Nausea and vomiting within 3–6 hours of receiving dose and lasting less than 1 day, followed by no symptoms for 2 weeks. Recurrence of symptoms for another 4 weeks. Number of white blood cells reduced	0
200–600	Nausea and vomiting lasting 1–2 days. No symptoms for 1–4 weeks followed by a recurrence of symptoms for up to 8 weeks. Diarrhoea, severe reduction of white blood cells, blood blisters on skin, bleeding, infection. Loss of hair above 300 rads	0–98% in 2–12 weeks from internal bleeding or infection
600–1,000	Nausea and vomiting starting within ½ hour of receiving dose of radiation and lasting 2 days. No symptoms for 5–10 days, then same symptoms as for 200–600 rads, for 1–4 weeks	98–100% from internal bleeding or infection
1,000–5,000	Nausea and vomiting starting within ½ hour of receiving dose and lasting less than a day. No symptoms for about 7 days, then diarrhoea, fever, disturbed salt balance in blood for 2–14 days	100% within 14 days from collapse of circulation
more than 5,000	Nausea and vomiting immediately followed by convulsions, loss of control of movement and lethargy	100% in 48 hours from failure of breathing or brain damage

Effects apply for a normal population of adults receiving total radiation doses over short periods of time, and may vary very widely in the 100–600 rad range

Source: Greene et al., *London after the Bomb*, p. 20

The longer-term effects of radiation exposure, even for relatively low doses, are an increased incidence of cancers and leukaemias, and the possibility of genetic abnormalities. These are discussed further in chapter 8.

As table 6.7 indicates, for those who receive fatal doses, death will not be instantaneous. For doses of over say 2,000 rads, the effect is likely to be almost immediate incapacitation, and death within a few days at the longest. But with lower dose levels, death may not ensue for several weeks. When numbers of deaths from radiation effects are calculated from doses received in the first two weeks after an attack, it is probable that a proportion of these people will not die for several more weeks.

For over 30 years, the body of opinion among radiologists has been that the human LD-50 value lies somewhere between 400 and 450 rads.[31] This value refers to doses to the whole of the body, not to separate limbs or organs; and to measurements made at the surface of the body. If the dose is measured to the 'mid-line' tissues, or to the bone marrow, the LD-50 is lower — since the radiation is attenuated as it passes through the flesh. The value also relates to 'acute' doses received over several hours or a day. The British Institute of Radiology say that for a dose protracted over one month, the LD-50 might be 600 rads, compared with 450 for one week.[32]

It is thought that the probability of death increases sharply with rather small increases in dose; and that for example the level of dose which would kill 90 per cent of the population (the 'LD-90') would be around 600 rads ('acute' dose).

The evidence on which these figures rests is, however, rather slim. Experiments have been made with high levels of radiation dose to animals. But for humans, the number of instances of such exposure is small. There were many who died from the effects of radiation in Hiroshima and Nagasaki of course; but the actual doses which they received, and the symptoms they displayed, were not measured or recorded with any precision. There have been several accidents to radiation workers. In some cases the victims were exposed to thousands of rads, and so they provided little information about the LD-50 value. Where the doses were in hundreds of rads, the sufferers mostly received intensive hospital treatment, with blood and fluid transfusions, antibiotics and in some cases bone marrow transplants. Since none of these forms of treatment are likely to be available to the survivors of a large-scale nuclear attack, the evidence is again not directly applicable to calculations of casualties in a nuclear war.

Another complication is the fact that many such victims in war would have burns or blast injuries in addition to radiation sickness. As the British Institute of Radiology say:

A radiation dose well below the lethal level could make recovery from the other injuries more difficult. Wound healing is inhibited in irradiated animals and the immune defences against infection are reduced. Serious burns cause shock and fluid loss and combined burn and radiation injuries have been shown to be synergistic, that is to lead to greater mortality than the simple addition of the casualties to be expected from each of the separate insults.[33]

On the basis of all these considerations we have assumed, for the purposes of the computer model, the relationships of dose level to percentage killed shown in figure 6.5. These refer to doses measured in rads (to the surface of the body) received over the two-week period

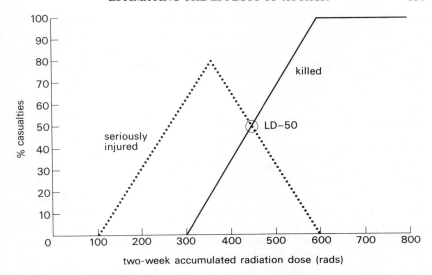

Figure 6.5 Assumed relationships of radiation dose (in rads) to percentage deaths and injuries from the acute effects of radiation. The values refer to surface-tissue doses, accumulated over two weeks. It is assumed that no specialized medical treatment is available.

following the attack. It is assumed that some deaths will occur at doses above 300 rads; that the LD-50 is 450 rads; and that deaths reach 100 per cent at 600 rads. We believe that if anything these values err on the high side, especially given that little or no medical treatment is likely to be available. Many authorities believe that some deaths could occur from 200 rads upwards. The dose is certainly extended over the relatively long period of two weeks. But because of the nature of the processes of radio-active decay, the greater part of this two-week dose — perhaps 80 per cent — is likely to be received over the first two days. Nor will the dose cease at the end of the nominal two weeks.

The figure also shows the percentages assumed to suffer 'serious injury' from radiation sickness, starting from a lower limit of 100 rads, and reaching 50 per cent at around 260 rads. The synergism between radiation sickness and other injuries is allowed for by assuming, as before, that those who suffer 'serious injury' from two causes (burns and radiation, or blast and radiation) will die.

Numbers of dead and injured from fallout are calculated on this basis from all grid-squares in turn. The final result is a series of totals for deaths from burns, blast and fallout, and for those who survive injured from any of these causes. These results for individual 1 km squares can be grouped together into larger units of area, as for example 10 km square units, by geographical boundaries such as counties, or right up to the national level.

Because of all the uncertainties, particularly those relating to the prediction of fallout patterns, as well as those to do with using census figures for the distribution of population, the aggregate predictions given for these larger areas are more meaningful than those for the individual 1 km squares.

EFFECTS OMITTED

Finally in this description of the computer model, we should re-emphasize that it takes into account only the immediate effects of attack; and that it counts just those who would be killed or injured, or else 'sentenced to death' from the radiation dose received, up to 14 days afterwards. Even some probable short-term effects are omitted, as we have mentioned, such as burns injuries received in fires, and the effects of initial nuclear radiation. We have not allowed for the possibility that additional fallout might reach southern England under certain wind conditions from bombs on the Continent. Nor do we make calculations relating to a whole range of possible longer-term consequences, some of which are listed and discussed in chapter 8.

7
Immediate Casualties and Damage

This chapter describes the results which the computer model gives for the eleven basic patterns of Attacks A to K, the attack on the dispersed cruise missiles, and the retaliatory 'MAD' attack described in chapter 5. The model has also been used to give predictions for the various home defence exercises and other historical scenarios mentioned in the same chapter. The sensitivity of these predictions to various changes in the assumed conditions of an attack, principally those to do with the weather, and with the amount of warning are shown. Also examined are the consequences of changing key assumptions to do with protection factors and the relation of radiation dose levels to percentage injuries.

The results can be presented in a variety of ways. The most obvious single measure is that of casualties: that is to say the number killed, the number seriously injured, and the total of killed plus injured. It is important to remember that even these totals exclude many possible cases of minor injury; and that most of those who are seriously injured are unlikely to receive anything but the most rudimentary medical aid, and may well die from their injuries in the weeks or months following.

Some people imagine that nuclear war will mean instant and painless death. But for millions this will not be the case. The accounts of the injured at Hiroshima and Nagasaki, and of the doctors who tried to tend them,[1] witness to the horrors and torments which would be magnified thousands of times over in the kinds of attack we analyse here.

It could take several weeks for some of those who had received radiation doses of hundreds of rads, to go through the successive stages, of nausea and vomiting in the first few days, followed by fever, bloody diarrhoea, skin haemorrhages and mouth ulcers, to their eventual deaths. It is hardly possible to imagine the conditions inside makeshift shelters for those who were suffering such symptoms or from extensive burns, bone fractures or skin lacerations. The situation would hardly be much better for those friends or relatives who might be sharing the shelters with the injured and trying to provide them with some comfort. The dry statistics of this chapter do little to convey the millions of individual realities which would lie behind them.

Total figures are given here for the whole of Britain (excluding Northern Ireland and the Channel Islands). They are also broken down by counties in England and Wales, and by regions in Scotland. There are 64 of these counties and regions. Statistics are also given in appendix 5 by 'Home Defence Regions', which are groupings of counties made for the purposes of civil defence planning, as described in chapter 10. There are 13 of these regions.

CASUALTIES IN ATTACKS A TO K

Table 7.1 gives the national casualties for Attacks A to K, as numbers killed, numbers seriously injured, and all casualties as a percentage of the initial population of 54 million. Figure 7.1 shows these same statistics plotted as a graph, against the total explosive power used in each attack in megatons. The reasons have already been given for believing that the

Table 7.1   Casualties (millions) in Attacks A to K, minimum retaliatory 'MAD' attack, and attack on dispersed cruise missiles

Attack	Total yield (megatons)	Killed	Seriously injured	Total casualties	Casualties as % of total population
A	42.5	6.4	2.7	9.0	17
B	87.0	13.3	6.0	19.3	36
C	116.9	20.1	6.2	26.4	49
D	129.45	20.8	6.4	27.2	50
E	163.75	25.6	6.4	32.0	59
F	185.75	28.4	7.1	35.5	66
G	213.65	35.4	5.4	40.8	76
H	218.7	37.5	5.1	42.5	79
I	257.65	39.9	4.4	44.3	82
J	306.65	42.9	3.6	46.5	86
K	347.65	45.3	3.0	48.4	90
'MAD'	37.8	18.3	4.9	23.3	43
Dispersed cruise missiles	698.7	42.8	3.9	46.7	86

Soviet Union is not likely actually to launch an attack much below the weight of H; and it has been explained that the lower levels of attack are introduced for the purposes of relating casualties to types of target and to progressively increasing numbers of weapons, in a systematic fashion.

The numbers of casulties increase in more or less direct proportion to megatonnage, from Attack A to Attack H. If the casualty total is divided by the total explosive yield, this ratio thus remains roughly constant, at about one casualty for every five tons of explosive equivalent. This is a very much lower rate than for example in the Japanese cities, where five or

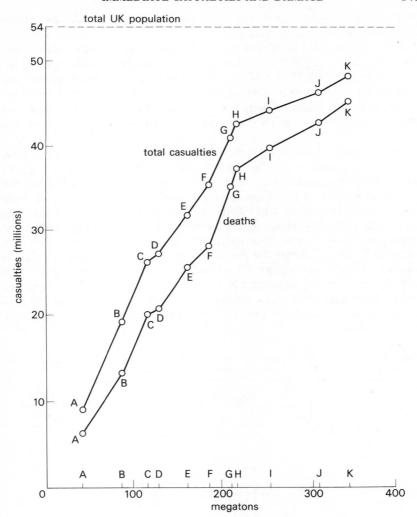

Figure 7.1   Total casualties (millions) from heat, blast and fallout related to total explosive yield (megatons) in Attacks A to K. The two curves show deaths and total casualties (deaths plus serious injuries) respectively.

six deaths were caused for every ton of explosive equivalent. The reason is partly because many of the weapons are on military targets, not cities; but mainly because of the enormous 'overkill' represented by weapons in the megaton range. There just are 'not enough people to kill'. (The slight departure from a straight line relationship at Attack D is due to the introduction at this stage of a large number of minor airfields, away from population centres, as targets.)

Even the minimal level of Attack A results in over 9 million casualties; and by Attack C, 26 million or half the population of the country are killed and injured. Attack H kills 37.5 million, and seriously injures another five million. Curiously, the number of seriously injured remains very much the same, at five to seven million, from B to H. This must be largely a consequence of the assumption that those who are injured twice or more will die.

After Attack H the rate of increase in numbers of deaths and in total numbers of casualties is rather slower. This is simply because the figures are now reaching close to the total population of the country. Most of the people in the towns and cities have been killed by this point, and those who remain are dispersed in villages or rural areas. The five million or so still uninjured after Attack K are mainly in the Scottish Highlands, the Welsh mountains and other such lightly populated regions with few targets. Table 7.2 shows the population in areas of different population density (persons per square kilometre) before and after Attack H. The population surviving uninjured in areas of lower density, 500 persons per square kilometre and less, is around 50 per cent or greater. In the highest density areas, above 2,500 persons per square kilometre, it is only 15 per cent or lower.

Table 7.2 The numbers and percentages of people surviving and without serious injury after Attack H, in areas with various initial population densities.

Population density (persons/km²)	Population (millions)		Uninjured as % of original population
	Before	Uninjured after	
1–50	1.5	0.9	64
51–200	2.1	1.1	52
201–500	2.7	1.3	47.5
501–1,000	3.9	1.6	41.5
1,001–2,500	10.3	3.3	32
2,501–5,000	16.8	2.4	14
5,001–10,000	13.1	0.7	5
more than 10,000	3.4	0.1	2
	53.9	11.4	

It should be remembered that up to Attack D the targets are exclusively military; and that heavy industrial targets are only included from Attack H onwards. It is simply not the case, as has sometimes been argued, that a strictly 'counterforce' attack, with relatively low-yield weapons, would result in only a small number of casualties. In Britain, as we have seen, many military targets are close to or actually within centres of population.

The consequence is that even in attacks which are very much more restricted than would be probable in view of Soviet targeting strategy and the number of weapons the Soviets have deployed, such as C or D, at least half the population of Britain would be killed or injured.

The closeness of some important military bases to cities is illustrated in the maps in figures 7.2, 7.3 and 7.4 which show the targets selected for Attack H in the London, Liverpool and Glasgow areas respectively. The extent of blast effects (at 1, 2, 5 and 12 psi) is illustrated in each case. This shows very graphically the enormous range of 'collateral damage' which even low-yield weapons are able to inflict.

Appendix 5 gives the casualties for Attacks A to K broken down by counties. The same statistics are illustrated in a series of maps in figures 7.5 to 7.15 in which the shading represents the percentage casualties (killed plus injured) in five different ranges. Of course these are dependent in detail on the particular targets chosen in each case. But some general features emerge. Taking Attack H for illustration, it is notable that the percentages surviving uninjured are very high in the Scottish Highlands and Islands, Dumfries and Galloway and the Borders. They are also high in the counties of north and central Wales. In counties such as the West Midlands, Greater London, Tyne and Wear, and Merseyside, by contrast, the uninjured barely exceed one per cent, for obvious reasons.

There are relatively few casualties in some of the counties along the south coast: Sussex, the Isle of Wight, Cornwall and Somerset. Devon and Kent also escape quite lightly. This is partly because there are rather few targets here, but is mainly because of the assumed wind direction, south-south-west, in the 'standard' calculations of effects. These coastal areas are not downwind of any groundburst weapons, and so the numbers of fallout injuries are few. This situation would change for other wind directions, obviously — and other coastal regions on the east, north or west would then be less seriously affected. It is also possible that if the wind were southerly, fallout from bombs on French coastal targets could reach Sussex and Kent.

The results of the attack on the ground-launched cruise missiles (see table 7.1) are perhaps slightly surprising. The total megatonnage is vastly increased over all the other attacks. At nearly 700 megatons the attack has double the weight of K. But the total casualties are not so numerous as in K. This is because the areas to which the cruise missile convoys are assumed to be dispersed are in the south and east of the country and in the Midlands, where casualties are already high (most uninjured survivors after J or K are in Scotland and Wales, on the South Coast or in the West, as we have seen); the dispersal areas are relatively lightly populated anyway; and the very high yield 20 megaton SS18s used in the attack represent a massive 'overkill' — eight separate 1 megaton explosions can destroy a greater area than can a single 20 megaton bomb.

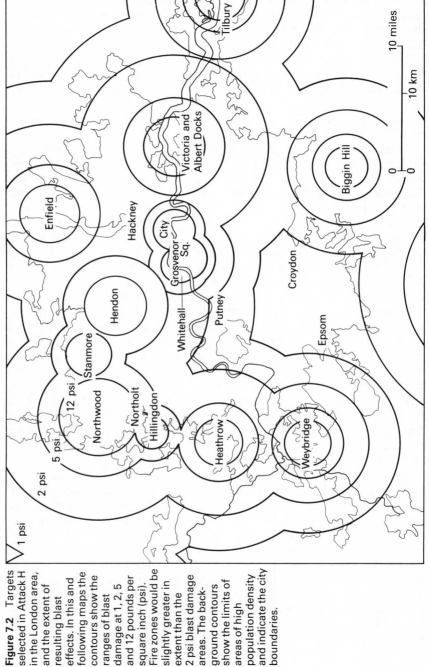

Figure 7.2 Targets selected in Attack H in the London area, and the extent of resulting blast effects. In this and following maps the contours show the ranges of blast damage at 1, 2, 5 and 12 pounds per square inch (psi). Fire zones would be slightly greater in extent than the 2 psi blast damage areas. The background contours show the limits of areas of high population density and indicate the city boundaries.

1 psi

2 psi

5 psi

12 psi

Northwood

Stanmore

Hendon

Enfield

Northolt

Hillingdon

Hackney

Whitehall

Grosvenor Sq.

City

Victoria and Albert Docks

Tilbury

Putney

Heathrow

Croydon

Biggin Hill

Weybridge

Epsom

0   10 km

0   10 miles

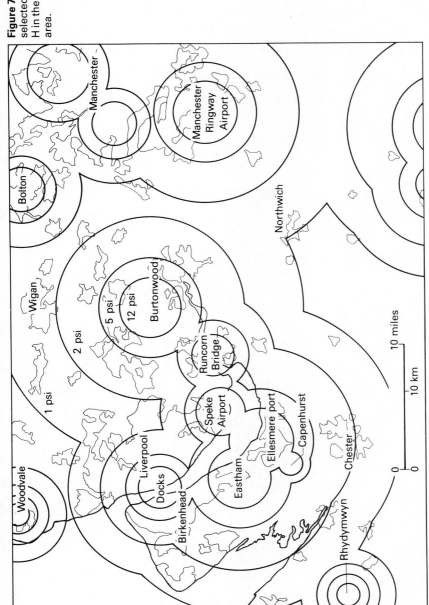

Figure 7.3 Targets selected for Attack H in the Liverpool area.

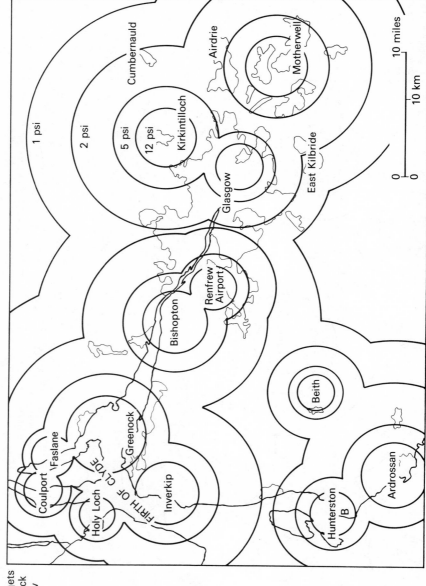

Figure 7.4 Targets selected for Attack H in the Glasgow area.

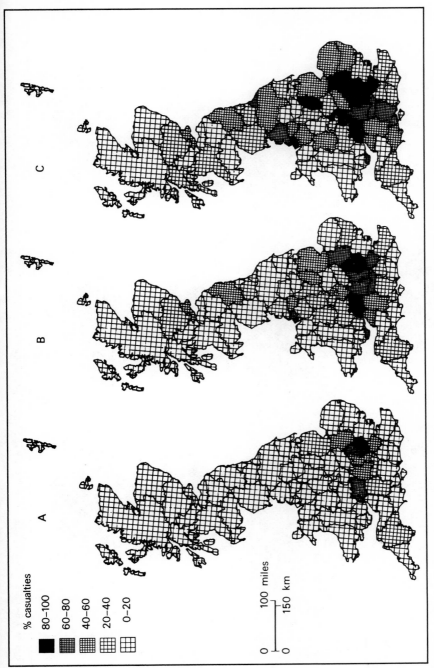

Figures 7.5–7.7 Total casualties (deaths plus injuries) from heat, blast and fallout, in Attacks A, B and C, shown by counties.

% casualties

■	80–100
	60–80
	40–60
	20–40
	0–20

0   100 miles

0   150 km

A   B   C

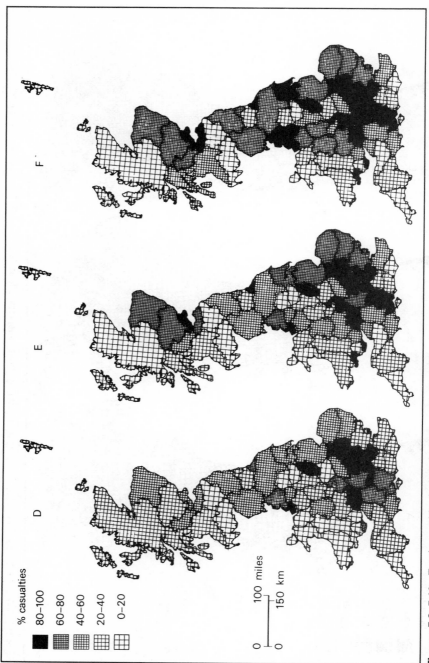

Figures 7.8–7.10 Total casualties in Attacks D, E and F, shown by counties.

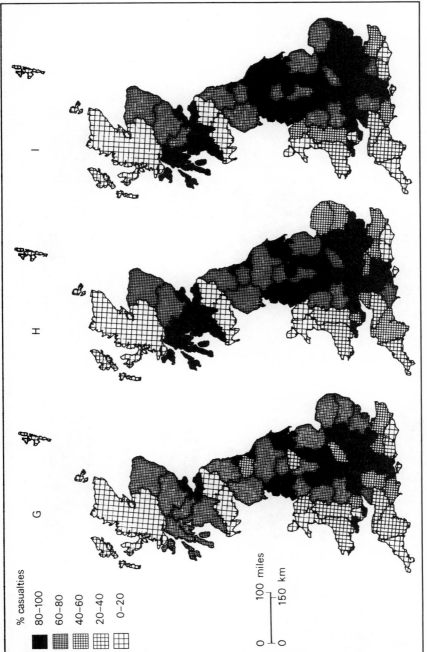

% casualties

	80–100
	60–80
	40–60
	20–40
	0–20

G   H   I

0   100 miles
0   150 km

Figures 7.11–7.13 Total casualties in Attacks G, H and I, shown by counties.

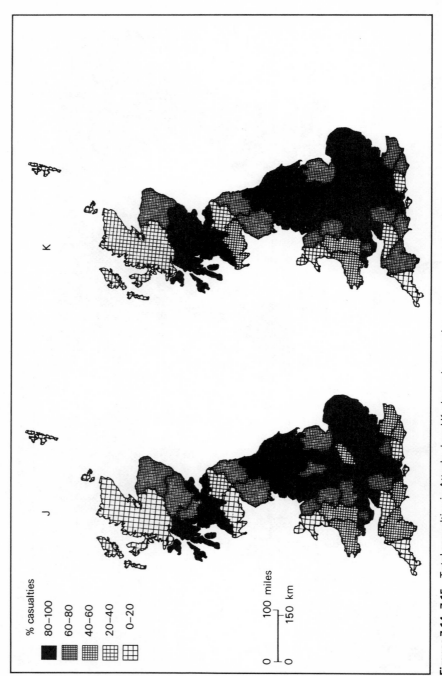

Figures 7.14–7.15 Total casualties in Attacks J and K, shown by counties.

Though it might be the case therefore that the dispersal of the cruise missile convoys could raise the expected level of Soviet attack, it does not follow — at least from this analysis — that casualty levels would be greatly increased as a consequence. This merely reflects of course the very high level of casualties in the basic Attack H, on which the targeting of the cruise missiles is superimposed. The SS18s on their own would be enormously damaging. Although casualties are not much increased, the extent of blast and fire damage is greatly magnified, especially in the agricultural shires.

ATTACKS ON CITY TARGETS

It is not probable, for all the reasons discussed in earlier chapters, that cities, in themselves, would be targets of high priority as such in an attack made early in a war. There is, however, the possibility, as discussed in chapter 5, that the Soviets could launch a small retaliatory attack against cities (together with energy resources such as oil refineries and power stations), after a very large fraction of their weapons had been knocked out in a disarming or damage-limiting first strike. The attack pattern constructed on the basis of this 'MAD' scenario (see table 7.1) gives casualties of 23.3 million, for a total yield of just under 40 megatons. We can compare this for example with B where more than twice the mega-tonnage, in a 'counterforce' attack, results in four million fewer casualties.

It is perhaps of some theoretical interest to look more systematically at this kind of difference which attacking principally military targets makes, in Attacks A to K, as compared with equivalent weights of attack against cities — as would have been the case when the MAD strategy was still in operation during the 1960s.

We have investigated this question in a slightly artificial way.[2] We have considered attacks made up exclusively from 1 megaton airburst weapons and have calculated only the resulting deaths and injuries from blast, not burns or fallout. The targets are selected by an automatic process. The computer searches all the grid-squares in the country for that target in which the resulting number of blast casualties is the greatest. (It is, as one might expect, in central London.) The numbers counted as dead are removed from the population data, and the computer then searches for the 'second worst' target, and so on, up to a limit of 200 weapons. In this way 'attack scenarios' with increasing explosive yields are constructed which represent the worst possible case with respect to blast casualties, given the chosen size of weapon. (For other yields of bomb the results would be somewhat different.)

Figure 7.16 gives the results, as total numbers of deaths plotted against total explosive yield. Two curves are illustrated. The lower curve gives numbers of deaths on the optimistic assumption that all those counted as injured survive, even if they are injured by blast more than once. The upper curve gives numbers of deaths on the pessimistic assumption that all those counted as injured (even if only once) die. Realistic estimates of the

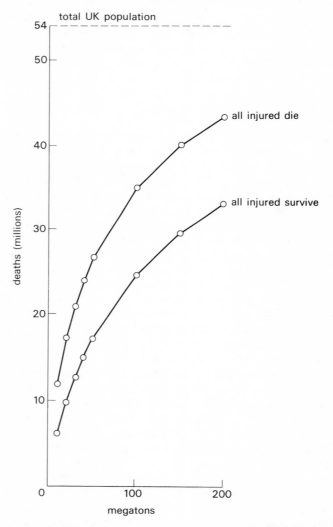

Figure 7.16 Deaths (millions) from blast effects only in 'worst case' attacks on population with increasing numbers of one megaton airbursts, up to a total yield of 200 megatons. The lower curve shows numbers of deaths on the assumption that all those injured by blast survive, even if injured more than once. The upper curve shows numbers of deaths on the assumption that all those injured by blast will die.

numbers of blast deaths would thus lie somewhere between the two curves. The curves rise very steeply at the beginning. The ten 'worst' bombs kill and injure over a million people each. (These are on different parts of London, on Birmingham, Manchester, Liverpool and Glasgow.) By 50 megatons, half the population have become blast casualties. However, the curves then begin to flatten out, as the later bombs are directed against cities and towns with ever smaller populations. At 200 megatons some 43 million people are casualties.

Comparing these results with our Attacks A to K in figure 7.1, the numbers of killed and injured are very much greater in the 'worst case' attacks against cities for total explosive yields below 200 megatons — especially remembering that figure 7.16 counts casualties from blast only. By the 200 megaton level, however, the total numbers of casualties in Attacks G and H are comparable with those in the 'worst case' analysis, at around 43 million. In both cases the casualty figures level off, as there become fewer and fewer people in the country remaining uninjured. The appalling conclusion emerges that at these, the minimum levels of attack on the UK that can be expected in the event of war, the numbers of dead and injured are determined not so much by the nature of the targets chosen, as simply by the total size of the British population.

Rather similar studies to this 'worst case' analysis were made in the United States in the 1960s, under the direction of US Secretary of Defense Robert McNamara, in order to determine the quantity of weapons which would be needed for 'mutually assured destruction'.[3] The percentage of the Soviet population killed, and the percentage of Soviet industry destroyed by blast effects, were calculated for increasing numbers of 1 megaton warheads. The resulting curves were found to rise sharply and then level off, in the same way as figure 7.16, according to what has been described as a law of 'strongly diminishing marginal returns'.[4] For the USSR, the curve of total deaths began to flatten out at around 400 megatons — the quantity accordingly fixed on by the Americans as the amount required for MAD.

CASUALTIES FOR THE HISTORICAL CIVIL DEFENCE SCENARIOS

Table 7.3 gives casualty estimates for the historical civil defence exercises. Those for 'Dutch Treat' and the 1960 attack pattern confirm how very damaging even low levels of attack can be when directed principally at cities. In both cases, roughly one casualty is caused for every two tons explosive equivalent. The results for the 1960 scenario are comparable with the 'worst case' analysis, in that just over 50 megatons produce a casualty total which approaches half the population of the country.

The numbers of casualties in 'Square Leg' are very similar to those in

Table 7.3   Casualties (millions) for historical civil defence scenarios

Attack	Total yield (megatons)	Killed	Seriously injured	Total casualties	Casualties as % of total population
'Dutch Treat' 1957	11	4.6	1.5	6.2	11
MoH Circular 1960	56.5	19.6	3.8	23.4	43
'Square Leg' 1980	205	27.2	7.4	34.6	64
'Hard Rock' 1982	48.4	6.5	4.8	11.3	21
Fission Fragments 1978	51	1.9	1.5	3.4	6

Attack F. The total weight of attack is some 20 megatons greater than in F; but on the other hand the number of weapons is smaller and hence the average weapon yield is higher. Some city targets are included in 'Square Leg', but not for example central London.

It has already been mentioned in chapter 5 that the attack pattern in the 'Hard Rock' exercise is largely nonsensical and has been chosen so that nearly all the nuclear warheads detonate outside of highly populated areas. Nevertheless, 11.3 million casualties would still result from it. In fact, in both 'Hard Rock' and 'Square Leg' one casualty is caused for about every five tons explosive equivalent — comparable with Attacks A to K.

The *Fission Fragments* attack pattern is explicitly restricted to high priority military targets that are well away from conurbations or cities of any size. The consequence is the surprisingly low casualty total of 3.4 millions. In this scenario, only one casualty results from every *fourteen* tons equivalent.

AREAS OF LAND AFFECTED IN ATTACKS

All these casualty figures refer to the 'night-time' or 'at home' distribution of the population which the use of census data implies. There is no easy way of simulating other distributions of the population, such as a day-time distribution, or one which represented an evacuated population. However, one way of approaching this problem indirectly is to examine, not the numbers of casualties caused, but the total *areas of land* affected by blast, heat and fallout in an attack.

Since the model records the damage or radioactive contamination occurring in each grid-square, it is possible to count all the squares experiencing a given level of damage and so derive a total for land area affected. Another possibility is to count just those grid-squares in which population is recorded in the census. This gives a total 'inhabited' area affected at the chosen damage level. It is likely that during the day, the majority of the population would still be somewhere within these 'inhabited' areas; and the same applies for an evacuated population. Thus the proportion of the total inhabited area which is seriously affected by heat, blast and radiation gives at least some broad indication — especially at higher levels of attack — of the likely level of casualties, wherever the population might be.

A comparison of the proportion of total land area with the proportion of inhabited area affected in an attack may also be interesting. A 'counterforce' attack might be expected to affect a large geographical area overall, but perhaps a smaller inhabited area; while an attack against cities would naturally affect a relatively larger area of inhabited land. (Although this might be less true for Britain, because of its high density and the siting of its military targets, than for some other countries.) These estimates of land areas affected will also be useful in the examination of the aftermath of attack which follows in chapter 8.

For heat effects, we take those areas which are exposed to thermal radiation at 6.7 calories per square centimetre or greater. We take the specific figure of 6.7 cal/cm^2 for convenience, since this is the level at which people would suffer fatal burns according to the OTA's assumptions (see p. 118), and the corresponding ranges are already calculated in the burns component of the casualty model. But a figure of around 6 or 7 cal/cm^2 is also the level at which readily combustible materials such as paper, dry wood or dry grass would be ignited by weapons in the megaton range. So this figure can be taken as defining the main zones in which fires would be started.

The ranges at which direct burns casualties and fires would be caused, would vary in practice with atmospheric visibility and cloud conditions, as described in chapter 6. We again assume clear visibility (19 km) for the sake of the results here. The radii of the 'fire zones' on this definition, for different yields of bomb, are given in table 7.4. (With the smaller-yield

Table 7.4 Distances from ground zero (in kilometres) to which main fire zones would extend, for weapons of different yields. There are taken to be areas where the level of thermal radiant exposure is 6.7 calories per square centimetre or greater

	Explosive yield (megatons)							
	0.15	0.5	1.0	1.5	2.0	3.0	5.0	10.0
Groundburst	4.6	7.5	9.7	11.2	12.3	14.0	16.3	19.8
Airburst	6.4	10.3	14.7	17.2	19.2	23.5	28.1	38.2

Assumes 19 km visibility, no cloud or snow cover
Height of airbursts taken to maximize 10 psi blast damage area

weapons a lower level of thermal radiant exposure would in fact be sufficient to ignite identical materials, since the same total quantity of heat is received over a shorter time.) These radii are somewhat greater than those of the 2 psi blast overpressure contours.

The areas subject to the most serious fire risk are liable to be those where the blast overpressures are in the range 2 to 5 psi, since here most buildings will be partly destroyed, rather than totally demolished, and in these circumstances fires are particularly likely to catch and spread. In the British raids on German cities in World War II, indeed, a deliberate policy was evolved of alternating high explosive bombing with incendiary attacks; since the blast damage created debris in which fires could readily take hold, and even firestorms could be generated. Similarly, in any plausible nuclear attack, many areas suffering blast damage from earlier weapons would then be exposed to thermal radiation from later bombs falling close by.

The OTA suggest that, in the 2 to 5 psi overpressure zone, perhaps five per cent of buildings might be set alight directly; and that those fires could spread, over a period of 24 hours or more, to destroy roughly half the buildings in this zone.[5] This assumes that no effort is made to fight the fires, which is probably realistic. Other important factors in the spread of fire would be the speed of the wind and the density and spacing of buildings — since one building can set light to its neighbour if the distance between them is say 15 metres or less. Obviously there is an increased danger from fire during periods of dry weather when materials and plants become desiccated.

Tokyo and Hamburg were attacked with incendiary bombs in World War II and experienced *firestorms*. It is well known that a firestorm also occurred at Hiroshima. In a firestorm the column of heated gases above the fire rises so fast that it pulls in air at speed from all directions into the base of the column. The fire cannot spread, but is contained, and burns at ever-greater intensity until everything combustible is consumed. Most people in the area of a firestorm would be killed, either by heat or by asphyxiation. It is thought that this phenomenon occurs however only in rather special circumstances: where the amount of combustible material in a given area is greater than it would be in most modern cities.[6]

In other conditions, isolated fires might join together to form a *conflagration* — a mass fire moving outwards along a front — as happened at Nagasaki. It is conflagrations which would be the more likely form of mass fire in an attack on Britain.

Figure 7.17 illustrates the extent of 'fire zones' as defined, in Attacks A to K. Both the total areas, and the 'inhabited' areas affected are shown. By Attack H the inhabited area affected is some 47,000 km². Levels in H represent about about one third of the total inhabited area, and one third of the land area of the entire country, respectively. In fact for all the attacks the proportions of inhabited and total areas affected remain roughly equal. By Attack K nearly half the country falls in the fire zones.

Figure 7.18 shows the total extent of areas affected by blast, at overpressures in excess of 1, 2, 5 and 12 psi. Figure 7.19 shows equivalent results for inhabited areas affected by blast. Recall that overpressures of

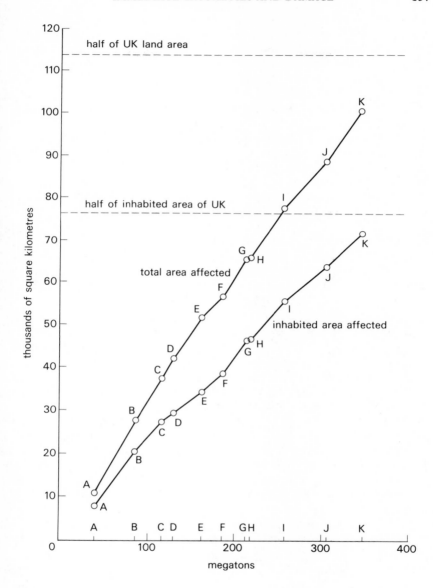

Figure 7.17 Areas (km²) of main fire zones in Attacks A to K. These are defined as areas exposed to levels of thermal radiation of 6·7 cal/cm² and above. The upper curve shows total areas affected. The lower curve shows the extent of 'inhabited' areas affected (where 'inhabited' refers to all 1 km grid-squares in which any population is recorded in the census).

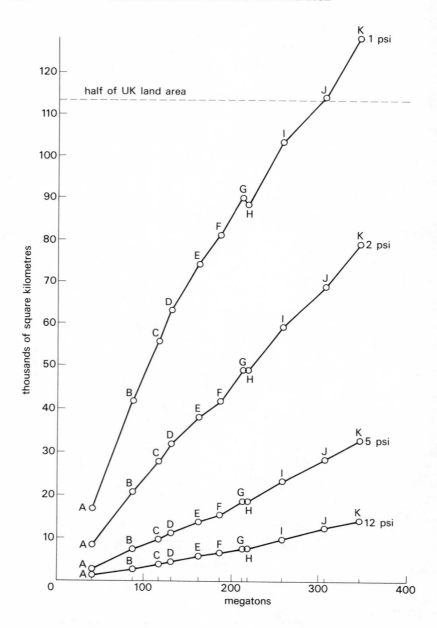

Figure 7.18 Total areas (km²) affected by blast in Attacks A to K, at overpressures greater than 1, 2, 5 and 12 pounds per square inch (psi).

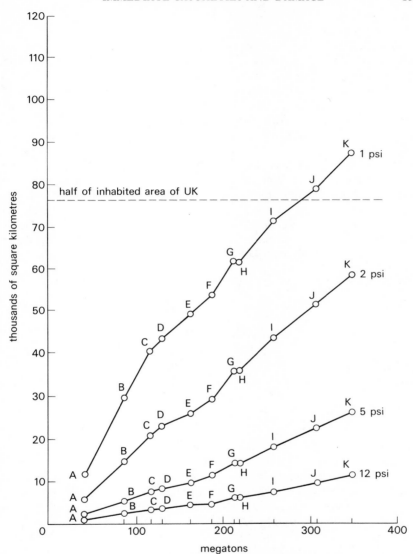

Figure 7.19   'Inhabited' areas (km²) affected by blast in Attacks A to K, at overpressures greater than 1, 2, 5 and 12 pounds per square inch (psi).

12 psi and greater will demolish most industrial and commercial buildings; overpressures of 5 psi and greater will demolish brick-built houses; overpressures in the range 2 to 5 psi will severely damage roofs, crack outside walls and blow out windows and doors; and overpressures of between

1 and 2 psi will cause light damage to buildings, for example the removal of doors and roof tiles.

At any plausible level of attack, vast areas of the country experience damage from blast. In Attack H for example the area affected at 2 psi and greater is some 22 per cent of the UK, and at 1 psi it is around 39 per cent. These figures rise to 35 and 56 per cent respectively in Attack K. For blast damage, as for fire zones, the proportion of inhabited land area affected does not differ greatly from the proportion of the total land area affected, in any of the Attacks A to K. The historical civil defence exercises show a slightly different picture. Table 7.5 gives total and inhabited areas experiencing blast pressures of 2 psi and greater in these attacks. In the 1957 and 1960 attacks on cities, the total area of blast damage in each case is not much greater than the inhabited area affected. But in 'Hard Rock' and the *Fission Fragments* scenario — both of them counterforce attacks — the total blast-affected area exceeds the inhabited area affected by a larger margin, as would be expected where most of the targets included are military and in lightly populated areas.

Table 7.5   Land areas affected by blast at 2 pounds per square inch or greater, in historical civil defence scenarios

Attack	Total area affected		Inhabited area affected		Pre-attack population density of inhabited area (persons/km^2)
	km^2	% of UK	km^2	% of total inhabited area	
'Dutch Treat' 1957	1,511	0.7	1,358	0.9	3,314
MoH Circular 1960	10,255	4.5	8,683	5.7	2,154
'Square Leg' 1980	42,958	18.7	31,432	20.7	836
'Hard Rock' 1982	10,387	4.5	7,845	5.2	777
Fission Fragments 1978	10,967	4.8	7,782	5.1	167

One reason these differences are not more marked, is that the definition of 'inhabited areas' here is a very generous one, and covers some areas of *very* low population density. All 1 km squares are included which contain any recorded population at all. The statistics in figure 7.19 should be set against the fact, for example, that the actual areas of land covered by urban, industrial and associated development amount, in England and Wales, to just 11 per cent of the total.

If we take the areas affected at 2 psi and over in the Home Office civil defence scenarios, and count the numbers of people recorded in those areas prior to the attack in each case, we can derive an *average population density* (in persons per affected km^2). There is now a very sharp contrast (see table 7.5) between the 1957 and 1960 attacks on the one hand, where the pre-attack population density in the blast-affected areas averaged 2,000 or 3,000 persons/km^2; and 'Hard Rock' on the other,

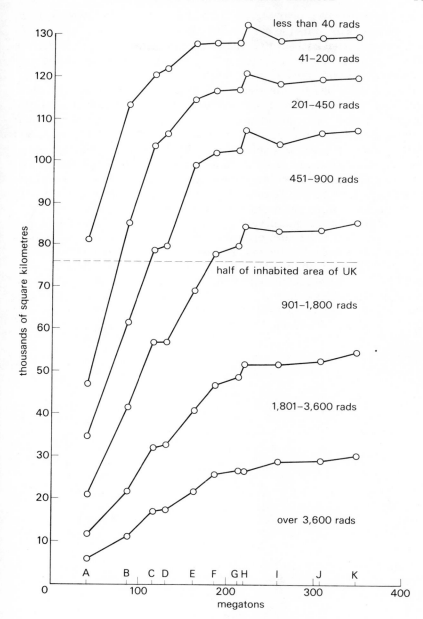

Figure 7.20 'Inhabited' areas (km²) affected by fallout in Attacks A to K. The curves show the extent of areas in which the two-week accumulated radiation dose, in the open, would exceed 40, 200, 450, 900, 1,800 and 3,600 rads.

where the density was below 1,000. In the *Fission Fragments* attack pattern the original density in the areas affected at 2 psi was only around 170 persons/km². (In Attacks A to K the average pre-attack population density of the 2 psi blast damage areas is much the same throughout, varying only between about 600 and 900 persons/km².)

Figure 7.20 shows the inhabited areas of the country affected by fallout at different levels of radioactive contamination, for Attacks A to K. These are presented in terms of the areas in which people in the open would accumulate radiation doses greater than 40, 200, 450, 900, 1,800 and 3,600 rads, in the first two weeks after the attack. People receiving 200 rads or more are almost certain to suffer radiation sickness. The chosen LD-50 value is 450 rads. The higher values are multiples of 450, and indicate areas in which protection factors of 2, 4 and 8 respectively would probably be insufficient to prevent death from radiation.

For all dose values, the curves rise steeply until Attack G or H, and then flatten out. This is because up until this stage the targets are predominantly military ones, and the majority are attacked with groundbursts (see chapter 5). It is groundbursts of course which produce local fallout. The additional industrial and city targets in I, J and K receive mostly airbursts, and thus the total amount of fallout is not increased. Figure 7.21 shows how the proportion of the total yield contributed by groundbursts declines from A to K as a consequence.

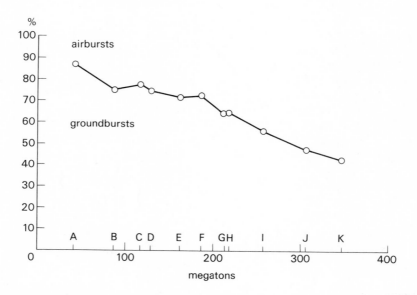

Figure 7.21 Percentage of total explosive yield contributed by groundburst weapons, in Attacks A to K. The remainder are airbursts.

For attacks above F, accumulated doses of more than 900 rads are received over half the inhabited area of the country. Doses greater than 200 rads, sufficient to cause radiation sickness, are received over three-quarters of the inhabited area.

EFFECTS OF CHANGING KEY MODELLING ASSUMPTIONS

We have examined the effects of varying weights of attack, and of different types of target. There remains the question of how sensitive all these results are to changes in some of the critical assumptions on which the calculations rest. Areas of particular uncertainty are the effects of the proportion of the population assumed to be outdoors on burns casualties; and the effects of wind speed, wind direction and average protection factors of shelters, on fallout casualties.

We have adopted a rather simple approach to this analysis. We have selected certain key variables, and have examined the effects on total casualties of making changes in each variable in turn, while all others are held constant. This excludes the possibility that some of the variables might be systematically linked together in their effects. However, earlier studies made with the model suggest that in general this is not the case. The results are presented for one scenario only, Attack H, since lower levels of attack than this are not probable, and for the heavier attacks, results of similar relative magnitude would apply.

The first area for investigation is the burns model. The difficulties of predicting what proportion of the population might be exposed to the fireball have been discussed in chapter 6 (p. 118). For the standard calculations of casualties 5 per cent exposed has been assumed. The consequences are illustrated in table 7.6, taking a range of values between 0 and 30 per cent exposed. Three different sets of assumptions were also described in chapter 6 (p. 119) concerning the relationships of levels of

Table 7.6 Effects of variations in burns casualty assumptions, and in percentage of the population assumed to be exposed, on total casualties (millions) from all causes in Attack H

% of population exposed	Burns casualty model		
	Glasstone and Dolan	Authors	Office of Technology Assessment
0	42.3	42.3	42.3
1	42.4	42.4	42.4
5	42.4	42.5	42.6
10	42.6	42.7	42.8
20	42.8	43.1	43.3
30	43.0	43.4	43.7

thermal radiation to resulting numbers of deaths and injuries: those of Glasstone and Dolan, the Office of Technology Assessment, and our own assumptions lying somewhere between the two. The results for all three models are shown in table 7.6. The changes in the assumed casualty rates for given heat levels have very minor effects; and only where the percentage of the population exposed is raised to 20 or 30 per cent is the number of total casualties significantly increased.

Table 7.7 shows the effects on fallout casualties, again in Attack H, of changing the assumed speed and direction of the wind. (The burns and blast parts of the model remain as in the standard version.) In all the results presented earlier in this chapter these were assumed to be 24 km/hr and south-south-westerly. In table 7.7 the results are shown of taking wind speeds between 16 and 40 km/hr, and wind directions in all four points of the compass. As the wind speed increases, the total area affected by fallout increases and any given point on the ground, the fallout arrives sooner, so the radioactivity has had less time to decay. The consequence is more casualties. As for wind direction, the results of changes here are more difficult to interpret, but are presumably related to the particular spatial pattern of groundburst explosions in the attack, and whether or not centres of population lie downwind of these. A westerly wind produces fewest casualties, a northerly wind the most (possibly because the heavily populated south coast is then seriously affected). Once again the effects overall are small. They might be more significant for lower levels of attack. In a heavy attack, more or less the entire country is affected by fallout, whatever the wind direction.

Table 7.7 Effects of variations in wind speed (km/hr) and wind direction on total casualties (millions) from all causes in Attack H

Wind speed (km/hr)	Wind direction				
	E	S	SSW	W	N
16	41.3	41.2	41.3	40.8	41.8
24	42.3	42.6	42.5	41.8	43.0
32	42.9	43.3	43.2	42.4	43.6
40	43.4	43.8	43.7	42.9	44.2

One area in which changed assumptions can have a very much more pronounced effect on fallout casualties is in the choice of values for protection factors of buildings. In chapter 6 we discussed the many considerations which could bear on effective pf values: house construction, extent of blast damage, questions of whether people could or would build and stay inside makeshift shelters. Table 7.8 shows the results of assuming different pf values from those taken in the standard model. The effects on fallout deaths, and on total casualties from all causes, are quite appreciable. In the extreme case, with the highest range of pf values, total casualties are reduced by some 5½ million. If the standard pf values are doubled in areas subjected to blast overpressures of between 1 and 12 psi, while the values in the remaining areas are left unchanged, the total casualties are reduced by 1.7 million and fallout deaths by 3.4 million. Reasons have been given for believing that these preferred values are reasonable or rather conservative ones. The uncertainties are perhaps greater in the areas suffering little or no blast damage (less than 1 psi), than they are in the blast-affected areas. In the latter not only will pfs be lowered by the damage to buildings (from both blast and fire), but arguably it will be more difficult for survivors to stay inside those buildings.

Table 7.8 Effects of variations in blast-dependent protection factors of buildings on casualties (millions) in Attack H

Average protection factors for areas with blast overpressures (psi) in ranges:					Total casualties (all causes)	Fallout deaths
more than 12	5–12	2–5	1–2	less than 1		
1	1	2	3.5	5	44.6	18.1
[a]1	1	2	5	8	42.5	16.0
1	1	2	5	16	40.6	14.9
1	2	4	10	8	40.8	12.6
1	2	4	10	16	38.9	11.5
1	3	6	15	24	37.1	9.1

[a] Authors' preferred values (assumed in the standard version of the model)

Table 7.8 shows the effects of keeping pfs in the blast-damaged areas the same as in the standard version of the model, while doubling the average pf in areas subjected to less than 1 psi, from 8 to 16. This reduces fallout deaths by one million, and total casualties by two million. That the difference is not greater is a function of how relatively large the inhabited areas affected by blast have become, in an attack the size of H. Total casualties would not be significantly decreased below the totals given in the table, by further increases in average pfs in areas subjected to less than 1 psi to values of say 30 or above.

Another uncertainty concerns the LD-50 value, and radiation dose levels causing other percentages of deaths and injuries. The result of raising the LD-50 from 450 to 600 rads, and all other death and injury rates in corresponding proportion, reduces total casualties in Attack H only from 42.5 million to 41.9 million. Thus changes in the LD-50 over the extreme range within which radiological opinion imagines the value might lie, are not so significant in their effects on fallout casualties as are the variations in protection factors shown in table 7.8.

There is some further discussion of the sensitivity of casualty predictions to various modelling assumptions in chapter 9, where the results are contrasted from this model with that of the Home Office. There are differences between the two models in key assumptions relating to all three main causes of casualties, heat, blast and fallout.

8

The Aftermath of Attack

If there are uncertainties in estimating short-term casualties from heat, blast and fallout — as emphasized throughout chapter 6 — then the task of assessing how many of the people surviving the attack itself might die from secondary consequences in the months following, is close to impossible. No very scientific or systematic attempts at estimates have been made. This chapter, therefore, simply presents some indications of the likely extent of physical damage to buildings and industry, of contamination of the land surface and consequences for agriculture, and in general of the destruction of the social and technological infrastructure of the country. Readers are left to draw their own conclusions about the long-term prospects for the 'survivors'.

Some readers may well say at this stage, 'Given that 35 or 45 million might be killed by the immediate effects, do we really need to go through a ghoulish recitation of the horrors of the aftermath?' However, the case for governmental civil defence preparations against nuclear war in this country has been argued on the grounds that although the level of casualties which would result from a 200 megaton attack would be 'grotesquely unacceptable . . . even then on the periphery there would be millions of people who could be helped. Are we to do nothing to help people who will be on the periphery of a devastated zone, or are we to plan to give them basic help?'[1]

Meanwhile there are those independent 'survivalists' who see the conditions after nuclear war as calling for the skills of the trapper, the hunter and the woodsman; and who are teaching themselves about self-defence, herbal remedies, edible fungi and 'making your own clothes from woodland materials'.[2] It is worth trying to paint a realistic picture, therefore, of what civil defence literature would call the 'post-attack phase', if only to examine whether current planning might be able to cope with the realities, or whether this is only fantasy.

There are some who argue that a massive programme of deep shelter building could reduce the short-term death toll very radically.[3] If that were true, then the question of what kind of Britain would confront the shelterers as they emerged from underground, assumes a new significance. We will take up the question of shelters in the following chapter.

HOUSING

No comprehensive data exist on the distribution of types and numbers of houses and flats throughout the country, broken down by small area units. However, since they record the locations of people 'at home', the census data which we use in our model must reflect rather closely the geographical distribution of the country's housing stock. Thus we can sum the total population present before the attack in those 'inhabited' grid-squares which experience a particular level of damage. This figure will then give an approximate guide to the proportion of national housing stock which would be affected at that damage level. For example in Attack H we find that 36,000 populated square kilometres are affected at 2 psi blast overpressures or above. The initial population in these affected zones is 33 million, which is 61 per cent of the national population of 54 million. Thus we can infer that roughly 60 per cent of the national housing stock will be either seriously damaged or totally destroyed in this attack. The figure rises to 80 per cent in Attack K. The 'inhabited' area of Britain exposed to overpressures in excess of 1 psi in Attack H is 61,500 km², and the number of people living in these zones, 42 million (76 per cent of housing stock). Corresponding figures for Attack K are 88,000 km² and 49 million (91 per cent of housing stock). Practically every window in Britain would be broken at these and indeed at much lower levels of attack.

Table 8.1 shows the percentages of national housing stock liable to be subject to damage from both blast and fire, calculated in the ways described, for the different scenarios. Figure 8.1 gives an indication of the geographical pattern of these effects. The map shows (shaded) those parts of Britain where the population density is greater than 100 persons per square kilometre. This density is rather low. Only villages and isolated farms would lie for the most part outside these areas. Superimposed is the extent of blast damage at the 1 psi level for Attack H.

Table 8.1 Approximate percentages of national housing stock affected at different levels of damage from blast and fire, in Attacks A to K; with total casualties as percentages of UK population, for comparison

	Attack										
	A	B	C	D	E	F	G	H	I	J	K
Serious blast damage (greater than 2 psi)	9	17	27	29	36	40	59	61	68	76	82
Some blast damage (greater than 1 psi)	16	32	46	48	56	61	75	76	82	87	91
Within fire zones	12	23	35	37	45	50	67	69	75	82	87
Total casualties as % of UK population	12	36	49	51	59	66	75	79	82	86	90

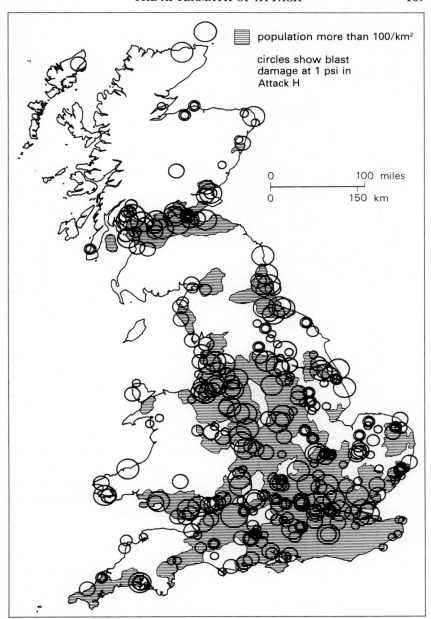

Figure 8.1 Areas of Britain in which population density exceeds 100 persons per square kilometre. The extent of blast damage at 1 psi and above in Attack H is shown superimposed.

These statistics are not presented to suggest that there would be any overall 'housing shortage' in the aftermath, but to give an indication of the huge extent of physical damage. The number of immediate casualties in any attack is so great, that the percentage of housing stock surviving only lightly damaged or undamaged in most cases (from Attack A to K) exceeds the percentage of the population surviving uninjured (see table 8.1). What is more, the areas with more survivors would tend obviously to be those in which damage to housing was not so severe. It seems reasonable to suppose, therefore, that lack of some form of crude physical shelter as such is not likely to be an overwhelming problem following an attack, although most remaining buildings will have windows broken, many will have damaged roofs, and most forms of heating other than open fires of wood and debris will be unavailable. Some survivors may thus be at risk from exposure or hypothermia.

As for buildings other than houses, there are again no suitable sources of comprehensive data at the national scale which would allow any precise estimates of damage. Building types such as offices, factories, shops and schools would, however, tend to be more highly concentrated in urban and suburban areas than housing. Hence they could be expected to suffer proportionately greater damage than houses, particularly in the heavier weights of attack, from Attack F upwards.

ENERGY

The country's fuel and power supplies, and the systems for their distribution, would certainly be high priority targets, as discussed in chapter 4. Quite apart from the military significance of oil and petrol stocks and nuclear installations, any attempt to destroy the economic and industrial structure of the country and hinder its chances of long-term recovery, is bound to concentrate on those sources which provide industry with the power to drive machinery and the fuel to fire industrial processes. A nation's economic life is heavily dependent on its transport system, and this too would be paralysed by a lack of petrol and oil.

Oil

Oil refineries are specifically included as targets in our scenarios from Attack E onwards. The fifteen refineries in Britain are shown on the map in figure 8.2. Refineries, being rather fragile above-ground structures, are very vulnerable to attack with airburst weapons. We have allocated a total of 14.5 megatons in Attacks E onwards for the destruction of refining and storage capacity throughout the country. Refineries and their storage tanks would be particularly susceptible to fire damage.

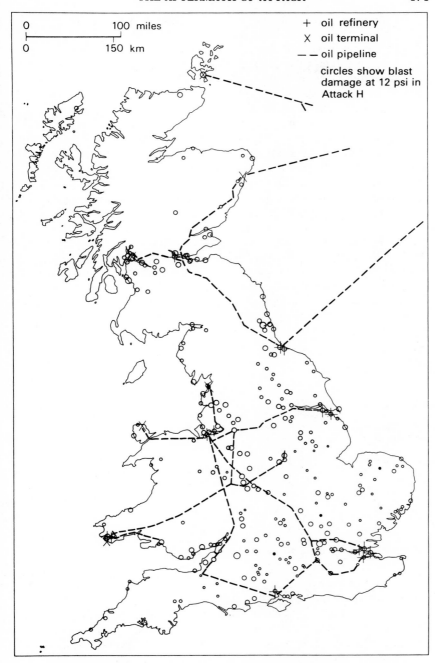

Figure 8.2 Oil refineries, terminals and pipelines in Britain. The extent of blast damage at 12 psi and above in Attack H is superimposed. This is more than enough to destroy the refineries, which would probably be vulnerable to 5 psi. All these are targets from Attack E onwards in any case. The pipelines would be broken where they run near the centres of the 12 psi damage zones from groundbursts.

As mentioned in chapter 4, it is very possible that the North Sea production platforms might themselves be attacked in a war, although these have not been included as targets in any of the scenarios. There are about 40 oil and gas platforms, British and Norwegian, in the North Sea, which would be vulnerable to either nuclear or conventional bombing attack. It has been estimated that a total of 4 megatons of nuclear weapons would be sufficient to uncap all these wells.[4]

Figure 8.2 also shows the locations of the terminals at which oil is loaded on or off tankers, and the pattern of the pipeline system by which oil is brought ashore from the North Sea, and is pumped around the country. Most of the terminals are targets themselves in Attack E upwards, or are within the range of 'collateral damage' from other targets. Clearly the destruction of the tanker terminals would make it difficult to bring in oil supplies from abroad after a war — assuming any international trade still continues.

The oil pipeline system, since it is buried, could be expected to survive an attack largely unscathed — although many of the controls and pumps on the surface would probably be damaged. A direct or near hit from a groundburst would nevertheless fracture any pipeline. Table 8.2 gives the sizes of crater caused by groundbursts of different yields. The size is given as an 'apparent radius' (in metres) in each case: that is, the radius of the

Table 8.2 Apparent crater radius (metres) for groundburst bombs of different yields, in different types of ground. (Underground pipelines would be fractured up to a distance from ground zero of twice the apparent crater radius)

Explosive yield (megatons)	Crater radius (metres)			
	Wet soil or wet soft rock	Dry soil or dry soft rock	Wet hard rock	Dry hard rock
0.15	110	85	80	65
0.5	160	120	115	95
1.0	200	150	140	120
1.5	220	170	160	130
2.0	240	180	170	145
3.0	280	205	190	165
5.0	320	240	230	190
10.0	400	300	280	230

Source: Calculated from data in Glasstone and Dolan, *Effects of Nuclear Weapons,* pp. 253–6

hole left after the explosion. The actual crater would be somewhat larger, but material would fall back into it. The size varies somewhat with the type of soil or rock. A pipeline would be ruptured up to a distance of twice the apparent crater radius from ground zero. For example, a 2 megaton bomb in dry soil or wet hard rock would fracture pipelines over a circular area of diameter 700 metres.

It is likely that the refineries and terminals shown in figure 8.2 would be seriously damaged by overpressures of around 5 psi. Since these are all targets in Attack E and above, there is not much to be learned from superimposing on the map the corresponding overpressure contours. Instead the areas affected in Attack H at overpressures of 12 psi and above are shown superimposed, in order to investigate possible damage to the pipelines. (For each weapon these areas are much larger nevertheless than the crater sizes in table 8.2.) The map is not accurate enough to determine where the pipelines would definitely be broken, or pumps and controls destroyed; but it serves to suggest that this could happen perhaps near Glasgow, Liverpool and Bristol, as well as at the refineries and terminals themselves.

Natural gas

Figure 8.3 shows the system of major pipelines carrying natural gas in Britain. North Sea gas is brought from the production fields through pipelines which come ashore at four terminals on the east coast, all of which are targets in the scenarios from Attack E upwards.

Similar damage criteria would apply for the principal underground gas pipelines as for oil pipelines. The gas network differs, however, in that it extends much more widely into houses and other buildings. These domestic and industrial supply pipes would be broken in many places through blast damage, and the resulting leaks could cause fires and explosions, unless special precautions were taken to shut down supplies before an attack. As with oil pipelines, we show superimposed on figure 8.3 the areas experiencing blast overpressures greater than 12 psi in Attack H. Within the limitations of the accuracy of the map, this suggests once again that the major gas pipelines would be broken in several places.

Natural gas storage tanks would also be vulnerable to blast and fire. We assume, as mentioned in chapter 4, that the very large gas stocks imported from Algeria and held on Canvey Island in the Thames estuary would be a target from Attack E upwards.

Coal

Mine workings underground would be very little damaged by the direct effects of attack, although surface installations could be affected by blast and fire. More importantly, should electricity supplies be cut, then underground ventilation and drainage systems would fail, and this in turn would make the pits unworkable.

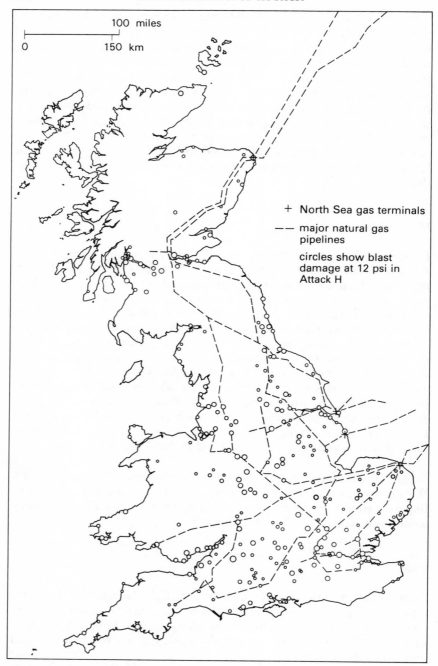

Figure 8.3 North Sea gas terminals and major natural gas pipelines in Britain. The extent of blast damage at 12 psi and above in Attack H is superimposed. The pipelines would be broken where they run near the centres of the 12 psi damage zones from groundbursts.

Electricity

Figure 8.4 shows the country's 14 operating civil nuclear power stations, plus the two under construction at Torness and Heysham. The four military and experimental reactors at Dounreay, Chapelcross, Calder Hall and Winfrith are also included. The map also shows 29 of the largest conventional power stations, including four under construction. Many smaller stations, in particular hydroelectric stations in Wales and Scotland, are not included. Nuclear power stations are targets in Attack E and upwards. Nineteen of the conventional stations are specifically targeted in Attack F and upwards. Many others are destroyed in attacks on nearby targets.

Besides the direct damage to the stations themselves, there would be other effects contributing to the destruction of the electricity supply system as a whole. Transmission cables and their supporting towers would be brought down at relatively low levels of blast overpressure.[5] Lightweight electrical transmission towers would be felled by a peak *dynamic* overpressure of 0.6 psi. (The same applies to lamp-posts and telephone poles.) The dynamic pressure is associated with the winds created by the explosion. It is not the same as the *static* overpressure, caused by the shock wave, for which values have so far been given in connection with blast casualties and damage to buildings. A dynamic overpressure of 0.6 psi would correspond to a static overpressure of 5 psi. Rigidly mounted and guyed towers would be brought down by a dynamic overpressure of 2.2 psi, corresponding to a static overpressure of 10 psi.

In addition to the power stations, figure 8.4 shows the routes taken by the 400/275 kV 'supergrid' of overhead power lines. Superimposed are the areas affected at 5 psi in Attack H. This would be sufficient to do serious damage to the cables, although rather higher overpressures — perhaps 10 or 12 psi — would be needed to bring down the towers. The main power lines could be broken, on the evidence of the map, in perhaps 70 places. Furthermore, some electricity grid control points are deliberately targeted in Attack F and upwards. Local transmission lines (not shown) would be broken all over the country.

Overpressures of around 200 psi would be needed to breach the containment vessel of a nuclear reactor, so this could only be achieved with a direct hit. However some of the vital systems such as air filters, auxiliary transformers and coolant pipes would be broken by overpressures in the range 4 to 20 psi, and this in turn could result in the meltdown of the reactor and the release of its contents.[6]

For those powerlines not affected by blast, severe damage could be caused by the electro-magnetic pulse (EMP), which would generate an electric field in the transmission cables, similar to the effect of a lightning strike but much more intense.[7] Because of the shorter rise-time with the

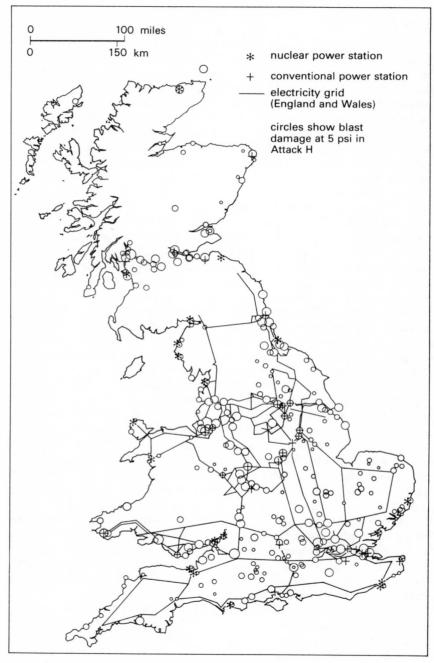

Figure 8.4 Civilian power stations and military reactors in Britain, including those under construction, and the 400/275 kV electricity 'supergrid'. (The grid is shown for England and Wales only.) The extent of blast damage at 5 psi and above in Attack H is superimposed. This would be sufficient to damage the power lines. The supporting towers would be brought down by 10 to 12 psi. Fifteen of the nuclear stations are targeted from Attack E upwards, and 19 of the conventional stations from Attack F. (Many others would be destroyed in attacks on nearby targets.)

EMP, some of the types of surge arrestor which are used to protect the network against lightning would not be effective. The microelectronic circuitry which is used in the control and switching equipment on the network and in the control systems for nuclear reactors is also vulnerable to the EMP.

Another potential cause of serious damage to electrical generating sets in stations not themselves directly hit by bombs, would be the sudden loss of electrical load resulting from massive blast damage elsewhere. This could only be avoided if the sets were switched off and isolated from the network before an attack. Finally, should any conventional stations with their equipment survive the attack unscathed, the problem of supplying these with coal or oil would still remain.

Nuclear attacks on nuclear reactors

Potentially, one of the most serious features of a successful attack with nuclear weapons on nuclear power stations would be the resulting release of radioactive fuel from the reactor cores, and the dispersal of this material mixed with other fallout. This problem has been discussed in a number of recent publications.[8] A nuclear reactor contains a relatively small amount of short-lived radioactive isotopes compared with a bomb, and so the resulting dose-rate from fallout would not be greatly affected immediately following the explosion.

The danger is created rather by the presence in the fuel of isotopes whose radioactivity is much longer-lived, as for example Strontium-90 and Caesium-137. Within three or four days such isotopes provide the major contribution to the radioactivity of the resulting fallout, as figure 8.5 indicates. After two weeks their effects dominate over those of the weapon. The curves in the figure relate to a 1 megaton groundburst on its own, and a 1 megaton groundburst on a reactor of nominal 1,000 megawatt capacity. The radioactivity from fallout would be even more long-lived — as also shown in the figure — if the storage tanks for high-level waste at Sellafield (Windscale) were hit. These tanks are not 'hardened' against blast effects and could all be destroyed by a single groundburst.

Figure 8.6 illustrates the magnitude of the problem. The map shows the twelve civil and three military nuclear reactors hit in Attack E. The shaded areas are those in which the resulting fallout dose accumulated, in the open, during the period from one month up to one year after the attack, would total 100 rads or more. A south-south-westerly wind direction is assumed. (The theoretical fallout ellipses are especially schematic here, since the wind would certainly not stay constant in speed and direction over the 500 km or so over which some of the ellipses extend.) Such a dose rate applies over large parts of the inhabited area of the country, as the map shows. Even this does not include the effects of the bomb on

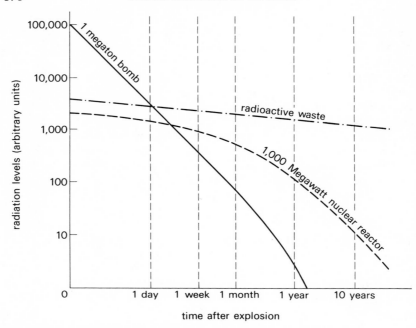

Figure 8.5 Comparative rates of decay of radiation levels from fallout, for a
1 megaton groundburst on its own; the contents of a 1,000 megawatt nuclear
reactor; and the contents of high-level radioactive waste storage tanks, such as
those at Sellafield (Windscale).

Source: adapted from data in S. A. Fetter and K. Tsipis, 'Catastrophic releases of radioactivity', *Scientific American*, April 1981, p. 33.

Windscale, or the fact that under these wind conditions, fallout from any
reactors attacked in northern France would also reach parts of England
and Wales.

    This level of accumulated dose of 100 rads would be reduced for people
inside buildings, although it is hardly credible that protection factors
much greater than 3 could apply over a period as long as a year —
especially given the extent of blast damage and the fact that survivors will
be obliged to spend time out of doors searching for food, clean water and
fuel. Nor would the only danger be from external doses of radiation, since
over this period the fallout particles could enter the body through wounds,
or they could be inhaled or ingested with food (see below). Radiation doses
of 100 rads would in themselves cause many cases of radiation sickness.
Furthermore it has to be remembered that these doses are additional to
those from the weapons fallout already considered, and thus would further
increase the number of early fallout casualties. Such doses would certainly
be very significant in producing longer-term biological effects including
genetic damage, cancers and leukaemias, as also discussed below.

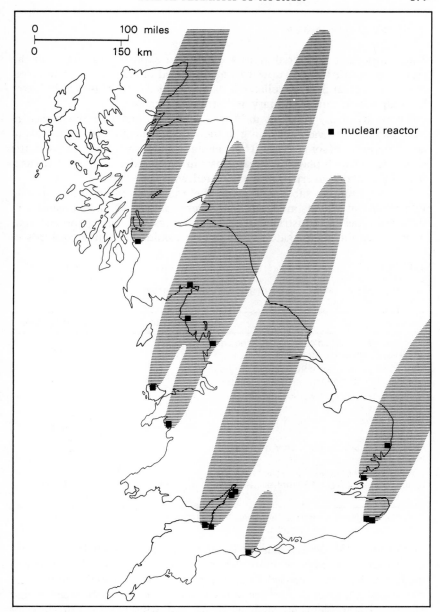

Figure 8.6 Extent of fallout resulting from successful attacks on twelve civil and three military nuclear reactors in Britain, in Attack E. The areas affected are scaled approximately to the output of the reactor or reactors in each case. The shaded areas are those in which the open-air dose accumulated from one month after the attack up to the end of one year would be 100 rads or greater. The wind is assumed to be south-westerly at 24 km/hr. Effects of attack on the high-level radioactive waste storage tanks at Sellafield (Windscale), or on reactors in northern France, are not included.

INDUSTRY AND TRANSPORT

Some important industrial areas are included explicitly as targets in the
scenarios from Attack H upwards, as discussed in chapter 5. At all levels
of attack, a great deal of 'collateral' damage will also be caused to industry
by weapons on purely military and strategic targets.

There are many types of industrial buildings and their resistance to
blast damage will vary according to their shapes, heights and materials of
construction. In some cases it is the static peak overpressure from the
shock wave which plays the greater part in causing damage; in other cases
it is the dynamic overpressure associated with the winds.

For illustration, table 8.3 gives the ranges from ground zero, in
kilometres, at which 'moderate' or 'severe' damage would be caused to
different types of industrial and office buildings by a 1 megaton airburst.
The ranges for a 1 megaton groundburst would be about two-thirds of

Table 8.3 Distances (kilometres) from ground zero at which 'moderate' and 'severe'
damage would be caused to factories, office buildings and road and railway bridges by a
one megaton airburst. (For a one megaton groundburst the distances would be two-
thirds of these values)

Type of structure	Moderate damage	Severe damage
Multi-storey reinforced concrete building with small windows, 3 to 8 storeys	5.2	4.6
Multi-storey reinforced concrete frame office building, 3 to 10 storeys	4.1	3.5
Multi-storey steel-frame office building, 3 to 10 storeys	3.7	3.4
Light steel-frame single-storey industrial building	6.1	5.5
Heavy steel-frame single-storey industrial building	4.0–4.6	3.7–4.3
Different types of railway and road bridges with spans between 20 and 120 metres, depending on construction	2.3–5.5	2.0–4.9

Source: Compiled from data in Glasstone and Dolan, *Effects of Nuclear Weapons,* table 5.139 and figure 5.140,
pp. 214–19

these values. 'Moderate' damage is defined as damage sufficient to render
the structure useless without major repairs. The distances at which
moderate damage is caused to all the building types listed, are those at
which the static peak overpressures would take values between 6 and
12 psi. 'Light' damage, such as doors and windows broken, interior
partitions cracked, and light metal or wooden siding ripped off, would
occur in all cases at a static overpressure of about 1 psi or more.

As for the national picture, this is again rather difficult to estimate without detailed data on the geographical distribution of industry. Industrial areas would, as mentioned, tend to be more concentrated geographically than are those devoted to housing. Thus the situation for industry might be expected to be at least as serious, if not more so, than that indicated for the national housing stock in table 8.1; for example, 65 per cent of buildings affected by fire or blast damage at the 2 psi and higher levels in Attack H, and a corresponding figure of 85 per cent in Attack K. Some offices and industrial buildings with steel or concrete frames are more resistant to blast than are houses as table 8.3 shows; but on the other hand, even 1 or 2 psi would remove the roofs and/or side walls from light factories and warehouses. One American study, by Katz, takes a level of blast overpressure of 5 psi or greater as the criterion for 'severe damage to industrial capacity'.[9] To give a very broad indication of what this might mean for this country, figure 8.7 shows the 5 psi blast damage areas in Attack H superimposed on a map of the major towns and cities in Britain.

It is sobering to compare the results of two other American studies, by the Stanford Research Institute and by the Metis Corporation, on the effects of hypothetical attacks directed exclusively at economic targets (and not at military sites as such) in the United States.[10] Both studies found that an attack with about 100 megatons was sufficient to destroy around 30 per cent of all US industry; and an attack with 300 megatons, around 50 per cent of industry. These figures should be seen in relation to the fact that the continental USA is over 30 times larger in area than the UK, and that urban densities are also in general lower in American than in Britain.

However, a simple measure of the extent of destruction of factories and commercial premises, even if this were calculated for the UK, would not give a true indication of the seriousness of the consequences for the economy of a given level of attack. As emphasized in chapter 4, industry is not a set of isolated parts, but a highly interconnected system in which the manufacture of one product can depend on supplies of components and processed materials from many other industries. Should the capacity of certain key industries be very much reduced, then the resulting 'bottle-neck' will have far-reaching effects elsewhere. The problems of lack of fuel and power for industrial processes, and the failure or contamination of water supplies, would be at least as important as physical damage to industrial structures. Shortage of fuel would also restrict the transport of raw materials and manufactured goods, if there are any.

Set against the problem of fuel supplies, any discussion of physical damage to the road and railway systems is perhaps academic — although this too could be very extensive. Some major transport links such as motorways and railway junctions are targeted in Attack F and upwards. The actual road surfaces or rail tracks themselves would be little damaged by blast except in the craters from groundbursts. The weak points would

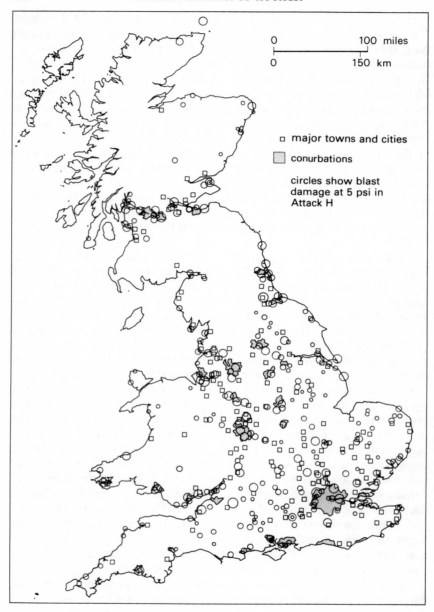

Figure 8.7   Major towns and cities in Britain, with the extent of blast damage at 5 psi and above in Attack H superimposed. 5 psi would be sufficient to cause serious damage to most industrial and commercial buildings; and so the map can be taken as indicating very broadly the extent of destruction of industry.

be bridges, and the overhead electrification lines on the railways. Table 8.3 gives some figures for the distances at which both road and rail bridges would be damaged or destroyed by a 1 megaton airburst. These are short-span bridges, up to 120 metres. Major long-span bridges such as the Tay, Severn and Forth bridges would be much more vulnerable. In addition both roads and railways would be blocked or broken at many points by land-slides and building rubble. Naval bases and dockyards are targeted from Attack C onwards, and other ports from Attack E.

Even very limited levels of attack directed wholly at military objectives, such as in Attacks C and D, are devastating in their consequences for the nation's continued economic life — since even here roughly one third of the country's built-up areas, including most of London and several other major cities, lie within the 2 psi and fire damage zones. By Attacks E and F, with the wholesale destruction of the country's energy supplies and transport system, the prospects for anything but the most primitive industrial activity following an attack must be limited indeed.

WATER

One key industry which we have not yet discussed is the water supply industry, which is not only crucial in manufacturing, but is of course literally vital to any survivors for drinking, cooking, in agriculture and in even the most rudimentary health care

Major water mains would be ruptured by blast in the immediate vicinity of craters from groundbursts, and smaller pipes broken over much larger areas due to the collapse of buildings and bridges. This in turn could result in a loss of water pressure throughout the whole network. Pumping and purification stations above ground would be damaged by blast and fire; and lack of fuel and the failure of electricity supplies could prevent the operation of undamaged pumps.

Reservoirs, streams, rivers and other bodies of open water would be contaminated by fallout. Any rainwater would be highly radioactive, unfit to drink, and even, in the period immediately following an attack, harmful to health merely by contact with the skin. The most dangerous radioactive contamination of water in the medium term would be from Iodine-131 and Strontium-89.[11] In addition, there would be widespread biological contamination from ruptured sewage pipes and from the large numbers of animal and human corpses. As water passes through the ground however, it is purified, and any water from deep aquifers — assuming it could be pumped to the surface — would be largely free of contamination.

Everything that has been said about industry as a whole would apply to the food processing and distribution industries. A certain amount of food would be in the shops and in the distribution system at the time of an attack. However, supermarkets hold only a few days' supply at one time. Civil defence planners have expressed doubts as to whether there would even be sufficient in the shops to provide the 14 days' supplies with which people are officially recommended to stock their fallout shelters.[12] There are also government food stocks containing a few weeks' supplies, held in a series of warehouses around the country (see chapter 10).

Food shops and warehouses would suffer blast and fire damage comparable perhaps with housing (see table 8.1). Any surviving stocks of refrigerated food would be liable to spoil quickly as a result of the failure of electricity supplies; and other stocks in damaged buildings could suffer radioactive contamination.

AGRICULTURE

The destruction of other industries would have serious consequences in turn for agriculture, since farming in Britain is highly mechanized and depends heavily on fossil fuels, electrical power, chemical fertilizers and pesticides, and a whole range of other industries supplying equipment, machinery and spare parts.

About three-quarters of the land area of England and Wales is devoted to agriculture. The main areas for arable farming are in the flat, rich land of East Anglia, Lincolnshire and Yorkshire, as well as in some parts of the Midlands and southern England, as shown in figure 8.8. Livestock farming is found mostly in the west, where the land is more hilly and the rainfall heavier. Figure 8.9 shows the extent of dairying and livestock production. On both maps there is superimposed the extent of 2 psi blast damage in Attack H. There is also the hill-farming concentrated in the Welsh mountains, the Scottish Highlands and the Lake District (not shown).

Agriculture would suffer very seriously from the immediate effects of blast and fire in an attack, especially the arable land in the east, as figure 8.8 indicates. Growing crops could be scorched or set alight, depending on the weather and the time of year. Figure 7.17, which showed the areas of fire zones throughout the country at the different levels of attack, reveals how widespread this damage could be: around 30 per cent of the land area by Attack H and over 40 per cent by Attack K.

Farm animals would be liable to burns and blast injury in much the same way as people. The main difference would be that animals would

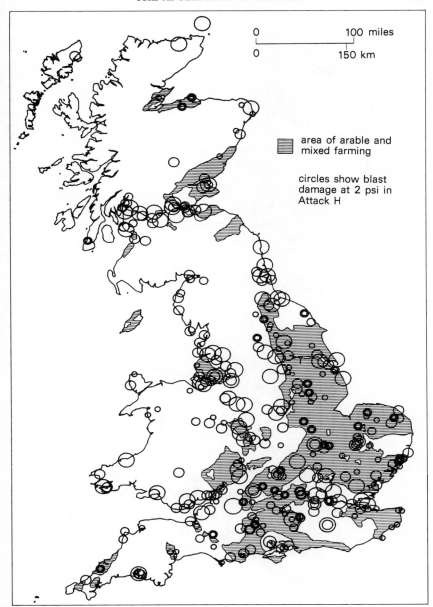

Figure 8.8 Areas of arable and mixed farming in Britain (horticulture, root and other crops, pig farming, fruit, and mixed cropping and livestock). The extent of blast damage at 2 psi and above in Attack H is shown superimposed. Main fire zones would be slightly greater in extent.

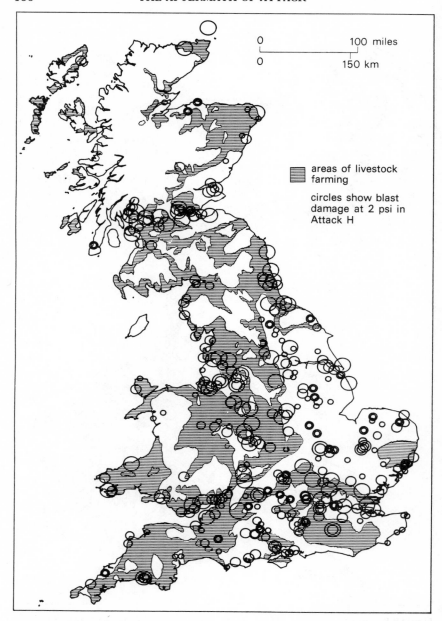

Figure 8.9 Areas of livestock farming in Britain (stock rearing and feeding, and dairying). Hill farming is not included. The extent of blast damage at 2 psi and above in Attack H is shown superimposed.

tend to be outdoors and away from buildings, and so would suffer proportionately more burns injuries. The same would apply for wild animals and birds.

The very high-speed winds produced by nuclear explosions would blow down trees over huge areas.[13] For example at 12 km from a 1 megaton airburst, up to 90 per cent of deciduous trees would be uprooted, and the remainder would have most of their branches ripped off. At 14 km, perhaps 30 per cent of trees would be felled. Coniferous trees are somewhat more resistant to the wind: the corresponding figures for these levels of damage would be 9 km and 11 km. These figures imply that orchard, woodland and forest trees would be either felled or set on fire — over 20 per cent of the UK in Attack H, and over 30 per cent of the country in Attack K. Britain is rather lightly wooded — over only about 7 per cent of the total land area of England and Wales. The most extensively forested areas of the Welsh mountains, and Scotland, would tend to escape the immediate effects of attack. Nevertheless by Attack H most of England's principal forests — Thetford Chase, the New Forest, the Forest of Dean — would be ablaze.

Those agricultural areas which escaped destruction by blast and fire would then face the effects of fallout. The sensitivity of animals to radiation varies widely with different species, but the effects on most larger domestic animals are broadly comparable with those on humans.[14] Table 8.4 shows the LD-50 values for different farm animals, for whole-body surface-tissue doses. For example in sheep the LD-50 is somewhat lower than in humans, while for poultry it is almost twice as great.

Table 8.4 Median lethal doses of radiation from fallout (LD-50 values) for farm animals. The doses measure exposure to gamma rays in roentgens. These can be taken as approximately equal to values in rads

	In barn	In pen or corral	In pasture
Cattle	500	450	180
Sheep	400	350	240
Swine	640	600[a]	550[a]
Horses	670	600[a]	350[a]
Poultry	900	850[a]	800[a]

[a] No experimental data available; estimates are based on grazing habits, anatomy and physiology of the species
Source: Glasstone and Dolan, *Effects of Nuclear Weapons*, table 12.248, p. 622

If ruminants such as sheep or cattle were to eat grass contaminated with radioactivity, then they would be at greater risk because of the combination of the external dose from gamma radiation, with the internal dose, mainly from beta radiation, from the contents of their stomachs. It seems that in these circumstances the LD-50 for sheep could be reduced to just over 200 rads, and for cattle could be as low as 70 rads.

Figure 7.20 showed that in Attack H, two-week radiation doses from fallout in excess of 200 rads would be accumulated in the open air over 120,000 populated km^2, more than half of the UK's land area. By comparison with the human population, farm animals would be more widely dispersed, away from cities and from at least some major military target areas. They would, on the other hand, be generally much worse protected from the effects of radiation. Some animals would be in barns or shed, with pf values of about 2 or 3, or could be rounded up and brought under cover before fallout arrived, but the problems of keeping livestock fed and watered indoors for periods of weeks or months would be prodigious, if not insuperable. For animals in the open, including all wild animals, the effective pf would, of course, be 1. It is difficult to escape the conclusion that the country's farm animal population — 8 million pigs, 12 million cattle and 27 million sheep — would suffer in numbers at least as seriously as would the human population. Animals in intensive factory production would be likely to fare worse than others, since their continued daily existence in peacetime is dependent on prepared foodstuffs, piped water supplies, and on electrical power for ventilation.

For those surviving farm animals which received non-fatal doses of radioactivity there would still be serious harm to their health. Ruminants would develop ulcers from the accumulation of radioactive material in their stomachs, their milk production would be depressed, and many animals would be rendered temporarily or permanently sterile.

Among other species, insects are particularly resistant to radiation. For example the LD-50 for bees is around 5,000 rads. It has been suggested that this great difference in sensitivity to radiation could lead to large differences in death rates between species, and consequent ecological imbalances. For example certain populations of insect pests might increase rapidly in the period following an attack, unchecked by their natural predators, with possibly disastrous consequences for crops.

As for food plants, their sensitivity to radiation is in general much lower than that of animals. The LD-50 value for many common crops lies in the range 1,000 to 20,000 rads, although these values could vary greatly at different stages of growth.[15] The time of greatest sensitivity is at the early reproductive stage. And crops which are just planted at the time of an attack will be exposed to radiation over a longer period before they are mature, than those which are ready to harvest.

Both farm animals and food crops on the ground, if not killed by radiation, could still be heavily contaminated with radioactivity and thus dangerous to humans as food. Larger fallout particles simply adhering to the surfaces of plants could be washed off (assuming uncontaminated water was available). But smaller particles, either on leaves or in the ground, would be actually taken up into the structure of the plant. Milk and meat would be affected where animals grazed on contaminated grass. It would be the longer-lived radioactive isotopes, such as those of Strontium and Caesium, which would come to present the greatest danger. Radioactive Iodine for example would find its way into milk, and if that milk was drunk, the Iodine would accumulate in the human thyroid gland.

Despite the seriousness of the long-term consequences of these increased radiation doses from diet, it should be said nevertheless that these levels of dose would be small compared with the direct external exposure from fallout; and that malnutrition and other diseases would present the greater medium-term threat to health.

Finally there are some complex and rather uncertain ecological and environmental effects of large-scale nuclear war which could have catastrophic results for food production. These have been discussed in the context of a full-scale war conducted over most of the Northern Hemisphere, and in those conditions would affect Britain as elsewhere.

EFFECTS ON THE EARTH'S OZONE LAYER

The first of these is the possibility, discussed in a report by the American National Academy of Sciences (NAS) in 1975, that nuclear war could have disastrous effects on the chemical composition of the upper atmosphere.[16] The explosion of high-yield nuclear weapons would have the result of injecting, among other materials, large quantities of oxides of nitrogen into the stratosphere. These in turn would react with, and so reduce, the quantity of ozone in the stratosphere. This layer of ozone shields the earth's surface from much of the harmful ultraviolet radiation which comes from the sun. Indeed biologists have argued that it was precisely the formation of the ozone layer, some 600 million years ago, which created the protected preconditions on earth for the evolutionary emergence of many of the higher species.

The NAS report calculated that a large-scale nuclear war could result in a reduction of the quantity of ozone in the stratosphere by between 30 and 70 per cent. No one knows for certain what the biological consequences would be of the resulting increased levels of ultraviolet radiation on the ground, but the scientific consensus is that they could be catastrophic. People would suffer severe sunburn from even short periods in the sun, and could be temporarily blinded, if they were not wearing protective clothing and glasses. They could develop skin cancer.

Animals and plants would not of course be so protected. Many animals would be permanently blinded, and would not survive. Some species of insects rely on ultraviolet radiation for navigation and other purposes, and their behaviour patterns would become disturbed. Some crop plants might be 'scalded' by the radiation and die as a result. And some species, for example the single-celled organisms in the shallower waters of the sea — on which many larger organisms feed, could be killed outright. What the combination of all these effects might be on the complex and fragile network of ecological relationships which link biological species together, no one can say. A depletion of the ozone layer could further have the consequence of altering the earth's climate, in ways which are also difficult to predict.

Since the publication of the NAS report, the models of the upper atmosphere which it used have been criticized. Nevertheless the magnitude of the effects which it predicted have been confirmed by more recent research.[17] Such consequences would result only from the explosion, in a global war, of thousands of weapons with explosive yields in the megaton range, or smaller weapons exploded at high altitudes. With lower-yield bombs detonated near the ground, the mushroom clouds would not reach high enough to have the same results. This fact has led Edward Teller (the 'father of the H-bomb' and not exactly a great campaigner for nuclear disarmament) to call for arms control, as a matter of urgency, to limit the yields of all nuclear weapons to a maximum of 400 kilotons.[18] Recent trends towards greater accuracy, and the introduction of MIRVing, have resulted in a general decrease in warhead yields. There remain today however very large numbers of weapons in the megaton range, especially in the Soviet strategic arsenal.

The second serious atmospheric effect of a large-scale nuclear war would be that resulting from the great number of fires. This question has been examined in a recent study by Crutzen and Birks.[19] They suppose that throughout the Northern Hemisphere around one million square kilometres of forest — equivalent to the combined areas of Denmark, Sweden and Norway — might be set alight. This is about 20 times the area burned annually worldwide in wild fires. They further suppose that a quantity of gas and oil would be released by the uncapping of wells, equivalent to current world consumption. Some of this might burn. Some of the gas might escape unburned, and be broken down in the atmosphere by photochemical reactions.

The effect would be to fill the atmosphere with small smoke particles, and to create in addition a photochemical smog similar to that produced by industrial pollution and vehicle exhausts. Crutzen and Birks calculate that this combination of smoke and smog could reduce the amount of sunlight reaching the ground at noon at least by half, and possibly to a hundredth of its normal level. There are some historical instances where this has happened as a result of forest fires, although not of course on such a huge scale. Burning grassland and burning buildings, not allowed for in the estimates, would further add to the smoke. This darkening of the sky could persist for weeks or months following the nuclear exchange, killing plants and making it impossible to grow any new crops. If the quantity of sunlight reaching the ground was reduced to a hundredth of its usual level, marine micro-organisms would be killed. Other features of the weather such as rain, wind and temperatures at ground level would be radically modified.

HEALTH

Hospitals and other health-care buildings are in general concentrated in areas of higher population density, and would thus tend to suffer damage in proportionately greater numbers in any level of attack, than would houses. Physicians, nurses and other health professionals, since they live near their places of work, would also be likely to be killed and injured in somewhat greater numbers proportionately than the population as a whole — unless some policy were instituted for their selective evacuation from likely target areas in advance of an attack (see chapter 10).

The number of hospital beds available in peacetime for the treatment of acute illness or injury in England is 127,000; in Wales 9,000; and in Scotland 18,000.[20] Of these, beds for the treatment of severe burns cases number only just over 100 throughout the country as a whole. These numbers of beds provide a measure of the capacity of the hospitals to deal with serious cases, since the capacities of medical and surgical facilities, operating theatres, X-ray suites and central sterile supplies are related in proportion to beds.

Medical plans exist to meet major peacetime emergencies, such as air crashes or terrorist bombings, but the criterion for such a major emergency is one involving more than perhaps 20 cases. In the pub bombings by the IRA in Birmingham in November 1974, for example, 22 people died and 162 were injured. This single incident stretched the medical facilities of the West Midlands to their limits.[21] As the British Medical Association have said in their report on the *Medical Effects of Nuclear War*, it is clear that the resources of the entire National Health Service would be overwhelmed by the tens or hundreds of thousands of blast and burns injury cases from even a single nuclear weapon used on a British city.[22]

In a large-scale attack, the prospects of injured survivors receiving treatment to accepted modern standards would be remote or non-existent. If, for the sake of argument, it was assumed that hospital buildings were damaged by blast and fire at the same rate as housing, then the numbers of beds given above might be reduced by half in Attacks F or G, and to one fifth or less by Attack K. The failure of electricity and water supplies could make normal working impossible in those hospitals which survived undamaged. The treatment of major injuries normally requires supplies of blood, plasma, antibiotics and other drugs, and these would rapidly run out.

Cases of radiation sickness are treated in peacetime with antibiotics, transfusions and in some cases bone marrow transplants. Such methods of treatment are hardly likely to be offered after a nuclear attack. In any case it would be difficult if not impossible in most cases to know what level of dose any individual had received, and whether he or she could be saved by treatment. The difficulty would be exacerbated by the fact that the early symptoms of radiation sickness — loss of appetite, vomiting, diarrhoea — are not easily distinguishable from those of gastroenteritis or psychological disturbance from which many of those in shelters could be suffering.

The sheer numbers of cases would put any complex medical procedures out of the question, and primitive operations might have to be carried out without anaesthetic. It has been argued that it would be necessary to institute something like the battlefield system of triage, developed by French military surgeons in World War I, in which patients are divided into three categories: those whose survival is thought to be improbable, those whose survival is thought possible, and those whose survival is thought probable.[23] Patients in the first category are left to die without treatment. Only patients in the second category are treated.

All this assumes that the injured actually reach hospitals or casualty stations. Many would be trapped in fallen buildings or fires. Disruption of communications, blockage of roads and possible shortage of fuel for emergency vehicles would hamper any rescue operations. More serious would be the question of levels of radioactivity from fallout; indeed it is probable that any rescue or medical teams would have to be held back from entering areas of heavy fallout — that is to say virtually the whole of the built-up area of the country in Attacks E and upwards — or else risk their own lives, for periods of several weeks or more. During this time the wounds of those surviving injured could become heavily infected.

For people in shelters, especially of a makeshift kind, there could be risks to health from the cold, insanitary, crowded, cramped and perhaps damp conditions. Many of them would suffer from shortages of food and clean water, and from severe psychological stress. Some shelterers might be in a state of shock, or be suffering mechanical or burns injuries. The effects of radiation sickness are to lower the body's resistance to infection, as well as to produce nausea and diarrhoea as mentioned. Under these conditions contagious diseases such as influenza and typhoid fever could spread rapidly.

In the medium term, perhaps when people emerged from shelters, there would be a high incidence of epidemic diseases, caused by the contamination of water and food by contact with sewage and the literally millions of human and animal corpses. There would be a resurgence of many of the diseases such as dysentery, infectious hepatitis, salmonellosis and cholera, which were once common in Europe and were largely conquered by the sanitary reforms of the nineteenth century. Even bubonic and pneumonic plague might make a reappearance.[24] Diseases such as tuberculosis and meningitis could increase as a result of poor nutrition and overcrowded conditions. The absence of drug supplies would mean that diseases which are controllable with modern medicine would become killers again — for example pneumonia or blood poisoning in the absence of antibiotics, and diphtheria, whooping cough and polio in the absence of vaccination.

In Britain, drug manufacturers hold six weeks to two months' supplies, and wholesalers perhaps one week's supply. Other stocks are held in hospitals.[25] Many of these stocks would be destroyed in an attack, and manufacturing, which is concentrated in a rather few companies, would be likely to cease altogether. Some drugs have a short shelf-life in any case, and stocks of others would be quickly exhausted. In the longer term, assuming no supplies were to reach Britain from abroad, traditional herbal remedies might be the only medication available.[26]

There are many invalids who rely on continuing drugs or other forms of treatment in peacetime and whose health or life would be at risk if their supplies were stopped: for example those suffering from heart disease, diabetes or kidney failure. There are others whose state of health is precarious at the best of times or who rely on others for help and support, and who would be ill-equipped to cope with the extreme rigours of life in the aftermath: the very old and the very young, the chronically sick, the mentally and physically handicapped. As for the psychological state of survivors, this is almost impossible to predict under the conditions of unprecedented horror which attacks of these magnitudes would bring about. The only possible guide to people's states of mind might be what happened at Hiroshima and Nagasaki. Here many survivors were reported as moving aimlessly like automata, incapable of organized activity.[27]

LONG-TERM RADIATION EFFECTS

Nuclear war differs from conventional war in many ways, but one of the most peculiarly horrible is that sickness and injury from the radiation effects will continue to be caused for decades afterwards, among those not even born at the time, as well as among the survivors of the attack itself. If the short-term effects of radiation are a matter for scientific controversy, then this is all the more true for the consequences in the longer term. That such effects will occur is not in question, however, only their magnitude. They will include higher incidences of cancer, abortions, abnormalities among the children of women pregnant at the time of exposure, and heritable genetic defects.[28]

There are several distinct ways in which people may receive significant doses of radiation, but insufficient to cause death from acute radiation sickness — most of which we have discussed already. There may be some instances in which people receive such doses from initial nuclear radiation (INR), especially with smaller weapons. This was the main source of radiation exposure among the Japanese survivors, but would be relatively rare among the survivors of the kinds of attack with higher-yield strategic weapons which have been described. In such attacks the greater risk is from local fallout. Almost all of the survivors of the immediate effects of blast and heat will receive some radiation dose from this source.

Figure 7.20 showed for example that in Attacks E onwards, open-air two-week doses of 200 rads and more are received over some 80 per cent of the inhabited area of Britain. There will be further doses accumulated from local fallout after people emerge from shelters, and these could be large if nuclear reactors are targeted, as discussed. And lastly there is the global fallout (see p. 111) which will descend from the stratosphere for several years following the attack. There would surely be few survivors who did not accumulate doses from all these sources of at least tens of rads over a period of months. Many would receive hundreds of rads. (Precautions governing radiation exposure in peacetime place an approximate upper limit on the dose to be received over a *lifetime* of ten rads.)

The doses from INR and the greater part of the doses from early fallout would be delivered to the external tissues of the body. But fallout particles could as mentioned also be inhaled, or ingested with food and water. The inhaled particles may lodge in the lungs and the ingested particles will be concentrated into other specific organs. The long-lived isotopes Strontium-89 and Strontium-90 will accumulate in the bones, and Iodine-131 in the thyroid. There was considerable alarm in the early 1960s, for example, about the levels of Strontium-90, originating from global fallout from the atmospheric testing of nuclear weapons, which were building up in cows' milk and hence in humans. Concern about such effects created strong pressure for the Test Ban Treaty of 1963.[29]

The fallout particles lodged inside the body continue to release radiation and this, and the radiation from external sources, can cause body cells to become cancerous. The most common form of cancer among the Japanese victims was leukaemia — that is cancer of the blood cells.[30] Other forms would include cancer of the thyroid, lung, bone and breast. Leukaemia could appear as soon as two years after the bombings. Among the Japanese survivors the peak occurrence of leukaemias was between five and ten years later. Skin or lung cancers on the other hand might not appear for 20 years or more.

When a number of the inhabitants of the Marshall Islands in the Pacific were exposed to fallout from the 'Bravo' test in 1954 and some received doses up to 200 rads, a high incidence of thyroid disorders resulted, especially among children, and there were several cases of thyroid cancer.[31] Exposure of part of the population of the state of Utah to fallout from weapons tests in Nevada in the 1950s is thought to have caused an increase in leukaemia among children.[32] In general children and infants are at greater risk than adults from the long-term (as from the short-term) effects of radiation exposure.

Exposure of the eyes to radiation can cause cataracts, leading to impaired vision and possibly blindness in one to ten years. The incidence among the Japanese survivors was over 50 per cent for doses in excess of 100 rads.

When a foetus is exposed to radiation in the womb, there is an increased risk either that the pregnancy will be aborted, or that the child will be born with physical abnormalities or mental deficiencies. This was the case with many of the children born to women pregnant at the time of the attacks on Hiroshima and Nagasaki.[33]

Finally there is the possibility that damage will be caused to the DNA molecules which carry the genetic information in the body. This in turn will result in genetic mutations and chromosomal aberrations, which may affect the children of exposed parents. Some of these genetic abnormalities could be passed on to later generations. Fortunately many genetic mutations are lethal, and foetuses carrying them do not survive pregnancy. Others however are the cause of hereditary disease or inherited physical abnormality.

The extent of such genetic effects is a particularly speculative and controversial question. They have been demonstrated experimentally in animals. However, intense study of the Japanese survivors has so far failed to show any clear increase in infant or child mortality, inherited malformation, or cancer rates in the next generation (as opposed to those directly exposed) which could be attributed to a genetic cause.[34] This is reassuring, but cannot be taken to mean — as it has been in some quarters[35] — that there would be no genetic damage from radiation exposure in a large-scale nuclear war. In the case of the Japanese victims the numbers studied are too few to determine the possible occurrence of certain rarer cancers; and some effects of recessively inherited mutations may still emerge in the future.[36]

As for making quantitative estimates of the numbers of cases which might be produced in a war, both of cancer and genetic defects, this is extremely difficult. No calculations have been made for the attacks on the UK. Figures have, however, been published in other studies which could give a guide to the possible magnitude of the casualty totals.[37]

It is usual to express the likely incidence of cancer statistically, in terms of the number of cases resulting from the exposure of a large population. The International Commission for Radiological Protection estimated in 1977 that the exposure of 10,000 people to a dose of 100 rads would result in 20 leukaemia deaths and 105 deaths from other forms of cancer.[38] The rates of non-fatal cancers would also be increased. Estimates published by the OTA are based on the assumption that the total number of cancer deaths (including leukaemias) could range between 40 and 200, for a similar exposure of 10,000 people to 100 rads. In the OTA study it is further assumed that the number of cases is related to the total collective dose of 1 million rads, and would remain the same if say a million people were exposed to 1 rad, or 100,000 people to 10 rads.[39]

The actual doses received by a population after an attack would obviously vary with many factors — not only the number and pattern of groundbursts in relation to the distribution of population, and average protection factors, as discussed in chapter 6, but also the extent of contamination of soil, food and water in the months following. The OTA nevertheless show calculations for different levels of attack, which indicate that cancer deaths could vary roughly between 200 and 2,000 for every megaton of yield. Equivalent figures for abortions range from 100 to 1,000 cases per megaton; and for genetic abnormalities, 300 to 3,500 cases per megaton.[40] Despite the wide ranges quoted such figures should still only be taken as highly approximate.

One thing which can be said for certain is that the numbers of long-term radiation casualties, great though they might be (potentially hundreds of thousands among the ten million or so short-term 'survivors' of Attack H), pale into insignificance relative to the immediate death toll. The threats of starvation and epidemic disease would loom much larger. Indeed few survivors might live long enough for these delayed consequences of radiation exposure to make their appearance.

9

Home Office Calculations of the Effects of Attack

The Home Office make calculations of the effects of nuclear attack on Britain, using a computer model which is in many respects similar to our own. Because it uses inappropriate data and overoptimistic assumptions, however, it predicts very much lower casualty levels than ours. This chapter describes the structure of the Home Office model, and some of the results obtained from it.

This account is based on the only two papers which the Home Office Scientific Research and Development Branch (SRDB) have released about their work. The first is a report by P. R. Bentley, published in 1981 in two slightly differing versions, with the title 'Blast Overpressure and Fallout Radiation Dose Models for Casualty Assessment and Other Purposes.'[1] The second is a paper, 'Scientific Advice in Home Defence', given by S. J. Butler at the 1981 meeting of the British Association for the Advancement of Science in York, and subsequently published in a book in 1982.[2] Bentley's paper gives details of the methods of calculation, and Butler's of the results.

When the British Medical Association (BMA) was conducting its inquiry into *The Medical Effects of Nuclear War*[3] during 1982, the BMA Working Party submitted a number of questions to the Home Office about their calculation methods. The Home Office's answers were published in the BMA's report, and provide a further source of information about some of the assumptions underlying their work.

Because of the similarities between the two computer models, we will concentrate on those areas in which the Home Office differs from our own approach.

For population data the Home Office use the same 1971 census results by 1 km grid-squares, as we do. They justify the implication of a night-time or 'at home' distribution of the population by reference to the current official 'stay-put' policy. The *Protect and Survive* leaflet advises people that they should not move away from home; and this advice is reinforced with the threatened sanctions that if people do move '. . . the authority in [the] new area will not help . . . with accommodation or food or other essentials'.[4] Local authorities, the leaflet warns, may take over any empty houses for others to use. The stay-put policy is also backed by plans to close many major roads, designated as 'essential service routes', to all but military and other official vehicles (see chapter 10).

Despite the fact that there are no plans at present to evacuate the general population, Butler nevertheless reports some experiments to show the effects of an evacuation policy on numbers of casualties. He does not however give any details about how the population is assumed to be redistributed.

The targets in an attack can be defined by National Grid co-ordinates. The explosive yields of bombs can take any of ten values between 100 kilotons and 20 megatons, and the heights of detonation of airbursts can be optimized for the 2, 4, 6, 10 or 20 psi blast damage levels. An upper limit is placed on the number of weapons in any attack of 300. However, in none of the results given by Butler are the individual targets in an attack pattern identified. All that is specified is the total megatonnage, divided between airbursts and groundbursts, and the general nature of the targets, 'military' or 'civilian'.

THERMAL RADIATION EFFECTS

The first main difference between the Home Office model and our own, is that the Home Office omit any consideration of burns caused directly by thermal radiation. (They also ignore, as we do, any indirect burns caused in fires.) Bentley says that 'Later, it is intended to establish whether the effects of thermal . . . radiation make any significant difference to total casualty figures. For the present, the philosophy of earlier work is followed and the effects of blast and fallout only are considered.'[5]

In evidence to the BMA inquiry the Home Office explained the omission of all burns casualties on two grounds.[6] First they assume that the population is fully warned of an attack, and that people have acted on these warnings and have taken cover. Second, they assume that no burns casualties would be caused by fire 'unless there were a conflagration or firestorm'. However the Home Office believes that mass fires of either type are unlikely to occur in the UK, and that in any case there are no reliable data on which to base any estimates.

Not only are the Home Office imagining that the warning system will be 100 per cent effective, therefore; but they make no allowance for the possibility that damage from earlier weapons will force people into the open to face the effects of later explosions.

As for burns caused in fires, Butler believes that 'the possibility of widespread fires could be greatly reduced by suitable precautions and by the control of incipient fires by survivors of the attack;'[7] but this is hardly credible. Survivors might be able to put out small fires, if they had stored some water for the purpose. (It is unlikely that the mains supply would still be working.) But they might have other preoccupations, such as reconstructing their fallout shelters, looking for friends and relatives, rescuing others from the wreckage, or simply trying to escape themselves. It does not take long for a fire to take hold.

There may be doubt over the possibility of firestorms, but there can be little question that conflagrations would occur in a heavy attack. The last chapter shows how enormous the areas covered by mass fires would be. And it has already been seen how poor the prospects are for any kind of serious fire-fighting effort, given the blockage of roads, the destruction of fire appliances, the failure of water supplies, and the radioactive dangers which any rescue workers would face. It should be remembered too that many survivors of an attack in the fire zones will be injured. Even those uninjured may find it difficult to escape from areas where fires are widespread.

BLAST EFFECTS

There is little essential difference between the ways in which our computer model and that of the Home Office predict the ranges of blast overpressure for bombs of given yield and height of detonation. Both use the same data for overpressure by distance, from Glasstone and Dolan.[8] Bentley describes how these data are approximated in the Home Office model (by plotting them on logarithmic paper and fitting straight lines); but says that these approximations produce a maximum error of 5 per cent, except in one very restricted distance band for airbursts, where the error can rise to 15 per cent.[9]

It should be noted that other Home Office publications give figures for these relationships of blast pressure to distance which differ, in some cases quite substantially, from Glasstone and Dolan. There are some small discrepancies with the Americans in the figures given for groundbursts in the two Home Office books, *Nuclear Weapons*[10] and *Domestic Nuclear Shelters: Technical Guidance*,[11] the effect of which is that the radii of the damage areas at higher overpressures are somewhat smaller according to the Home Office. For example the Home Office predicts for a 1 megaton airburst an area affected at 6 psi and greater of 38 km^2, compared with 50 km^2 according to the American data.

Much more serious are the discrepancies which arise in relation to airbursts, because of a crude rule of thumb which the Home Office use in several places. The booklet *Nuclear Weapons* says that 'For practical purposes it can be assumed that the ranges of various categories of damage for groundburst bombs . . . would be increased by 30 per cent if the same sized weapon were air burst near the optimum height.'[12] The same rule is repeated in *Domestic Nuclear Shelters*.[13] The truth is, however, that the increase is something more like 50 or 60 per cent depending on the exact height of detonation of the airburst. Table 9.1 compares the distances at which certain levels of maximum overpressure would be experienced from a 1 megaton airburst, according to this Home Office rule and Glasstone and Dolan respectively. In the latter case the height of burst is optimized for the 10 psi damage level. The four overpressure values given in the table are those which the Home Office use for convenience to define four concentric blast damage zones labelled A, B, C and D from the centre outwards.

Table 9.1   Distances (kilometres) at which certain peak overpressures would be experienced from a one megaton airburst, according to the Home Office and Glasstone and Dolan respectively

		Distance (km)	
Ring	Peak overpressure (psi)	Home Office	Glasstone and Dolan[a]
A	11	3.25	4.25
B	6	4.55	6
C	1.5	11.7	14.5
D	0.75	18.2	24 approx.

[a] Height of burst taken to maximize 10 psi blast damage area

Sources: Glasstone and Dolan, *Effects of Nuclear Weapons*, pp. 114–15; Home Office, *Nuclear Weapons*, p. 35; Home Office, *Domestic Nuclear Shelters: Technical Guidance*, p. 9

These discrepancies in the radii of the rings give rise to very large differences in the estimated *areas* of blast damage. For the two inner, A and B, rings the areas according to the Home Office are only about three-quarters of the areas according to Glasstone and Dolan.

When the BMA Inquiry questioned the Home Office on the matter, the Home Office agreed that the rule of adding 30 per cent to the range for a groundburst:

. . . is too great a simplification for many practical applications (as well as 1.3 being a rather atypical factor) and it may have originated in the early days when detailed information on weapon effects was inhibited by security restrictions . . . It is unfortunate that the old 30 per cent rule has been re-quoted (even though it is only intended to serve as a general indication and it is not actually applied in any calculation) in *Domestic Nuclear Shelters: Technical Guidance* . . .[14]

It is worth remarking that this reference to 'the early days' must mean prior to 1957 at least, when the first edition of *The Effects of Nuclear Weapons* appeared. Some might think it worse than 'unfortunate' that figures have not been revised in the intervening quarter century. Despite the fact that the '30 per cent rule' has also been used to calculate figures for airbursts in Butler's papers, it is, however, clear from Bentley's account, that the approximation is *not* used in the Home Office computer model.

The principal way in which the Home Office model diverges from our own in relation to blast effects, is in the assumed relationships of over-pressure values to percentages of the population killed and injured. The Home Office do not define these in relation to *ranges* of overpressure value, as do the Office of Technology Assessment (compare table 6.4). Instead they have a set of curves which give the percentages assumed to be 'killed', 'trapped' and 'seriously injured' at any chosen overpressure (figure 9.1). These were published under the title 'Exercise ARC' in a Home Office pamphlet of 1959.[15] In figure 9.1 the casualty rates are illustrated in terms of distances from ground zero for groundburst weapons of different yields. (It has been pointed out that at a distance of about 1 mile for a 1 mega-ton bomb, and correspondingly for other yields, the three categories of casualties sum to 115 per cent!) Besides being used in the computer model, these figures are built into the pocket 'weapons effects calculators' which are issued to civil defence workers. In estimating total casualties in an attack the Home Office generally assume that those counted as 'trapped' will die.

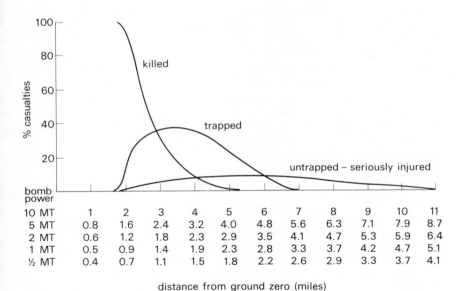

bomb power											
10 MT	1	2	3	4	5	6	7	8	9	10	11
5 MT	0.8	1.6	2.4	3.2	4.0	4.8	5.6	6.3	7.1	7.9	8.7
2 MT	0.6	1.2	1.8	2.3	2.9	3.5	4.1	4.7	5.3	5.9	6.4
1 MT	0.5	0.9	1.4	1.9	2.3	2.8	3.3	3.7	4.2	4.7	5.1
½ MT	0.4	0.7	1.1	1.5	1.8	2.2	2.6	2.9	3.3	3.7	4.1

distance from ground zero (miles)

Figure 9.1 Home Office blast casualty rates ('Exercise ARC'). Percentage casualties are shown at varying distances (miles) from groundbursts of different yields. Those 'trapped' are generally assumed to die.
Source: Home Office, *Control of Civil Defence Operations*, p. 10.

Figure 9.2 compares what the OTA assumptions and these Home Office blast casualty rates would predict for a 1 megaton airburst detonated at a height of 2,200 metres. It is clear that the differences are enormous, especially since these rates apply to circular damage areas. If the population is assumed to be uniformly distributed, then the OTA rates would predict about twice as many deaths as the Home Office (assuming those 'trapped' die). For injuries the discrepancies are greater still: in the inner part of the C damage ring, on the Home Office definition, the percentage of the population injured declines from around 7 per cent to zero, where according to the OTA, 45 per cent of the population would suffer injuries. The OTA predict 25 per cent injuries in areas in the D ring where the Home Office expects no casualties at all.

The explanation is that the Home Office does not derive these blast casualty rates from studies of nuclear weapons. They originate from information collected about the effects of conventional chemical explosions in World War II. But these are by no means comparable with the effects of nuclear explosions. Many more casualties would occur from a nuclear weapon, at the *same* level of blast overpressure, because that overpressure and the associated winds last for much longer than in a chemical explosion.[16]

Statistics for the Blitz on Britain show roughly that for every 1 ton of bombs dropped, one person was killed. Taking the two bombs dropped on Hiroshima and Nagasaki together, their combined yield was equivalent to some 35,000 tons of conventional explosive. It is now thought that more than 200,000 died in the two cities.[17] This gives nearly six deaths per ton of explosive. By no means all of these deaths were caused by blast, but the crude comparison still gives an indication of how much greater are the capacities of nuclear weapons to cause death and injury, even allowing for their hugely magnified explosive power.

When the BMA Inquiry asked the Home Office to comment on the discrepancies between their own blast casualty rates and those of the OTA, they replied as follows:

The original blast damage/injury rules used by the Home Office were derived from the results of a study by members of the British Mission to Japan of blast damage to buildings at Hiroshima and Nagasaki, combined with an analysis of casualty rates in the then typical UK houses with various degrees of HE [high explosive] bomb damage. These rules represented the only information of its kind that was available for official use for some years. It has often been suggested that they might under-estimate casualties from megaton range weapons on account of the possibly severer effects of the longer duration blast wave. Over recent years, note has been taken of the changes occurring in UK house construction, and of recent research carried out in the USA. Currently this Branch is, as a priority item in its Civil Defence Research programme, reviewing the blast damage/injury rules with the aim of producing a revised set of rules that are more soundly based and applicable to the current UK situation.[18]

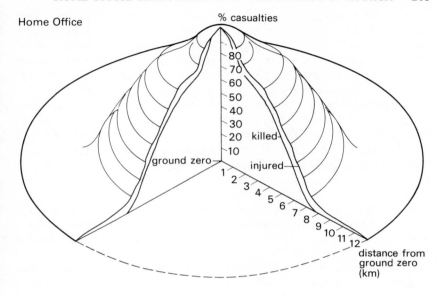

Home Office

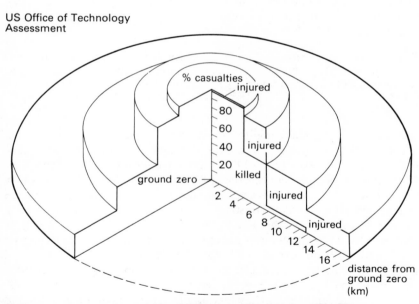

US Office of Technology
Assessment

Figure 9.2   Percentage casualties (killed, and seriously injured) at different
distances (km) from a one megaton airburst detonated at 2,200 metres altitude,
according to the Home Office (above) and the Office of Technology Assessment
(below) respectively. These are shown diagrammatically as three-dimensional
solids, where the circular area in plan represents the zone, centred on ground zero,
in which casualties are predicted to occur, and the vertical dimension represents
percentage casualties. Thus the total estimated *number* of casualties is
proportional to the *volume* in either case.

The published report of the British Mission to Japan referred to here contains findings which do not, however, support the Home Office casualty rates.[19] The Mission give figures for the percentages of the population present who were killed at different distances from ground zero, averaged for the two cities. If the current Home Office rates are applied to weapons of relevant yield and height of burst, they 'predict' percentages of deaths (killed plus 'trapped') which are substantially smaller at all distances. The comparison is not *entirely* fair, in that the Mission's figures refer to deaths from all causes, and the Home Office's relate to blast deaths only. On the other hand the current Home Office methods of calculation would omit completely the other principal causes of death in the bombings in Japan: thermal radiation and initial nuclear radiation.

In chapter 6 it was argued that the Office of Technology Assessment's blast casualty rates by contrast give a reasonably good 'prediction' of the numbers of casualties which actually occurred in Hiroshima — allowing for all the uncertainties, for differences in building construction, and especially for the very small yield of the weapon used. Home Office blast casualty rates applied to the same data give about half the actual number of casualties. The Home Office told the BMA Inquiry, nevertheless, that they do not accept the OTA rates, and do not believe that they are appropriate to the UK:

Not only are they too broad to be of use for many analyses, but they are based on data relating to USA house construction (it would appear wood frame) and incorporate arbitrary assumptions for the distribution of persons around houses, and their posture. Thus the OTA rules are likely to be unduly severe for assessments of attacks on the UK.[20]

It is possible that there might be differences between typical methods of house construction in the UK and the USA, which could affect their blast resistance. However, this could account for only a small fraction of the very great difference between the OTA and Home Office blast casualty rules. It is not in fact the case that the OTA rates are based on the assumption of wood-frame construction. They are based, as mentioned in chapter 6 (p. 123), on the assumption that 'a typical residence will be collapsed by an overpressure of about 5 psi'. In the 1950s actual houses were exposed to nuclear explosions in the Nevada desert. They were of wood-frame construction similar to many American houses, and of brick and cinder-block construction, similar to many modern British houses. The results are reported by Glasstone and Dolan.[21] The wooden house was demolished by about 4 psi, and the brick-built house by 5 psi.

What is more, there are certain features of many of the buildings which have been put up in Britain over the last 20 years, which might be expected to make them particularly vulnerable to blast: for example the prefabricated construction used in many high-rise blocks of flats, the large areas of glass in both office buildings and some houses, and the use of other lightweight building materials.

Despite these Home Office criticisms of the OTA blast casualty rates, they have, as we shall see, experimented in their own computer model with a 'more severe blast criterion', which they told the BMA Inquiry was 'not directly related to, but was not in fact far different from, the OTA assumptions'.[22]

FALLOUT EFFECTS

There are no large differences between the ways in which open-air accumulated radiation doses from fallout are calculated in the Home Office model and our own. Both take Glasstone and Dolan as the basic source, and predict fallout patterns using the idealized elliptical contours (see chapter 6). The method of approximating the 'time of maximum' and 'time of completion' in our own model is taken directly from Bentley's account of the Home Office model (see appendix 2). Both models assume a fission fraction of 0.5 and a ground roughness factor of 0.7. The only difference of substance is that the number of different dose-rate ellipses is greater in our model. We measure dose-rates down to 1 rad/hr, and extrapolate from Glasstone and Dolan's figures up to 9,000 rads/hr; where Bentley considers dose-rates only in the range 10 to 4,000 rads/hr.

PROTECTION FACTORS OF BUILDINGS AND SHELTERS

Far more significant differences arise in the assumptions made in relation to protection factors of buildings. Neither Butler nor Bentley give the precise figures taken for pfs by the Home Office which, as described in chapter 6, are not measured by a single national average, but are expressed as a 'spectrum' of values to represent different types of house and flat. Butler says, however, that, for the results which he publishes, the protection factor spectrum used was taken to represent 'general adherence to *Protect and Survive* advice . . . as regards fall-out precautions'.[23] And when the Home Office were asked by the BMA Inquiry for some more specific information, they said that the spectrum of pf values used for the calculations in Bentley's paper corresponded to an average of something greater than 20.

For the purposes of more recent calculations the Home Office have issued a new set of provisional pf values, which they described to the BMA as follows. The figures have been derived by '(a) selecting a range of representative house types for which estimates of the protective factors in the best location within the house (but without special adaptation) have been made, and (b) estimating (via liaison with Directorate of Works) the distribution of these types in the UK as a whole'.[24] The values are given in table 9.2. They correspond to an overall average pf of 21. The Home Office adds that these figures '. . . may well be modified when used in assessments, through assumptions about precautionary measures, regime followed, modified population distribution, etc.'

Table 9.2   Home Office protection factor 'spectrum'

% of dwellings	2	4	27	34	18	8	7
Protection factor	2	5	9	18	26	40	70

Source: BMA, *Medical Effects,* p. 78

Chapter 7 showed the great sensitivity of predicted numbers of fallout casualties to assumptions about protection factors. The consequences of the Home Office taking average pf values of 20 or higher is for the number of predicted fallout deaths to be of the order of hundreds of thousands, and certainly under one million, in a 200 megaton attack.

Chapter 6 discussed the considerations on which values for protection factors in these kinds of studies must be based. The Home Office are in effect assuming that the entire population are able and willing to do what *Protect and Survive* tells them: to block doors and windows, to build 'inner refuges', and to stay inside these for at least two weeks and possibly longer. More important, the Home Office make no allowance whatsoever for the effects of blast damage in reducing the protection offered by buildings against radiation. The BMA Inquiry asked the Home Office what their reasons were for this omission. They said 'We recognize that a degradation effect would occur and that it would be desirable to allow for it. However, there is no reliable information available to us on which to base quantitative estimates and, moreover, it is believed that the effect is likely to be small, on the basis of observations of the behaviour of fall-out-like particles (e.g. volcanic dust).'[25]

There is certainly an area for legitimate debate, as to exactly what might be the extent of the reduction of protection factors by blast. But to make *no* allowance, and to assume that pfs of 20, or higher, still obtain in areas where houses have no roofs, doors, windows or even are demolished altogether, is obviously absurd. Notice that the Home Office comments imply that the effect of blast damage is just to allow fallout particles to enter the building. But this is not the only consequence, since more *radiation* from fallout *outside* the building will also enter through any apertures caused by blast (see p. 133).

INJURY AND DEATH RELATED TO RADIATION DOSE

The uncertainties which exist on the question of fatal levels of radiation dose in humans are discussed in chapter 6. In our own model we take an LD-50 value of 450 rads; although this is itself a conservative value, and some studies have concluded that given the likely conditions following a nuclear attack, an LD-50 of 400 rads might be a more reasonable assumption.[26]

The Home Office up until recently concurred with the generally held view among radiologists that the LD-50 should be taken to be about 450 rads. For example in the booklet *Nuclear Weapons* it is stated that 'The best estimate that can be given at present for this lethal dose of whole body radiation for human beings is that the LD-50 lies somewhere between 350r and 550r if the dose is received quickly, within the space of an hour or two.'[27] The value would be greater if the dose were spread over longer periods. (The unit of radiation dose used here is the roentgen *r*, which for the present purposes can be taken as approximately equal to the rad.) In the *Operational Handbook for Scientific Advisers* the LD-50 value is given as 450 rads, for 'brief exposures' to surface tissues; and the LD-90 (the dose killing 90 per cent) as 600 rads.[28]

In the last couple of years, however, these assumptions have been radically revised. In 1975 the Home Office Scientific Advisory Branch sought new advice on the effects of radiation from the Protection against Ionising Radiation Committee (PIRC) of the Medical Research Council. A working party was set up under the chairmanship of J. C. Vennart, and this group reported to the Home Office in the form of a letter in 1977. A number of supporting scientific papers, including papers by Vennart and R. H. Mole were submitted 'in confidence'. Neither these papers nor the PIRC letter have yet (May 1983) been published; but some details are given in the report of the BMA Inquiry.[29]

The effect of the PIRC advice was to raise the basic LD-50 value used in casualty calculations, to 600 rads. This value again refers to brief exposures, to generally fit persons, and to doses received to the surface tissues. The corresponding LD-50 value for a dose to the bone marrow would be 450 rads. The level of dose which the PIRC take to be fatal to 95 per cent of the exposed population, is 800 rads.

These new figures were based on an analysis of the case histories of some 20 patients receiving radiation therapy and some 19 victims of accidents. Most of these people received doses between 150 to 350 rads, and none received doses of more than 370 rads. Only one person in the sample died. So the lethal effects of higher doses are extrapolated from these non-fatal doses. The PIRC told the Home Office that their recommendations for the relationship of dose to effect, to be used in calculations, were provided 'as a working hypothesis only and must be regarded as only tenuously based on evidence'.[30] They have nevertheless been incorporated into the Home Office computer model, as described by Bentley.[31]

Thus the first consequence of the PIRC advice is to raise the basic LD-50 value by roughly one third. The assumed levels of dose required to cause other percentages of deaths are increased in similar proportion. *However*, these values are intended by the PIRC to apply only to doses received within a *few minutes*. When doses are received over a period of hours or more, the actual dose values are modified in Home Office calculations according to what is termed the 'operational evaluation dose' formula or OED. This formula is applied both in the computer model and in casualty estimates made by hand.

The OED formula is intended to allow for two distinct mechanisms of recovery, the first of which is imagined to take place in a matter of hours, and the second of which occurs in the longer term. The formula has been in use for a number of years,[32] and previously was expressed as:

$$OED = x - 150 - 10t \text{ rads}$$

where x is the actual dose received, and t is the number of days after the start of exposure. The body is supposed to be able to recover from 150 rads without ill effects in the course of a day — hence the deduction of 150. And it is supposed to be able to recover from 10 rads/day thereafter (up to a limit of 100 days) — hence the deduction of $10t$.

According to Bentley's description of the Home Office computer model, however,[33] the OED formula has also recently been revised (but not it seems on PIRC advice) and now takes the form:

$$OED = x - 200 - 15t \text{ rads}$$

so that the two allowances are now even greater. Suppose that the actual dose x received over seven days ($t=7$) was 900 rads. Then the OED value would be $900 - 200 - (15 \times 7) = 595$ rads. This is very close to the (new) Home Office LD-50 value of 600 rads; and in the Home Office calculations, half of those exposed to such a dose would be counted as dead. But the *actual* dose which these people have received here is *900* rads. Seven days is taken as the exposure period for this illustration, since in the Home Office model accumulated doses are computed up to that limit of time. The percentages of an exposed population assumed to be killed and 'seriously injured' at different values of the OED, are illustrated in figure 9.3 which is taken from Bentley's paper.[34]

To recapitulate, the effect of using the OED formula is to raise the LD-50 from a basic value of 600 rads for a dose received in minutes; to 800 rads for a dose received over some hours; to just over 900 rads for a dose received in a week (and with a further addition of 15 rads/day, for periods longer than that). Recall that the LD-50 figure given by the British

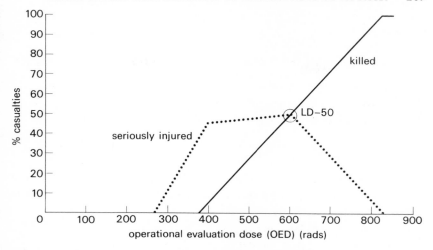

Figure 9.3   Assumed relationships of radiation dose (rads) to percentage deaths and injuries from acute effects of radiation, incorporated in the Home Office computer model. The values refer not to the actual dose received, but to the 'operational evaluation dose' (OED).
Source: Bentley, 'Casualty assessment', fig. 15, p. 18.

Institute of Radiology for a dose received over a week, as quoted in chapter 6, was by contrast 450 rads, just half of the corresponding Home Office figure.

It is difficult for those like ourselves who are not radiologists to comment on the scientific validity of the PIRC advice and the Home Office interpretation of that advice. It is not easy for radiologists to evaluate the PIRC recommendations either, since they are based on experimental work which remains unpublished. What is quite clear, however, is that the Home Office is now far out of step with almost all other British and international bodies on this subject. The National Radiological Protection Board in Britain, and the National Council on Radiation Protection and Measurements in the USA, which are the authorities officially charged with the evaluation of radiation hazards in the two countries, both continue to give figures around the 400 to 450 rad level for the human LD-50.[35]

Individual scientists have criticized the Home Office OED formula, even in its previous version. Professor P. Lindop says, for example, that 'From limited clinical experience and animal data I would expect that this dose rate [10 roentgen (r) per day] given after an acute dose of 150r would result in severe bone marrow damage several weeks later. No data show that 10r or more per day can be repaired indefinitely.'[36] The controversy seems certain to continue.

SUMMARY

The main ways in which the Home Office model differs from our own are:

1 Omission of burns casualties caused directly by thermal radiation.

2 Blast casualty rates based on data from the effects of conventional explosions in World War II.

3 Higher average protection factor values, with no allowance for the effects of blast damage in lower pfs.

4 Higher levels of radiation dose assumed to cause given percentages of deaths and injuries, in particular through the use of the 'operational evaluation dose' formula.

The next two sections describe those results which the Home Office have published from their model, and compare what all these differences mean precisely for numbers of predicted casualties.

HOME OFFICE PREDICTIONS OF CASUALTIES IN AN ATTACK

Table 9.3 is reproduced from Butler's paper, and gives the casualties predicted by the Home Office computer model for an attack with 193 megatons. The targets are not listed in detail, but they are described as being a mixture of military sites attacked with groundbursts, and cities attacked with airbursts. The average weapon yield is just over one megaton. Assuming, as the Home Office do, that those 'trapped' by blast will die, the total predicted number of deaths is 17 million, and of seriously injured 3½ million. According to Butler 'In this case, perhaps 70 per cent of the population would survive the first 60 days.'[37]

One point in the table should not pass without notice. The 'severe fall-out area' is given as covering about 9 per cent of the land area of the country. By 'severe' here is meant 14-day accumulated doses in the open of *4,000* rads; roughly nine times the LD-50 value, and fatal to all people in buildings with protection factors around seven or lower. Severe indeed.

Figure 9.4 is also from Butler's paper, and shows the effect on casualties (as a 'percentage surviving') for the same attack, of altering some key assumptions in the radiation injury and blast injury models. The nature of these changes is not explained; and in any case the 'less severe fall-out radiation criterion' has little effect.

The Home Office told the BMA Inquiry that the 'more severe blast criterion' on the other hand was very similar to the US Office of Technology Assessment assumptions (cf. table 6.4). The effect is to add about 10 million more blast deaths, compared with the 'standard current casualty model'. One (relatively minor) deception in the presentation of these statistics is in the labelling of the graph. The 'percentage' includes, without comment, those counted as 'seriously injured' among the survivors.

Table 9.3 Results from the Home Office computer model: 'Casualty and damage summary for a multiple nuclear attack'

	129 airbursts	Power	84 megatons
	50 groundbursts	Power	109 megatons
	179 weapons	Total power	193 megatons

Key assumptions The attack includes city targets
There is no blast shelter provision
There is full adherence to *Protect and Survive* advice
Stay-put or *night-time* residential population

A Ring area	(11 psi +)	2¾%	(24% population)
A and B Ring area	(6 psi +)	5%	(38% population)
A, B, and C Ring area	(1½ psi +)	15%	(60% population)

Severe fall-out area   9%
(Dose rate DR7 – 100 rph or more seven hours after attack – accumulated dose in open 4,000 *r* or more in first 14 days)[a]

Initial population	56 million	
Killed or trapped	16 million ⎫	30%
Fall-out sickness deaths	under 1 million ⎭	
Serious injured	3½ million ⎫	32%
Other homeless	up to 14 million ⎭	
Immediately available housing	40%	
Housing reparable in wartime	10%	

[a] Dose is measured in roentgens (*r*)
Source: Butler, 'Scientific advice', p. 154

Another change in initial assumptions which is illustrated by Butler concerns the distribution of the population. The purpose is to investigate the consequences of a policy of evacuation, by substituting for the standard 'stay put' distribution (using census data), a 'dispersed' distri-bution of the population. (The exact nature of this distribution is again, however, not explained.) Where the attack is primarily on military targets, the 'percentage surviving' an attack with 181 megatons is increased, from roughly 90, to 93 per cent for the dispersed population. Where the attack is on military targets and population centres, the percentage surviving rises from 72 to 88 per cent. For an attack primarily on civilian targets, the percentage rises from 66 to 87 per cent. (Presumably these 'survivors' again include many seriously injured.)

In view of the fact that no evacuation is now planned, and officially the public are told to 'stay put', there is a considerable irony in these findings

— since, if taken seriously, they show that evacuation of the population would result in millions more 'surviving'. Nevertheless the fact of the matter is that mass evacuation is probably unworkable in practice, and is of dubious value in saving lives, as the Home Office themselves recognize (see chapter 10).

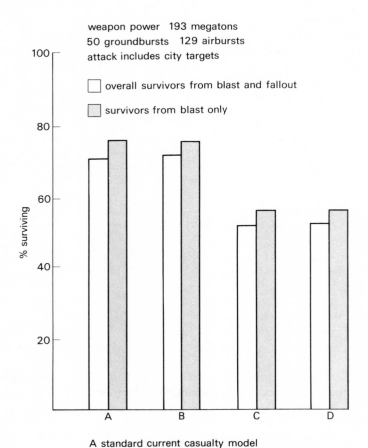

A standard current casualty model
B with less severe fallout radiation criterion
C with more severe blast criterion
D with both criteria changed

Figure 9.4 Effects on predicted casualties, for an attack with 193 megatons, of changing certain key assumptions in the Home Office computer model. Casualties are shown as a 'percentage surviving'. (Some of the survivors are seriously injured.) The 'more severe blast criterion' approximates to the assumptions of the Office of Technology Assessment.

Source: Butler, 'Scientific advice', fig. 10, p. 156.

Finally Butler's results include some experiments on the effects of increasing the total weight of attack from 180 megatons (the lowest figure considered), up to 500, 1,000 and even the quite fantastic total of 3,000 megatons. The results are once more shown for military targets, for civilian targets, and for a mixture of both. For mixed military targets and cities, the 'percentage surviving' is given as around 60 per cent of the population for 500 megatons, and around 15 per cent for 3,000 megatons.

The analysis of previous chapters will have made plain the utter and tragic preposterousness of these figures. Butler does not seriously argue that an attack with 3,000 megatons is militarily credible. The intention is simply to make a polemical point about the supposed value of civil defence. Even at this level, Butler says '. . . millions of survivors would be expected to need assistance and there would still be limited prospects for national revival, though in a very impoverished state.' Reflect that 3,000 megatons represents *60 tons* of high explosive equivalent for every man, woman and child in the country. It is sufficient to carpet the entire inhabited area of the country with blast pressures in excess of 12 psi.

ASSESSING THE EFFECTS OF HOME OFFICE ASSUMPTIONS

However, for more realistic levels of attack than 3,000 megatons there is some interest in investigating what exactly the consequences are, for predicted casualties, of the various differences between the Home Office assumptions and our own. Clearly our results and those of the Home Office are very far apart, for comparable levels of attack. For example Butler's 193 megaton attack results in 17 million deaths and 3.5 million serious injuries, according to the 'standard current' version of the Home Office model. Perhaps the closest pattern of attack to this which we have examined with our model, is the scenario used in the 'Square Leg' exercise (see p. 102), which totalled 205 megatons, was also directed at a combination of military and city targets, and for which we predicted 27.2 million dead and 7.4 million injured.

This comparison indicates the magnitude of the differences in total estimated casualties. But since Butler does not specify the actual targets chosen in his attack pattern, it is impossible to know whether the scenarios are strictly comparable in targeting terms. (One notable feature of 'Square Leg' for example was that no bombs were dropped in central London, only around the outer suburbs.) Also, it would be valuable to know which of the various discrepancies between the two models are more significant in their effects on total casualties.

In principle, the simplest way of doing this would be to run both models for a series of identical attack scenarios. Since the staff of the Scientific Research and Development Branch have for the most part refused to discuss their work, either in public, in private meetings or in print, this has not been possible. As the next best alternative, we have, therefore, built a duplicate version of the Home Office model going by the description in Bentley's paper. We cannot be certain that the replica is entirely accurate. But we have been as fair as possible, and we believe that the resulting approximations to the Home Office work are reasonably close.

One important feature of the Home Office model about which Bentley is not entirely specific, is the assumed relationship of blast overpressures to percentage casualties. However, the Home Office evidence to the BMA Inquiry confirmed that this is the same as in 'Exercise ARC' and the 'weapons effects calculators' (see p. 201). So we have worked from these sources, and have approximated the casualty rates in a series of over-pressure ranges. Details are given in appendix 6. The significant features of our replicated Home Office model are:

1 No burns casualties.
2 Blast casualty rates as specified in appendix 6.
3 Protection factor 'spectrum' as given in table 9.2 above.
4 Protection factors not dependent on blast damage.
5 Radiation dose casualty rates, calculated using the (new) OED formula, as shown in figure 9.3 above.
6 Those counted as injured more than once assumed to be killed.

Table 9.4 Total casualties (millions) predicted for different attacks, by authors' computer model, and by authors' replica of Home Office (HO) model. Also, for comparison, total casualties predicted by authors' model with burns effects omitted

Attack	Authors' model	Authors' replica of HO model	Authors' model with burns omitted
A	9.0	2.7	8.9
B	19.3	4.2	18.9
C	26.4	7.4	26.1
D	27.2	7.9	26.9
E	32.0	10.2	31.7
F	35.5	11.4	35.2
G	40.8	16.0	40.5
H	42.6	15.8	42.3
I	44.3	19.5	44.1
J	46.5	23.0	46.3
K	48.4	25.5	48.2
'Dutch Treat' 1957	6.2	1.9	6.0
MoH Circular 1960	23.4	9.8	23.1
Fission Fragments 1978	3.4	0.5	3.3
'Square Leg' 1980	34.6	12.2	34.2
'Hard Rock' 1982	11.3	2.1	11.1

Table 9.4 shows the total predicted casualties for Attacks A to K, and for the historical civil defence exercises, according to our own model and the replicated Home Office model respectively. For Attacks A and B our model predicts three to four times as many casualties as the Home Office. This ratio declines, for increasing weights of attack, until by J and K our model is predicting around twice the number of total casualties. The reason for this is presumably the fact, as discussed in chapter 7, that in the heavier attacks the casualty totals predicted by our model are reaching the limit imposed by the size of the UK population. For some of the very small attacks assumed in the civil defence exercises, our estimates differ from those of the Home Office by a factor of five or six.

Table 9.4 also shows the total casualties predicted by our model when burns effects are omitted. The differences from the standard version of the model are not great, partly because the burns casualties are relatively few in any case compared with blast and fallout, and partly because if people are not counted as killed by burns, they are likely to become blast or fallout casualties instead. In relation to the Home Office results, this shows that the Home Office omission of burns is not so significant as are the other differences.

Table 9.5 shows separately the numbers of deaths and injuries from blast, calculated by the two different models for all the attack scenarios. The numbers of blast deaths predicted by our model, following the OTA

Table 9.5 Numbers (millions) predicted as killed and seriously injured by blast, in different attacks, by authors' computer model, and by authors' replica of Home Office (HO) model

Attack	Killed		Seriously injured	
	Authors' model	Authors' replica of HO model	Authors' model	Authors' replica of HO model
A	2.4	1.2	2.6	0.2
B	3.9	2.0	5.3	0.4
C	7.0	3.5	7.3	0.7
D	7.6	3.8	7.7	0.7
E	10.6	5.2	8.4	1.0
F	11.7	5.7	9.2	1.1
G	19.7	9.8	10.2	1.9
H	19.8	9.8	11.0	1.9
I	24.0	12.7	9.9	2.3
J	30.7	16.0	8.8	2.8
K	34.4	18.3	8.2	3.1
'Dutch Treat' 1957	1.6	1.0	2.2	0.2
MoH Circular 1970	8.5	5.7	7.2	0.8
Fission Fragments 1978	0.4	0.2	0.9	0.05
'Square Leg' 1980	14.5	8.5	10.2	1.3
'Hard Rock' 1982	1.9	1.2	3.8	0.3

assumptions, are consistently around twice the number given by the Home Office. The differences in the numbers injured from blast vary much more widely. For lower weights of attack our model predicts between 10 and 15 times as many injured, while for heavier attacks such as I, J and K, the difference is only a factor of three or four.

Finally there are the differences in estimated fallout casualties. These are somewhat more complex to investigate, since they are affected by the differences in blast casualties. If more people are counted as *killed* by blast effects in a given area, then fewer remain who can subsequently be injured or killed by radiation. On the other hand, if more people are counted as *injured* from blast, then there is a greater chance that some of those people might be counted as injured by radiation also, and so be assumed to die from the combination of injuries.

One way to examine the differences due to the fallout components of the models alone, is to take the numbers predicted as surviving either uninjured or injured by blast, from the Home Office model. These numbers are then introduced as data, first into the Home Office's fallout model, and second into our fallout model. The effects of the differences in fallout assumptions can then be measured from the same base population. The results are shown in table 9.6. Our model predicts in general about five or six times as many deaths, and about twice as many injuries. The

Table 9.6 Numbers (millions) predicted as killed and seriously injured by fallout, in different attacks, by the fallout components of the authors' computer model and of the authors' replica of the Home Office model. (Both sets of calculations start with the numbers of survivors from blast effects, either injured or uninjured, as predicted by the replica Home Office model)

	Killed		Seriously injured	
Attack	Authors' model	Authors' replica of HO model	Authors' model	Authors' replica of HO model
A	4.4	1.3	1.6	0.9
B	9.7	1.5	4.8	1.6
C	14.7	2.9	5.2	2.4
D	14.9	2.9	5.3	2.4
E	18.1	3.6	5.6	3.0
F	20.1	4.1	6.1	3.6
G	22.7	4.0	4.8	3.3
H	23.3	3.9	4.9	3.1
I	24.3	4.3	4.2	3.2
J	24.1	4.2	3.5	3.0
K	23.8	4.1	2.8	2.9
'Dutch Treat' 1957	3.2	0.6	0.7	0.7
MoH Circular 1960	10.9	3.4	2.2	3.2
Fission Fragments 1978	1.4	0.2	1.2	0.2
'Square Leg' 1980	14.6	2.2	5.2	2.1
'Hard Rock' 1982	4.3	0.5	3.2	0.6

difference in the numbers of injured, however, is very variable, and in some cases the Home Office predictions actually exceed our own. This is simply because the large numbers of radiation deaths predicted by our model leave fewer people remaining to become injured.

On the basis of the sensitivity analyses carried out with our own model and described in chapter 7, it would seem that the major cause of these differences lies in the assumptions relating to protection factors: an average value of over 20 in the Home Office case, and an average of something under eight (depending on the extent of blast damage) in our model. The effects of changing the assumed relationships of radiation dose to percentage casualties — by increasing the LD-50 to 600 rads, for example — are relatively less important.

Going back to the predictions of total casualties from all causes shown in table 9.4, it will be seen that the discrepancy between the results from the two models is greatest for the 1978 *Fission Fragments* scenario and the 1982 'Hard Rock' exercise. The totals differ here by a factor of five or six. These are both scenarios for which the targets are mostly rural or remote. The numbers of blast deaths are few, and there are no great differences here in the predictions from both models. But our model predicts very much higher numbers of blast injuries. Many of the people injured by blast subsequently become the victims of radiation sickness; hence the large differences in the final casualty totals.

AREAS OF LAND AFFECTED IN AN ATTACK

Butler gives some figures, for his sample attack with 193 megatons, for the areas of land affected at certain levels of blast damage. These are as shown in table 9.7. We can compare these with the results from our own model given in figure 7.18. Butler's scenario lies somewhere in total megatonnage between Attacks F and G. Figure 7.18 shows that at this level of attack, we find some 16,000 km^2 affected at 5 psi or greater and 44,000 km^2 affected at 2 psi or greater. Interpolating between the values for 1 psi and 2 psi, we find over 60,000 km^2 affected at 1.5 psi or greater; as against 36,600 km^2 at 1.5 psi on Butler's figure.

Again, without knowing the exact targets and weapons used, it is difficult to determine the exact causes of the discrepancy. So far as blast overpressures go, both models rely on identical date from Glasstone and Dolan, so the explanation cannot lie there. The main reason is almost certainly the difference in total numbers of weapons and average weapon size in either case. In Butler's attack the average yield of weapon is over 1 megaton; whereas in our attacks it is much lower. As explained in chapter 6, the area affected by blast from a bomb does not increase in direct proportion to the yield, but at a much slower rate. It follows that if

Table 9.7 Areas of land affected by blast in an attack on the UK with 193 megatons, as predicted by the Home Office computer model

	% land area	Square kilometres[a]
Greater than 11 psi	2.75	6,710
Greater than 6 psi	5	12,200
Greater than 1.5 psi	15	36,600

[a] Butler gives only percentage figures. These have been converted into square kilometres on the assumption that Northern Ireland is included in the total land area

Source: Butler, 'Scientific Advice in Home Defence', figure 9, p. 154

the *same* total megatonnage is divided into more lower-yield weapons, the extent of blast damage will be greater. It is the weapons in our own scenarios, of course, which correspond to the actual Soviet weapons likely to be used in an attack on Britain. (Against this should be set the fact that the proportion of *airbursts* in Attacks F and G is much lower than in Butler's scenario. For the equivalent ratio of airbursts to groundbursts, the discrepancy would be even greater.)

Another possible cause of the difference in estimated total areas of blast damage might perhaps be that the weapons in Butler's scenario are targeted in such a way as to create a large amount of overlap of the areas affected by adjacent bombs.

Whatever the explanation, the figure of 15 per cent is one which features in Home Office literature in several places, as the fraction of the land area of the UK likely to be 'affected by blast' in an attack with around 200 megatons. Thus in *Domestic Nuclear Shelters: Technical Guidance* it is stated that in such an attack 'on about 80 targets', 85 per cent of the land area '. . . would be subject to little or no blast effects'.[38] The remaining 15 per cent is calculated, as in Butler's results, to experience blast pressures in excess of 1.5 psi. Thus 'little or no blast effects' in Home Office terms here would refer *inter alia* to areas in which for example the OTA would predict up to 25 per cent serious injuries.

In the pamphlet version of *Domestic Nuclear Shelters* intended for the non-specialist reader, the same figures are given in an even more anodyne form. 'Estimates suggest that around 5 per cent of the land area of the UK might suffer seriously from the effects of blast [that is, at overpressures of 6 psi and greater]. We cannot, of course, know in advance where the bombs would fall, but about 80 per cent of the land area might suffer no blast effects at all.'[39] The Home Office's own criterion for the limit of 'light' blast damage is 0.75 psi, at the outer edge of the 'D' damage-ring (see table 9.1). On this figure, our own calculations show that a figure of 40 or 50 per cent for the area 'unaffected by blast' would be closer to the truth. Window glass would be broken at even lower overpressures than this.

A rather different picture is painted by Home Office scientists in documents intended for circulation among civil defence workers. Calculations of areas of land affected by blast in a 200 megaton attack are given for example by J. K. S. Clayton in the Introduction to the Scientific Advisory Branch *Training Manual for Scientific Advisers* issued in 1977. 'An attack of this weight would cause heavy damage over about 10,000 square kilometres, moderate to heavy damage over about 50,000 square kilometres, and light damage over an additional 100,000 square kilometres . . .'[40] This gives a total of 160,000 km^2, or about 65 per cent of the UK affected (if Northern Ireland is included). From this rare case where it is possible to make a direct comparison, it emerges, therefore, that the Home Office presents its figures for private and for public consumption in very different ways.

10

Civil Defence and its Effectiveness

It is not our intention in this chapter to provide any very extensive description of existing civil defence plans in Britain. Admirably detailed accounts have recently been published by Campbell[1] and Crossley,[2] and Home Office policy is set out in a series of 'Emergency Services Circulars'.[3] Instead we will focus on some of the arguments in the current civil defence debate, and how the findings of previous chapters bear on these issues.

A first point which needs to be clarified is the distinction between 'home defence' and 'civil defence'. In government documents the terms are sometimes used interchangeably, but they have in fact subtly different connotations. Civil defence is usually taken to mean any precautions, other than actual combat, to protect the civilian population against the effects of attack by a foreign power. It is defined legally in these terms by the Civil Defence Act of 1948. 'Home defence', however, is rather broader. The Home Office *Training Manual for Scientific Advisers* lists four aims for home defence:

(a) to secure the United Kingdom against any internal threat
(b) to mitigate as far as is practicable the effects of any direct attack on the United Kingdom involving the use of conventional, nuclear, biological or chemical weapons
(c) to provide alternative machinery of government at all levels to increase the prospects of and to direct national survival and
(d) to enhance the basis for national recovery in the post-attack period.[4]

The first item on this list is thus concerned with the defence of the UK against *internal* enemies. This function is the responsibility of central government assisted by the police and the armed forces. Local government is involved only in the remaining three functions.

The *Training Manual* envisages the 'internal threat' to be that of terrorism, sabotage by enemy agents, and the activities of 'dissident extremist groups' who might be active in 'fomenting strikes in key industries, promoting anti-war demonstrations to turn the populace against the Government and disruptive activities concerned with war preparations'.[5] Much has been made of the civil liberties implications of this internal policing role for 'home defence'. We will not enter into that debate here, except to make one point. Government spokesmen may choose to emphasize the humanitarian and civilian protection aspects of home defence. But the fact remains that at least one of the explicitly declared purposes of current planning — even if this aspect is not widely publicized — is the maintenance of law and order and the control of dissident factions before and after an attack. This serves to explain something of the balance of emphasis in present planning.

What do these home defence measures consist of? They can be listed under four headings: advice to the public; systems for giving warning of an attack and for plotting the movement of fallout clouds, which are the responsibility of the United Kingdom Warning and Monitoring Organisations (UKWMO); preparing the proposed 'alternative machinery' of regional government to be put into action after an attack; and plans for the organization of various emergency services — medical facilities, fuel supplies, food stocks and so on — in the aftermath.

ADVICE TO THE PUBLIC

The Home Office has provided information to the general public about the effects of nuclear war, and measures to protect against these, in the form of a booklet *Nuclear Weapons*,[6] and two pamphlets, *Domestic Nuclear Shelters*[7] and the now notorious *Protect and Survive*.[8]

Nuclear Weapons is a generally reliable account of the physical and biological effects of nuclear explosions, drawing heavily on Glasstone and Dolan. Apart from serious underestimates of the ranges of damage from airbursts (by using the '30 per cent rule' — see p. 199), some questionable assumptions in calculating the protection factors of buildings, and the recommended use of the OED formula in assessing radiation risks, there are no great differences from the account which we have given here. On the other hand the booklet gives no estimates of the likely scale of attack on Britain, no calculations of the possible extent of damage or casualties, and no information or advice whatsoever on civil defence.

Protect and Survive was originally intended for distribution only when a nuclear attack seems imminent, but was made public in 1980 'for those who wish to know what they would be advised to do at such a time'.[9] The same advice would be promulgated through advertisements inserted in newspapers, and in pre-prepared films and tapes broadcast on television and radio. *Protect and Survive* instructs the householder — as by now almost every person in Britain must know — to 'stay put' and to prepare a fallout room and 'inner refuge' using doors, boxes, sandbags and heavy furniture. The fallout room is to be stocked with water, food and other supplies sufficient for a stay of at least two weeks. Some advice is given about limiting fire risks before the attack, and about controlling small fires after the attack. Shelterers are to listen to the radio for instructions and information, especially about fallout hazards; and to listen for sirens which will give warning of an attack and will sound the 'all-clear'. This is the only immediate aid which the government intends to give the general population.

The pamphlet has been the object of well-merited ridicule and scorn because of the huge gulf between its bland aseptic primary school style, with its neat little diagrams of paper tissues and teddybears, and what any half-way imaginative reader knows would be the reality — crouching in fear for days on end, in the dark, behind a couple of doors, with a bucket for a lavatory, perhaps with some of the shelterers injured or suffering radiation sickness, picturing what ruin and chaos might be found in the world outside. There is more substantial criticism to be made, however, of what *Protect and Survive* omits than of what it contains.

It gives no indication of the likely extent of blast and heat effects on a national scale, and no suggestion of the vast numbers of casualties which would certainly be caused by blast. Our own calculations for example predict just under 31 million killed and injured by blast in Attack H (see table 9.5). The pamphlet describes no means at all of obtaining protection against these effects of blast.

Perhaps only a few readers might be seriously misled into thinking that *if* they protect as instructed, *then* they will with luck survive, wherever they live. But the title is surely intended to carry something of that comforting impression, and there is little hint that for perhaps half the population the recommended 'protection' measures — since they relate almost exclusively to fallout — will be worse than useless. If a shelter is collapsed by blast, it could trap or bury people rather than protect them. Many other readers of *Protect and Survive* will probably appreciate that its advice in reality applies just to the periphery of the main blast and fire zones. But even they are likely to be unaware just how few people actually live in such 'peripheral' areas in Britain.

The only effective form of blast protection would be a system of properly-designed and equipped underground shelters. We will come to consider deep shelters shortly. Given that no such public shelters and very few private underground shelters exist in the country today, however, the emphasis on fallout precautions in Home Office advice is at least a realistic recognition of where last-minute *ad hoc* preparations could be of some use.

There is no doubt that the protection factor offered by an 'inner refuge' constructed according to the *Protect and Survive* plans could be substantially greater than that of the unmodified house. If the shelterers succeeded in staying inside, even for a few days, this might make the difference in some areas between life and death.

The problem is, as mentioned, that this would only be true in parts of the country more or less free of blast damage. In an attack with 200 megatons or more, over two-thirds of the built-up area of Britain will experience significant blast effects. Where the overpressures are not sufficient to cause large numbers of blast casualties, they may still be enough to cause serious damage to houses, to knock away the temporary barricades from doors and windows, and to collapse the 'inner refuges'. (Perhaps a few of the shelterers could rebuild these — but they would have to work fast, or be caught exposed at the time of greatest radiation risk.)

Chapter 8 showed that around 70 per cent of national housing stock could be expected to experience blast overpressures of 1.5 psi and above and to lie within the main fire zones, in Attack H. In this case it is only in the remaining 30 per cent of dwellings therefore that any inner refuges and prepared fallout rooms are likely to be left intact. This fact explains our results in chapter 7, where we experimented with raising average protection factors in areas experiencing less than 1 psi blast overpressures, in Attack H, from 8 to 16 (see table 7.8). The effect was to reduce fallout deaths from 16 million to just under 15 million. (Most of the fallout deaths occur within the blast-damaged areas, many of these resulting from the *combination* of blast injury with radiation injury.)

Even when average pfs are raised to 24 where overpressures are less than 1 psi, and to 15 where overpressures are between 1 and 2 psi — much higher values than we believe could be attained in practice even with inner refuges — fallout deaths in Attack H still total 9 million, and total casualties 37 million. Raising the pf values higher than these would have very little effect in reducing the casualty total.

Thus the great claims which have been made by government spokesmen for the numbers of lives which could be saved by people following *Protect and Survive* advice are clearly exaggerated. They completely overlook, as in all Home Office calculations, the crucial effects of blast damage on the radiation protection which houses and temporary shelters could provide.

The Home Office pamphlet *Domestic Nuclear Shelters* offers two designs of improvised fallout shelter to be built in the garden from doors, timber, scaffold poles, plastic sheets, and earth.[10] More details are given in the design manual *Domestic Nuclear Shelters: Technical Guidance*.[11] These shelters are quoted as giving blast protection 'up to 1.5 pounds per square inch'. The same arguments apply to these therefore, as to the *Protect and Survive* refuges: they will be demolished by blast in an attack with 200 megatons or more, over perhaps 70 per cent of the built-up area of the UK.

All this assumes that everybody actually does what *Protect and Survive* tells them. Many critics have doubted whether this will happen. We have discussed some of the issues involved in chapter 6. The pamphlet itself acknowledges that the advice does not apply to many who live in flats, bungalows or caravans, and that they will have to seek 'alternative shelter accommodation' with neighbours or relatives. Some people may give higher priority to contacting relations or friends say, or to collecting food, in the period when an attack is expected, than to building shelters. (Of course it is no criticism of civil defence planning that the public might choose deliberately to ignore advice.) Others, imagining themselves to be near likely targets, might quite sensibly decide to try to evacuate their families to areas which they perceived to be safer.

The physical difficulties of building the shelters and 'inner refuges' are also appreciable. A number of television programmes have filmed volunteers constructing the Home Office designs, and shown that very substantial quantities of earth and several person-days of labour are required.[12] Many elderly people, invalids and people living alone would find the work unmanageable. There would be difficulties in obtaining timber and scaffolding at the last minute. Many houses and flats do not have gardens suitable for the outdoor types of shelter. In some areas the excavations for the outdoor shelters would fill rapidly with water since the water table is close to the surface. Then there is the vexed question of how long people would or could stay inside — assuming they actually completed the shelters and that these were not knocked down again immediately by blast.

WARNING OF ATTACK

One key question is how much warning time would be given. We have looked at this question in chapter 5. It is necessary to distinguish two types of warning. The first is that given during a 'period of international tension', when a political crisis or a conventional war seems likely to escalate to a nuclear exchange. The second is the warning that enemy missiles or bombers are launched and on their way. Obviously in the nature of things the first form of warning must be indeterminate and uncertain. Home Office planning assumptions as to the amount of time available for civil defence preparations have been progressively revised downwards in recent years, from a period of several weeks, to what is now envisaged might be only a week or less. 'The basic essentials of plans should be capable of implementation within forty-eight hours.'[13]

The discussion in chapters 2 and 3 has made clear that Soviet strategic thinking lays great emphasis on surprise in attack. We have also explained the premium which 'counterforce' targeting places on the early use of nuclear weapons without warning. Even if the British government had sufficient indication of the possibility of a nuclear attack to put some covert official defence plans discretely into action, there still remains the question of whether warning would be issued to the general public. There are strong disincentives to doing this, as indicated in chapter 5. Clearly if public warning is not given, few if any householders will have temporary shelters prepared when an attack comes.

The short-term warning of the actual approach of Soviet missiles would be a matter of minutes only. There might be no warning at all of submarine-launched missiles fired from the North Sea or from the Atlantic. The public warning of the approach of missiles or bombers is to be relayed to the UK Regional Air Operations Centre at High Wycombe, and from there via the network of the United Kingdom Warning and Monitoring Organization, to 'carrier control points' installed in 250 major police stations. There are 7,000 automatic sirens throughout the country controlled from this network. Warning messages can also be sent out from the carrier control points to receivers in other public buildings throughout the country, where volunteers have been issued with some 11,000 hand-operated sirens.

Protect and Survive recognizes that people may be caught at work or in the open air, and that they have only a 'couple of minutes' to take cover. The pamphlet advises people in the open to get inside the nearest building, or if there are no buildings nearby, to lie flat in a ditch. This will give little or no protection against blast, but would shield people from direct exposure to thermal radiation from the fireball.

Chapter 9 showed that Home Office calculations assume that there will be no burns casualties at all. This would only be valid if warning was successfully conveyed to, understood by and acted on by everyone in the country within the few minutes available. This is unlikely. Our own calculations allow for 5 per cent of the population exposed. It should be remembered that not all weapons in an attack will arrive simultaneously, so that people forced into the open by earlier explosions will be exposed to the heat from later weapons.

Furthermore, a large part of the warning system itself will probably be destroyed by the first wave of the attack. Fylingdales is reported to be vulnerable to the effects of the electro-magnetic pulse,[14] as are practically all other radar and receiver installations. These would in any case be high priority targets (see chapter 4). The UKWMO network relies on land-lines which could also be damaged by the EMP.[15] In many areas the staff of the warning system will probably be killed, and the equipment destroyed, during the early stages of attack.

Even on the highly unlikely assumption that the warning system continued to be 100 per cent effective, and that the entire population took cover and so escaped direct burns injuries, this would only, however, reduce the overall casualty total in Attack H, for example, from 42.5 million (for 5 per cent exposed) to 42.3 million (for none exposed) —

as the experiments reported in table 7.6 showed. This is once again explained by the fact that the number of blast casualties in an attack of this magnitude is quite overwhelming. Where people escape burns injuries, there is still a high probability that they will face subsequent injury or death from blast effects, against which the *Protect and Survive* measures are powerless.

As for the Home Office advice on controlling incipient fires — by white-washing windows against the heat flash, removing curtains and other inflammable materials, and keeping buckets of water at hand — although such measures might be effective in some cases, it is hardly credible, as we said in the last chapter, that these could make much impact on the scale of mass fires (covering more than 60 per cent of the built-up area in Attack H) which our calculations predict. Conventional fire precautions were largely impotent in the face of the conflagrations caused by incendiary bombing in World War II, or in the Chicago and San Francisco fires. Indeed this fact seems to be recognized in civil defence planning for the fire service, in which it is intended that 'approximately 50 per cent of manpower and appliances' will be withdrawn from the cities and dispersed away from target areas before an attack. Fire services are only to be risked where 'the return is judged worthwhile' and 'planning should be directed towards the preservation of the fire service for its role in the longer survival period'.[16]

This concludes the discussion of measures currently taken to 'mitigate the effects of any direct [nuclear] attack on the United Kingdom'. As we have seen, the measures consist for the most part of encouragement to individuals to make their own last-minute low-cost preparations with little government assistance. On a very optimistic estimate the fallout precautions might save one or two million lives, and the precautions against thermal radiation exposure perhaps another couple of hundred thousand, out of a casualty total of 42 million in Attack H. If there is only a chance that this could be achieved, then in the absence of any more substantial forms of protection, the precautions are obviously well worth taking in areas less likely to be targets. What is reprehensible in official policy and government statements is the attempt made to create the illusion that these rather desperate remedies would be any more effective than sober analysis shows them to be.

The total civil defence budget in Britain is very modest. In 1983 the level of government funding to local authorities was planned to be around £45 million. In fact the authorities are spending only £13 million.[17] (Compare this with the civil defence budget in 1938, which was £42 million. Today's figure is of course worth only a fraction of that amount in real terms.) The major part of this money does not go on direct protection for the general public as such, but rather on the third function of home defence, that of providing 'alternative machinery of government'.

Figure 10.1   Home Defence Regions in Britain, as established in 1973.

'ALTERNATIVE MACHINERY OF GOVERNMENT'

The system of government planned to take effect in time of nuclear war is a regional one. England and Wales are to be divided into 10 regions, each of which contains one or two sub-regions. Scotland is split up into three zones. These zones, regions and sub-regions are shown on the map in figure 10.1 The planned structure of government is set out diagrammatically in figure 10.2.

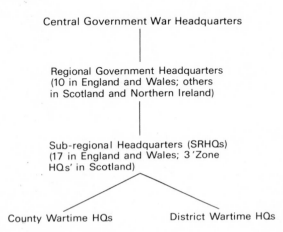

Central Government War Headquarters

Regional Government Headquarters
(10 in England and Wales; others
in Scotland and Northern Ireland)

Sub-regional Headquarters (SRHQs)
(17 in England and Wales; 3 'Zone
HQs' in Scotland)

County Wartime HQs   District Wartime HQs

Figure 10.2   Planned governmental structure in the event of a nuclear war.

Although it seems possible that some form of national government might be conducted, alongside military operations — according to Campbell from the underground headquarters at Hawthorn[18] — the plans envisage that 'central command and control agencies may not survive a nuclear strike',[19] in which case the functions of government will pass directly to the *sub*-regional level. Of the lower levels in the hierarchy only sub-regional headquarters (SRHQs) are housed in substantial bunkers. It is intended that the sub-regional governments take control in the period immediately following an attack, for perhaps some weeks or months, until the regional governments could be re-formed (in above-ground, unprotected accommodation).

Each of the SRHQs will provide space for between 200 and 400 people. One of them (in sub-region 8.1) remains to be built, but most are complete, either specially incorporated into the basements of government office buildings, or else adapted from World War II stores, military bunkers and ordnance factories, or from old RAF 'sector controls' and radar stations. The degree of protection of the SRHQs against blast and fallout would appear to vary. The newer basement bunkers, at least, are built to withstand blast pressures of 15 psi, to have pfs of around 400, and are equipped with air-conditioning and filtration systems and independent water and power supplies sufficient for a month's occupation.[20]

Each SRHQ is to be directed by a Sub-Regional Commissioner appointed by Parliament, who will have absolute authority, and a staff consisting of local government officials together with representatives of some other organizations and industries (such as British Telecom and the water authorities), working closely with the police and army. The main activities of these sub-regional governments are seen as being to do with the control of public order and the conservation of food, fuel and other supplies for the longer term. Other tasks would be the organization of road clearing operations, emergency sanitation and water supplies and burial of the dead. Little emphasis is placed on rescue operations, which are seen as putting staff and equipment at unprofitable risk, especially under heavy fallout conditions.

According to the Home Office circular *The Machinery of Government in War,*

Sub-Regional Commissioners would be concerned with the administration of justice, with the maintenance by the public of law and order, and with the general behaviour and morale of survivors . . . the function of the Sub-Region would be to process and disseminate information on the extent and effect of attack; to determine priorities and arrange for the re-allocation, where appropriate, of resources to meet immediate needs . . . and to prepare the administrative groundwork for the establishment of regional government.[21]

Although Sub-Region would rule on conflicting priorities, its intervention would aim at the *conservation of resources*, both manpower and materials, for longer-term survival — rather than immediate short-term aid to the hardest hit areas.[22]

At County level the chief executive is to serve as County Controller, directing a small emergency committee of local authority officials (but with no role for elected representatives). Each county would have a county headquarters and a 'standby headquarters' with accommodation typically for up to 150 staff between them. The premises designated for these County HQs are mostly adapted basements with rather little equipment and providing very variable standards of protection. The District HQs would be similar, but with fewer staff. Below these levels the proposed administrative system would depend on volunteers and would involve such organizations as the Red Cross, St Johns' Ambulance and the Women's Royal Voluntary Service — the intended role of the WRVS being mainly in emergency feeding.

While it is probably more sensible to rely on the initiative and training of individual volunteers to give some real help to survivors than on elaborate paper bureaucratic structures, it should be appreciated that these volunteers will face formidable difficulties. Fallout will prevent rescue workers from getting first aid to the injured until perhaps two weeks or more after the attack, by which time it may be too late. Members of the voluntary organizations are of course themselves likely to be killed and injured in similar proportion to the population generally.

A very important role, on the dubious assumption that all this actually comes into effect, would be that played by the UKWMO, whose principal function in the period following an attack would be that of monitoring and plotting the extent of fallout.[23] Messages about fallout hazards would be passed to the SRHQs, who could use this advice in controlling the exposure of their staff and in giving warnings to the general public. It is intended that police in surviving stations should issue such warnings by setting off maroons.

The UKWMO has 870 monitoring posts across the country, each housed in a concrete bunker with space for three volunteer members of the Royal Observer Corps. The posts are linked together into groups, and the groups into 'sectors', through a network of land-lines and radio links. Each post contains equipment for detecting nuclear explosions, for pin-pointing their ground zeros, and for measuring local radiation levels. Thirteen of the group controls are equipped with the AWDREY system (Atomic Weapons Detection, Recognition and Estimation of Yield) which performs similar functions, but works at longer range. The UKWMO would also act as an emergency meteorological office, on the assumption that the peacetime facilities at Bracknell are knocked out. This would obviously be crucial to any effective system of fallout prediction. Expenditure of some £20 million is budgeted over five years for the replacement of outdated equipment and improvements to the UKWMO communications system. It is not clear what protection will be incorporated against the effects of EMP.

Like *Protect and Survive*, the whole system of sub-regional government has attracted widespread condemnation, from all points across the political spectrum — in this case because of the priority it apparently gives to preserving the lives of a small number of officials over the safety of millions of the population at large. Critics have pointed to the hypocrisy of the government building hardened and specially-equipped bunkers for a bureaucratic elite, while the average householder is offered only ramshackle arrangements of doors and sandbags. Thus the Nuclear Protection Advisory Group, who exist to advocate that much more be spent nationally on 'effective' civil defence, have argued that 'It is quite illogical for government officials and military personnel and not the public to have shelters, because the only role of such people is to protect the public. It follows that, if one section of the community needs shelters, so do the others.'[24] Similar views have been expressed by David Owen: 'The Home Secretary reveals the paucity of his approach [and] goes on to advocate spending to ensure that the ruling establishment survive . . . But millions of others lose their lives. Money is to be spent on Sub-Regional Head-quarters; the governors will go underground, the governed will stay on top.'[25] Even the Society of Emergency Planning Officers, who carry the responsibility for civil defence planning in local authorities, have gone so far as to say that they sometimes get the impression '. . . that the government's home defence policy is to protect the government and not the people'.[26]

The declared purpose of the 'alternative machinery of government' is to increase the prospects of 'national survival'. One is perhaps entitled to ask in what sense 'the nation' could be said to be surviving, in circumstances where four-fifths of its population is killed by the immediate effects of attack. The proposed system of administration, consisting as it does of independent quasi-military regional authorities entrusted with summary and dictatorial powers, can hardly be said to provide any continuity with national government in its peacetime form. Perhaps such an authoritarian regime would be the only kind which would be at all workable in the aftermath. But it would certainly not continue the country's democratic traditions; none of its membership is directly elected (indeed the identity of most of the staff of the SRHQs remains secret); and in our view its moral authority to exercise power seems very dubious.

However this may be, the question at issue here from the strict civil defence point of view is would it actually work, and if so could it contribute to saving lives? Many people have wondered whether in the event the designated staff would be prepared to leave their families and take their places in the bunkers. There are the uncertainties about the amount of warning time available for the staff to get to the bunkers. There are question marks over whether radio and telephone communications systems would survive the effects of EMP and blast damage. And there is the possibility of the destruction by blast of the Sub-Regional, County and District HQs themselves.

In a recent study of an attack with 261 megatons, very comparable in its targeting and in the weapons used with our Attacks H and I, Crossley assumes that both the National Seat of Government and all the SRHQs are directly attacked.[27] (The SRHQs are not taken as targets in our own scenarios.) Of the County HQs and County stand-by HQs, Crossley finds that 36 fall within the 5 psi damage zones, and 34 outside. He concludes that half would be destroyed; although given that many are in buildings of ordinary construction it could be argued that lower overpressures than this would be enough to make them unusable. Our own map of the extent of 5 psi damage in Attack H (see figure 8.7) indicates that 5 out of the 20 SRHQs would be affected at this damage level.

The network of buried teleprinter and telephone lines, provided they survived the initial EMP, would, Crossley assumes, be little affected by blast except where directly hit, which seems reasonable.

He argues on the other hand that much of the long-distance microwave network would be knocked out by damage to the towers and microwave aerial dishes at overpressures of 2 psi and above. Since the system of government is designed to be highly decentralized this might not be so serious — although the loss of communication between regions could prevent effective monitoring and warning of fallout risks.

EMERGENCY SERVICES IN THE AFTERMATH

Since little rescue effort is planned by the regional governments, they would not contribute much to lifesaving in this respect. On the other hand the measures for advising any sheltering population of continuing radiation dangers, and the other planned public health precautions are obviously of value. It should be said though that the latter are paper plans only. Sites have been earmarked for mass graves, and records compiled of the locations in peacetime of supplies of chemicals, insecticides and other equipment. But, for example, no special emergency stockpiles of these materials exist.

As for emergency food supplies, these are under the control of the Ministry of Agriculture, Food and Fisheries (MAFF). Local authorities hold only stocks for their own bunkers. In the period preceding an attack, plans allow for the government to control the food market by means of rationing. Existing stocks of food within the normal distribution system would be identified, and those concentrated at ports would be dispersed to safer areas. As mentioned in chapter 8, the Home Office itself in its Circular *Food and Agriculture Control in War* believes it unlikely that shops could meet the demand from householders seeking to stock their *Protect and Survive* refuges with 14 days' supplies.[28]

For the period after the attack, MAFF has stocks of foodstuffs in a series of 'buffer depots' around the country, together with cooking equipment, utensils and such items as mobile bakeries. The buffer depots contain flour, sugar, fats, glucose sweets and biscuits. Campbell has published a list of just over a hundred of these, which he does not claim to be complete or entirely accurate.[29] We have nevertheless used this list to plot their distribution on the map in figure 10.3. Campbell calculates that these depots hold sufficient stocks in theory to feed 20 million survivors for a month.[30]

Large numbers of the buildings, which are of brick construction with asbestos roofs, would, however, be damaged or burned in an attack. Even light damage would result in the stocks becoming unusable from the effects of weather and radioactive contamination. Figure 10.3 indicates that in Attack H some 47 of the buffer depots shown would be affected by blast damage at 2 psi or greater. There is the problem of transporting

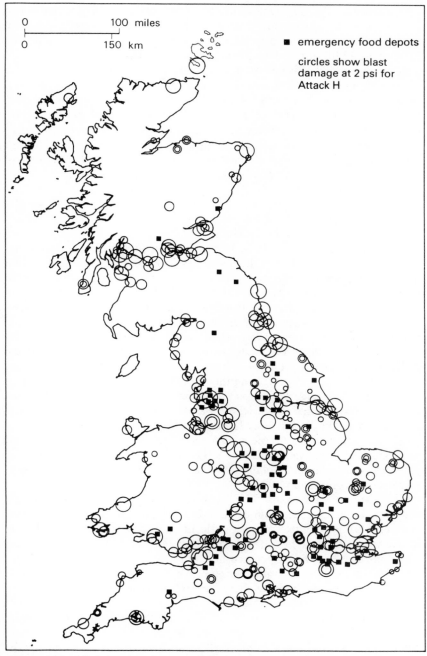

Figure 10.3 Ministry of Agriculture, Fisheries and Food (MAFF) buffer depots holding emergency food stocks. The extent of blast damage at 2 psi and above in Attack H is shown superimposed.

Source: from an incomplete list in D. Campbell, *War Plan UK*, table 16, pp. 359–61.

and distributing undamaged food stocks to survivors. When stocks ran out, there would remain only such food as could be found wild or could be grown. We have reviewed in chapter 8 all the problems which face any kind of agricultural effort in the aftermath.

It is almost impossible to come to any quantitative estimates of the impact on medium-term casualties which might be achieved. But in view of all the overwhelming difficulties of lack of fuel, lack of communication, lack of transport, extent of fire and blast damage and of radioactive contamination which we examined in chapter 8 — not to mention simple shortage of manpower — it appears implausible that any very significant action could be organized, other than in the less-affected regions of northern Scotland, north Wales and perhaps the far west of England.

DISCUSSION

Our analysis of existing plans, in the light of our earlier findings, has brought us to the conclusion then, as it has for numerous other critics, that official civil defence in Britain today is an emperor with few clothes. What motive might government have for exercising such a 'cruel deception' on its people, for pretending that measures would offer real defence, when on examination it turns out that their actual impact would be marginal?

It was not always so. In 1957, when the anticipated magnitude of bombardment was a fraction of what can be expected today, the Conservative government issued a Defence White Paper in which it recognized that 'there are no means of protecting the population against the consequences of a nuclear attack'.[31] Over the following decade the civil defence organization was run down, and in 1968 the old Civil Defence Corps, first formed out of the World War II Air Raid Precautions organization, was finally disbanded, its equipment disposed of, and civil defence placed on a 'care and maintenance' basis only. The recent revival in civil defence publicity and 'emergency planning' — although it involves little expenditure — dates only from 1972.

There are several reasons. The first is perhaps a certain wishful thinking amongst the older generation of civil defence enthusiasts and emergency planners, who look back even a little nostalgically to 'the spirit of the Blitz', and cannot see how utterly different nuclear war will be. A second factor is the sheer incompetence and bureaucratic inertia of the Home Office Scientific Research and Development Branch. It is said of generals that they are always fighting the previous war. This seems to be all the more true of civil defence planners.

We saw in the last chapter how Home Office calculations of blast casualties in a nuclear attack are based on the effects of high explosive bombing in World War II. Campbell has drawn attention to the way in which much of the Home Office's advice to the public about sheltering remains similarly unchanged over the last 40 years. *Protect and Survive* carries curious echos of *The Protection of your Home against Air Raids*, its predecessor of 1938.[32] (The 'refuge room' was intended then to protect against poison gas.) Two of the designs in *Domestic Nuclear Shelters* published by the Home Office in 1981 were identical, as Campbell points out, to the World War II 'Anderson' and 'Morrison' types – but with the dimensions now given in metric units.[33] Perhaps, working in an atmosphere of secrecy, and under pressure always to produce 'politically acceptable' results, the Home Office scientists have even convinced themselves up to a point about their very optimistic predictions.

However, none of this explains the sharp differences between some of the figures given publicly and privately by the Home Office about the effects of attack; nor the abandonment in the 1960s and now the revival of civil defence once again. To find the principal reason for this about-turn, we must look at those trends in nuclear strategy discussed in chapter 2. Where both sides held the other's cities hostage in the policy of 'mutual assured destruction' of the 1960s, it was consistent with the military posture that there be no civil defence. Indeed the protection of the civilian population would actually 'undermine deterrence', since if one side felt that its people were moderately well protected, it might be more prepared actually to risk a war. When the military strategy turns towards counter-force targeting and plans for limited nuclear war, as NATO doctrine did after 1967, it becomes an integral part of the 'credibility' of that strategy, that an opponent believe that one would be prepared to enter into such a war. This means presenting an impression in public that nuclear war is in some measure 'fightable' and 'winnable', or at the very least 'survivable'.

At the same time governments are unwilling to spend large sums on civil defence, or to give much publicity to the effects of nuclear weapons, since this seems to suggest that the 'deterrent' on which so much money *is* being spent is liable to fail, and that war is possible. As observed in chapter 1, governments also wish to avoid causing any alarm which might in turn bring calls for nuclear disarmament. Thus government is caught in a strange dilemma, which serves to explain much of the confusion and ambiguity surrounding present civil defence arrangements in this country. The result is a compromise, whereby a strategy that was intended to deceive the enemy, ends up as an attempt to bluff the population at home.[34]

In Britain, during 1982 and 1983, this bluff has been called. The Home Office, mainly as a result of CND's 'Hard Luck' exercise, the publication of the BMA report and the activities of the 'Nuclear Free Zone' local authorities, have to all intents and purposes lost the argument over the likely level of short-term casualties in an attack with 200 megatons. Their response so far has been to do two things. The first is to avoid all public debate, to postpone any new home defence exercises, and to withdraw from publication several proposed new documents — including a revised (and retitled!) version of *Protect and Survive* — presumably in an effort to damp down general discussion of the issues.[35] The second is to argue that civil defence is intended to defend against other eventualities besides a nuclear attack on this magnitude, and even that massive nuclear bombardment is the least probable of these threats.

Chapter 5 has described the scenario for the cancelled 'Hard Rock' exercise, planned for 1982, which envisaged a nuclear attack with under 50 megatons. The response of the Home Office to the BMA's report referred to a 200 megaton attack as being 'at the upper limit of foreseeable possibilities'. And in a letter to *The Times* on 24 March 1983 — which was quoted in chapter 3 — Lord Renton, President of the National Council for Civil Defence, together with several other signatories, wrote that:

Hostile attacks for which we should be prepared include:
1 A conventional attack in which no nuclear bombs are dropped.
2 One or two nuclear bombs dropped on us as 'blackmail' to bring a conventional war to an end.
3 An 'all-out' nuclear holocaust, or even 'germ' or chemical warfare on a large scale.

Some people wrongly assume that this third possibility is the only one which is conceivable, arguing that there would be no survivors and that all civil defence preparations are a waste of time even to protect people on the periphery and in remote areas from fall-out. Their argument is then falsely extended to the denial of civil defence in all circumstances.[36]

There is a considerable irony to these last remarks, since civil defence advocates are now putting forward arguments whose falsehood is of a perfectly symmetrical nature. *They* argue that we must have civil defence to protect against an attack involving only one or two nuclear bombs, or conventional weapons alone; and then try to extend that argument to cover a system which is still intended to sustain the illusion that it provides real defences against a substantial nuclear bombardment.

In our experience, emergency planners have, in debate, even argued the case for the whole civil defence system *solely* on the grounds that its principal concern is with contingency planning for civilian disasters such as air crashes or accidents at nuclear power stations. It goes without saying that coping with peacetime emergencies is a perfectly proper and desirable function of 'emergency planning'. But that is not the present subject, which is civil defence in war. In truth, as we have shown, most of current planning including that of the whole SRHQ and UKWMO systems *is* directed towards the threat of nuclear attack. For chemical fires or for accidental releases of radioactivity one would expect plans for evacuation, not the 'stay-put' policy. Out of some 60 'Emergency Services Circulars' issued by the Home Office since 1972, only four deal with peacetime disasters.[37]

Our account of Soviet strategic thinking has, we hope, made it perfectly clear that the Soviet Union does not subscribe to NATO or American concepts of limitations on nuclear war, and certainly regards the notion of a blackmail or 'warning shot' with one or two weapons as 'the height of strategic foolishness'. It is not impossible that Britain might experience conventional bombing by the Soviet Union. But it has been argued in chapters 2 and 3 that many factors make this very unlikely. By the time that a European war extended to British territory, it would almost certainly have gone nuclear. These factors include the very large numbers of battlefield and medium-range nuclear weapons in central Europe, the pressure to mount pre-emptive attacks on nuclear forces, and not least the NATO doctrines of flexible response and first use.

Civil defence designed solely against conventional air-raids is likely to be of little use, if these are followed (or preceded) by nuclear attacks. Many of the requirements in the two cases are contradictory. For conventional bombing it would be sensible to concentrate rescue teams, emergency hospitals and fire services, whereas for nuclear attack the only hope is to disperse these. Evacuation of the cities might be feasible in a conventional war, but hardly so in a nuclear war (see below). Fallout precautions are obviously only applicable in the latter.

There remains the possibility that a single Soviet weapon might be launched by accident. In times of tension, with the high state of readiness on which warning systems and nuclear forces would be placed, this would probably trigger all-out nuclear war. In other circumstances it might not provoke retaliation; and this remains an event whose probability we find it difficult to estimate, but which perhaps should be something for which civil defence plans are prepared. Maybe more likely is the use of a small nuclear device by a terrorist group.[38] As our analysis in chapter 8 indicates, and as the BMA have said, the resources of the entire National Health Service would be overwhelmed by the casualties from a single small nuclear weapon on a British city.[39] However, there would be much that could be done by bringing in a massive rescue effort from the rest of the country, and in protecting people in areas away from the explosion from the effects of fallout — for example by evacuation.

The new emphasis on conventional war and limited nuclear attacks in the official rationale for civil defence represents a complete *volte-face*, and has not been supported by any explanation, in terms say of some supposed change in Soviet strategy, or imagined threats from other possible enemies. Up until 1981, the primary threat was said repeatedly by the Home Office to be massive Soviet nuclear attack. Thus the Scientific Advisers' *Training Manual* of 1977 states that 'It is possible that a nuclear war would be preceded by a conventional war in Europe and the possibility of attacks on this country armed with non-nuclear devices cannot be ruled out'; but that 'The current assessments point clearly to nuclear war as the overriding consideration in determining the preparations to be made for home defence in the United Kingdom.'[40] The introduction to the *Manual* suggests that a nuclear attack by 'the Warsaw Pact Nations' would be with 200 megatons.[41]

The last chapter showed how Butler's experiments with the Home Office computer model, reported in 1981, started from a lowest level of attack studied of 180 megatons. The 1980 'Square Leg' exercise was based on a 200 megaton attack. *Domestic Nuclear Shelters: Technical Guidance*, issued in 1981, contains the statement that '. . . in a nuclear war the UK might expect about 200 megatons of nuclear weapons of various sizes to be delivered against about 80 targets'.[42] In 1983 the Home Office is ordering over 30,000 'Radiac' instruments for measuring radiation levels, at a cost of £20 million. As Campbell points out, this hardly supports any thesis that conventional bombing is now the major concern.[43]

It is worth reiterating the point that even a massive attack at the level, for example, of Attack H, although it is intended to bring about the complete destruction of the UK's military forces and to prevent economic and industrial recovery, can still in a certain sense be said to be 'limited' (although not part of a 'limited nuclear war' strategy) in two respects. It still uses less than half and perhaps less than a third of the megatonnage which on our calculations the Soviet Union has allocated to the UK (see chapter 4); and it is targeted primarily against military and strategic objectives, not cities as such.

It is difficult to escape the conclusion that these new arguments about conventional or reduced nuclear threats represent a desperate attempt on the Home Office's part to scale down the problem to a point where 'low-cost' civil defence *would* arguably have more than marginal value, now that they recognize that against a realistically assessed level of Soviet nuclear attack, the plans lack all credibility.

It remains for us to look briefly at what the case is for putting much more effort and money into civil defence than at present; and of what the value might be of such policies as mass evacuation, or a large-scale programme of deep shelter building.

EVACUATION

In the 1960s, British civil defence plans involved organizing mass evacuation from the cities.[44] These plans are shown being put into action in the film *The War Game*. They have now been abandoned in favour of the 'stay put' policy. Recently evacuation plans have once again been under consideration by the government.[45] In the autumn of 1982 government committees were looking at the results of a study prepared by a Shelter and Evacuation Working Party at the Cabinet Office. It seems that two proposals, involving either 12 million or 30 million people, were being examined. Both schemes were turned down however; and the new civil defence regulations, intended to come into effect in 1983, will not now require local authorities to prepare evacuation plans.

This is probably wise. On detailed analysis the practical and logistic difficulties facing mass evacuation in Britain are insuperable. In the first place, no parts of the country can be predicted to be very much safer from the effects of fallout than any other, and very little of the built-up areas can be guaranteed immune from heat and blast — as *Protect and Survive* acknowledges. In those areas where the risk *is* less (northern Scotland, the Welsh hills) there is rather little accommodation and shelter. In the US and in the Soviet Union there are large parts of the country which would probably escape direct attack; but even in the US the practicability of evacuation, or 'crisis relocation' as the Americans call it, has been seriously questioned.[46]

Moving millions of people would present vast problems of organization, would almost certainly result in widespread chaos and panic, and could hardly be achieved in the few days of warning time now thought likely to be the maximum available. There would be the problems of housing and feeding the millions in the areas to which they were moved.

There is also the double bind which applies to many civil defence precautions in countries which are themselves nuclear weapons powers: that a large-scale evacuation could be seen by the other side as part of preparations for nuclear war. It is even possible that an attack could be made while evacuation was in progress, in which case the situation could be much worse than if people had 'stayed put'.

At present in Britain not only is evacuation not envisaged, but the government, recognizing that many people are likely to attempt to escape from obvious target areas on their own initiative, have actually made plans to control such an exodus by sanctions and even by force.[47] As mentioned in the last chapter, *Protect and Survive* warns people that authorities in other areas will not provide accommodation or food to evacuees. 'So stay at home.'[48] There are plans to designate motorways and other major roads as 'Essential Service Routes' which would be kept clear for military and official traffic, but whose simultaneous (and it seems deliberate) effect is to seal off any other movement out of the cities.[49]

DEEP SHELTERS

If evacuation is not promising, then what about deep shelters? Here it seems that some real protection could be obtained against all the principal effects, of thermal radiation, blast and fallout. Many publications have appeared in which designs are presented for below-ground reinforced

concrete or steel shelters with reinforced entrance doors, separate escape
tunnels, and ventilation systems equipped with filters to trap fallout
particles.[50] One such design is included in the Home Office's *Domestic
Nuclear Shelters: Technical Guidance*.[51]

We do not intend to discuss shelter design in detail. No doubt some
unscrupulous cowboy operators have been offering worthless and
dangerous designs to unsuspecting purchasers who will not be in a
position to complain when their shelters fail. On the other hand there are
certainly properly-engineered designs of shelter published and on the
market, which would protect against almost all of the effects of a nuclear
explosion anywhere but in the immediate vicinity of ground zero. Clearly
it is essential that an effective shelter be stocked with sufficient food and
water for a long stay, and that it has a lavatory and its own independent
power supplies. It is also important that a shelter be sited in such a way
that all exits will not be blocked by building rubble and the occupants
permanently entombed.

The *technical* problems associated with otherwise adequately-designed
shelters are mainly to do with the equipment to control temperature,
humidity and air quality inside. If it was necessary to limit the ventilation rate because of smoke outside, then the internal temperature and
carbon dioxide concentration could rise and even cause death.[52] The
difficulties would be exacerbated in hot and humid weather. And, as the
OTA points out 'Fires are also a threat because of extreme temperatures
(possibly exceeding 2,000°F) and carbon monoxide and other noxious
gases. A large fire might draw oxygen out of a shelter, suffocating
shelterees. World War II experience indicates that rubble heated by a
firestorm may remain intolerably hot for several days after the fire is put
out.'[53] It has been suggested that shelters might have their own
independent oxygen supplies, in cylinders, and chemical means for
reducing carbon dioxide levels;[54] but this still does nothing to stop the
temperature rising.

In many areas where fires were less serious, the protection against blast
and fallout could nevertheless be virtually complete. There are, however,
three main considerations to do with deep shelters, besides their technical
functioning. The first is cost. Most experts agree that the cost per person
of small 'domestic' blast and fallout shelters with perhaps four to six places
in each, would be around £1,000 to £1,500.[55] This view is shared by the
Home Office.[56] Thus a programme to shelter the population of the whole
country might cost between £50,000 and £80,000 million. This is a fearsome amount — four to six times the annual defence budget of the UK.
It seems unlikely that such a programme could gain public or government
support, particularly at a time when so many essential services are being
cut back. However, if such shelters really would be effective, perhaps the
cost involved should be the least of the considerations.

The second question is once again that of warning time, and whether there might be a large number of people who would be caught above ground in a surprise attack. In large communal shelters, especially those purpose-built as part of other buildings such as blocks of offices, flats or even multi-storey car parks, the cost per place could be much less than in small household shelters — perhaps as low as £150 to £300.[57] However, it would take longer for people to reach and get inside community shelters; and so the considerations of cost and warning time work against each other.

Civil defence enthusiasts point to the examples of Switzerland and Sweden as countries which have invested heavily in shelters for the general population, and which now have shelter capacity for large fractions of their populations (about 90 and 70 per cent respectively).[58] The crucial difference from Britain however, is that these are neutral countries, without nuclear weapons, whose military posture is defensive in the true sense. This does not of course make them immune from direct nuclear attack. But it does mean that they are unlikely to face heavy bombardment, and that the greater threat is that of fallout from nuclear war in other parts of Europe.

For this there would be a longer period of warning, measured in hours rather than minutes. It would be possible for people to go home from work say, make some hurried preparations, and get inside the communal shelters. Governmental instructions to the population to take cover will not be seen by an enemy as provocative, or as signalling any intention to attack. If Britain were to adopt a non-nuclear defence policy, then civil defence on the Swiss and Swedish models would be worth considering. The investment and building effort involved should not be underestimated though. Switzerland and Sweden are rich countries, they have been building shelters for 20 years, and they have not finished yet.

The difference between the positions of these countries and Britain in relation to the nuclear threat is also relevant to the third and most important consideration to do with deep shelters: what will the shelterers find when they come up to the surface again? In Switzerland and Sweden they will emerge to a landscape perhaps heavily polluted with radioactivity, and with all the damage and chaos caused by leaving agriculture and industry untended for days or weeks, but without great physical destruction of buildings, technological infrastructure or crops.

In Britain this would not be the case. There is no need for us to go over again the picture of devastation painted in chapter 8. Surely in these circumstances most of those who were safely sheltered from the immediate effects of attack would have been condemned instead to more protracted and unpleasant deaths in the months following. Extraordinarily enough some of the advocates of deep shelters themselves acknowledge the truth of this. For example R. N. Ormerod, author of *Nuclear Shelters: A guide to Design*, has written:

The reason that civil defence and shelters will never be supported by a government facing the scale of threat we currently do is that for the 'good' of the nation it is best to maximise the initial casualties from a nuclear attack. . . . The more people that perish immediately, the less acute the strain on the survivors fighting for the (very) limited resources.[59]

Studies have been made in the United States of the possibility of hardening or otherwise protecting industrial buildings and machinery from some of the effects of blast and thermal radiation, for example by burying equipment temporarily or transferring it to shelters.[60] Another possibility is that stockpiles of goods and essential equipment could be built up in protected accommodation — although there is still the possibility that such stocks could be targeted by an enemy if their sites became known.

Even if machinery or some industrial plant could be sheltered, it is difficult to see how, say, the country's transport system, its housing stock or its agriculture could be 'hardened'. We seem to be faced with a kind of infinite regress, in which the search for passive defences against the effects of nuclear war would lead towards the construction of a complete secondary underground world, like that depicted in E. M. Forster's story *The Machine Stops*.[61] But this is to descend to the realm of science fiction.

Anyone who argues against civil defence preparations for nuclear attack tends to meet with the indignant response that the concerns of civil defence are wholly humanitarian, and that any criticisms must, therefore, have sinister motives. The argument that civil defence in nuclear weapons states is intimately bound up with strategies for fighting nuclear war, meets with the riposte that this is like saying that the existence of the fire brigade encourages the arsonist.

Readers who have come with us this far will see that we have not condemned all civil defence as futile. We have, however, shown that existing plans, preparations and levels of expenditure in Britain are minimal; that defence of the civilian population is only one of their concerns and a minor one at that; that the number of short-term deaths and injuries averted by present precautions would be very few in comparison to the total death toll; and that even much greater investment and much more elaborate civilian defences offer little hope. We have condemned official attempts to conceal the truth about these questions, and to exaggerate the extremely marginal effectiveness of civil defence measures.

The analogy of the fire brigade is false. Where two nuclear weapons powers confront each other, it would be more apt to compare the situation to that of two arsonists, each surrounded with drums of petrol, and each threatening to set fire to the other's house. The first priority is to get rid of the petrol from both houses.

Appendix 1

List of targets and details of attack scenarios

A   Airburst   D   One groundburst and one airburst
G   Groundburst   K   Two groundbursts
W   Waterburst   T   Triple attack (a combination of ground and airbursts)

SS4	1 Mt warhead	SS5	1 Mt warhead	SS11(SS11mod3)	1	Mt warhead
SS20	0.15 Mt warhead	SSN5	1 Mt warhead	SS19/1(SS19mod1)	0.5	Mt warhead
Badger	1 Mt warhead	Fencer	1 Mt warhead	SS19/2(SS19mod2)	5	Mt warhead
Blinder	1 Mt warhead	Backfire	1 Mt warhead	Kingfish	0.2	Mt warhead

The National Grid system divides the UK into 100 km squares which are identified by two letters e.g. NH etc. In this appendix the targets have been grouped together according to these squares. Considerations of space have obliged us to omit the detailed grid references for each target. These can be obtained from the authors on request. The same applies to the details of the warheads used in attacks A–G and I–K.

Scenario H was constructed at an earlier time (May/June 1982) than the others and its attack pattern differs in detail from theirs (for instance, a groundburst instead of an airburst or a bomber instead of a missile attack might be assumed for some targets). None of these small differences is of any qualitative significance.

Many of the descriptions of the targets in this appendix require the use of abbreviations which are listed at the end.

		Included in attack										Weapon
	Description	A	B	C	D	E	F	G	H	I	J	K	in H
Grid square HU												
Sullom Voe	Oil termnl, US Coastguard stn, sub. navigation base(?)	–	A	A	A	A	A	A	A	A	A	Badger
Sumburgh	Radar, airport	–	–	G	G	G	G	G	G	G	G	Kingfish
Grid square HP												
Saxa Vord	Radar (Ace High, NADGE)	–	–	A	A	A	A	A	G	A	A	Kingfish
Grid square NB												
Kyle of Lochalsh	RN base	–	–	–	G	–	–	–	–	–	–	–
Stornoway	US ASW base (Orion P3), (plans for 2000 m rway), power stn nrby	G	G	G	G	G	G	G	G	G	G	SS11
Grid square NC												
Dounreay	UKAEA prototype fast breeder reactor, nuclear waste storage	–	–	–	G	G	G	G	G	G	G	SS4
Brora	Intelligence facility	–	–	–	A	–	–	–	–	–	–	–
Grid square ND												
Thurso	US microwave stns	–	–	–	A	–	–	–	–	–	–	–
Flotta	Oil termnl	–	–	–	–	A	A	A	A	A	A	Badger

	Description	A	B	C	D	E	F	G	H	I	J	K	Weapon in H
		Included in attack											
Grid square NF													
Benbecula	Radar, airfield, rocket range	–	–	–	A	–	–	–	–	–	–	–	–
Grid square NG													
Loch Ewe	POL depot	–	–	–	G	–	–	–	–	–	–	–	–
Grid square NH													
Invergordon	RN base, aluminium, fuel depot, oil pipeline nrby	–	–	G	G	G	G	G	G	G	G	G	SS20
Dalcross	Airport (minor), Inverness nrby	–	–	–	G	–	–	–	–	–	–	A	–
Grid square NJ													
Kinloss	RAF (air def., Nimrod) (rway 2500 m), prob. wartime nuc. wpns store	G	D	D	D	D	D	D	D	D	D	D	SS20
Milltown Airfield	Radio commns base	–	–	A	–	A	A	A	–	A	A	A	–
Lossiemouth	RAF (Buccaneers) (rways 3000, 2000, 1300 m). nuc. wpns store	D	D	D	D	D	D	D	D	D	D	D	SS20
Mormond Hill	USN & USAF long-range commns, NADGE radar, NATO relay stn	–	A	A	A	A	A	A	A	A	A	A	SS20
Dyce	Civil airport (rways 2000, 2 × 1400 m)	–	–	G	G	G	G	G	G	G	G	G	SS20
Aberdeen	Port, B.Sh., fertilizers gas/oil pipelines, commns links, USN microwave stn	–	–	–	G	G	G	G	G	G	G	G	Blinder
Grid square NK													
Buchan	RAF radar	–	–	–	A	–	–	–	–	–	–	–	–
Buchan	RAF sector operational control	–	G	G	G	G	G	G	G	G	G	G	SS20
Crimond W/T Stn	RN radio stn	–	–	–	A	–	–	–	–	–	–	–	–
St Fergus	N. Sea gas termnl	–	–	–	–	A	A	A	A	A	A	A	Badger
Grid square NN													
Pitlochry	NSHEB electricity grid control	–	–	–	–	–	G	G	G	G	G	G	Badger
Grid square NO													
Edzell	USN & USAF commns & SIGINT centre	–	A	A	A	A	A	A	G	A	A	A	SS20
Arbroath	45th Royal Marines	–	–	–	A	–	–	–	–	–	–	–	–
Kinnaber	USN microwave link stn	–	–	–	A	–	–	–	–	–	–	–	–
Dundee	Docks, oil ref. (350 kt/yr), Tay bridge nrby, engineering, UKWMO sector control	–	–	–	–	G	G	G	G	G	G	G	Blinder
Leuchars	RAF (Lightings, Phantoms) (rways 2700, 1500 m)	–	D	D	D	D	D	D	D	D	D	D	SS19/1 SS11
Balado Bridge	NATO Satcom III (sat. link)	–	A	A	A	A	A	A	–	A	A	A	–
Hawklaw	SIGINT centre	–	A	A	A	A	A	A	A	A	A	A	SS19/1
Perth	Ind./urban	–	–	–	–	–	–	–	–	–	–	A	–
Grid square NR													
Machrihanish	US ASW base (nuc. weapons) (rway 3,000 m)	T	D	D	D	D	D	D	T	D	D	D	SS20
Grid square NS													
Greenock	USN/US Army trnspt termnl & store, docks, shpbldg	–	–	–	–	–	–	–	–	–	A	A	–
Glasgow Airport	Civil airport (rways 1900, 1200m)	–	–	G	G	G	G	G	G	G	G	G	Backfire
Beith	RN air def., poss. nuc. weapons store	G	G	G	G	G	G	G	G	G	G	G	SS19/1
Glasgow	Several major military-related	–	–	–	–	–	–	A	G	A	A	A	Backfire
	inds (e.g., GEC, Dunlop,	–	–	–	–	–	–	–	–	A	A	A	–
	Yarrow & Co., Courtaulds),	–	–	–	–	–	–	–	–	–	A	A	–
	steel, lead, US store												
Inverkip	Power stn (over 900 MW)	–	–	–	–	–	–	–	A	–	A	A	Backfire
Dalry	Chem. ind.	–	–	–	–	–	–	–	–	–	A	A	–
East Kilbride	Ind./urban, SRHQ	–	–	–	–	–	–	–	G	G	G	G	SS4

| | | Included in attack | | | | | | | | | | | Weapon |
Description	A	B	C	D	E	F	G	H	I	J	K	in H

Grid square NS — continued

Place	Description	A	B	C	D	E	F	G	H	I	J	K	Weapon in H
Kirkintilloch	SSEB Elect. grid control	–	–	–	–	–	–	A	A	A	A	A	Backfire
Stirling	Urban/ind.	–	–	–	–	–	–	–	–	–	–	A	–
Bishopton	Royal Ordnance Factory, USN & US Army trnspt termnl & store nrby	–	–	–	–	–	–	A	A	A	A	A	Backfire
Bathgate	Heavy ind., Plessey	–	–	–	–	–	–	–	A	A	A	A	Badger
Motherwell	Heavy ind.	–	–	–	–	–	–	–	A	A	A	A	Badger
Grangemouth	USN/US Army trnspt termnl store	–	–	–	A	–	–	–	G	–	–	–	Backfire
Grangemouth	Oil ref. (8600 kt/yr), chem. ind.	–	–	–	–	A	A	A	A	A	A	A	Backfire
Longannet	Power stn (2400 MW), bridge	–	–	–	–	–	G	G	A	G	G	G	Backfire
Kilmarnock	Ind./urban	–	–	–	–	–	–	–	–	–	A	A	–
Cumbernauld	Ind./urban	–	–	–	–	–	–	–	–	–	A	A	–
Airdrie	Ind./urban, pharmaceuticals	–	–	–	–	–	–	–	–	A	A	A	–
Firth of Clyde	US & UK nuc. subs, flooding	–	–	W	W	W	W	W	W	W	W	W	SS19/2
Gare Loch	Entrance to Faslane	W	W	–	–	–	–	–	–	–	–	–	–
Coulport	Nuc. missile store/sub. store	G	G	G	G	G	G	G	G	G	G	G	SS19/1
Holy Loch	US Poseidon/Trident subs base	G	G	G	G	G	G	G	G	G	G	G	SS19/1
Holy Loch	Entrance	W	W	W	W	W	W	W	W	W	W	W	SS19/1
Faslane	UK Polaris nuc. sub. base	G	G	G	G	G	G	G	G	G	G	G	SS19/1
Glen Douglas	NATO weapons store/sub. store, Finnart oil termnl nrby	–	–	G	G	G	G	G	G	G	G	G	SS19/1
Hunterston B	Nuclear power stn (AGR) (2 × 616 MW), Hunterstone A magnox nuc. power stn (2 × 15 MW) nrby	–	–	–	–	G	G	G	G	G	G	G	Backfire
Ayr	Ind./urban, fertilizers, drug ind.	–	–	–	–	–	–	–	–	–	A	–	–
Ardrossan	Oil ref. (275 kt/yr), port	–	–	–	–	A	A	A	A	A	A	A	SS4
Irvine	Chem. ind., Dundonald NADGE radar stn	–	–	–	–	–	–	–	–	A	A	A	–
Prestwick	Civil airport (rways 3220, 1970, 1540 m), USN trnspt & ASW, USAF & RAF airlift cmnd, radar, B.Ae., Air Traffic Control (Scotland)	–	D	D	D	D	D	D	G	D	D	D	SS11

Grid square NT

Place	Description	A	B	C	D	E	F	G	H	I	J	K	Weapon in H
Rosyth	Polaris and hunter-killer nuc. sub re-fit & repair dockyards	–	G	G	G	G	G	G	G	G	G	G	SS19/1
Forth Bridge	Bridge (& Dalmeny oil termnl)	–	–	–	–	–	–	W	W	W	W	W	SS19/1
Pitreavie Castle	NATO naval and COMMAIR cmnd (N. Atlantic and NE channel), HQ Nthn Maritime Air Regn (& GEC, power stn (140 MW))	G	G	G	G	G	G	G	G	G	G	G	SS19/1
Galashiels	Ind./urban	–	–	–	–	–	–	–	–	–	A	A	–
Leith	Edinburgh docks, fertilizers	–	–	–	–	G	G	G	G	G	G	G	Backfire
Edinburgh	Ind./urban, pharmaceuticals	–	–	–	–	–	–	–	–	A	A	A	–
Turnhouse	Civil airport (rways 2100, 1100, 800 m)	–	G	G	G	G	G	G	G	G	G	G	Backfire
Craigihall	Dist. Army HQ and barracks	–	–	–	A	A	A	A	A	A	A	A	SS19/1
Cockenzie	Power stn (1152 MW)	–	–	–	–	–	A	A	A	A	A	A	Backfire
Kirknewton	RAF (rways 1100, 1100, 800 m), SRHQ	–	–	–	G	–	–	–	–	–	–	–	–

Grid square NU

Place	Description	A	B	C	D	E	F	G	H	I	J	K	Weapon in H
Boulmer	BMEWS, RAF (rways 1700, 1300 m), radar (Ace High, NADGE)	A	A	A	A	A	A	A	A	A	A	A	SSN5

Grid square NX

Place	Description	A	B	C	D	E	F	G	H	I	J	K	Weapon in H
Whitehaven	Chem. ind.	–	–	–	–	–	–	–	–	A	A	A	–
Dumfries	Urban/ind.	–	–	–	–	–	–	–	–	–	A	–	–

Description	A	B	C	D	E	F	G	H	I	J	K	Weapon in H
Grid square NY												
Chapelcross — BNFL nuc. power stn (4 × 49.5 MW), Powfoot ordnance factory nrby	–	–	G	G	G	G	G	G	G	G	G	Backfire
Anthorn — VLF commns with nuc. subs	–	–	A	A	A	A	A	A	A	A	A	SS20
Calder Hall — BNFL nuc. power stn (4 × 49.5 MW)	–	G	G	G	G	G	–	G	G	G	–	–
Sellafield (Windscale) — Nuc. reprocessing plant	–	–	G	G	G	G	G	G	G	G	G	SS5
Broughton Moor — USN depot (run by RN)	–	–	A	A	A	–	–	A	–	–	–	SS20
Carlisle — RAF maint. unit, ind./urban	–	–	–	–	–	A	A	A	A	A	A	SS20
Grid square NZ												
Blyth B — Power stn (1100 MW)	–	–	–	–	A	A	A	A	A	A		Blinder
NE regn Airport — Civil airport (rway 2500 m)	–	G	G	G	G	G	G	G	G	G	G	Backfire
Tynemouth, Sth. Shields, Jarrow — B.sh., GEC, Dunlop engineering, chem. inds	–	–	–	–	–	–	A	A	A	A	A	Badger
Tynemouth, Sth. Shields, Jarrow (cont.)	–	–	–	–	–	–	–	–	–	A	–	–
Newcastle — Vickers, steel, non-ferrous metals	–	–	–	–	–	–	A	A	A	A	A	Blinder
Birtley — Royal Ordnance factory	–	–	–	–	–	–	G	G	G	G	G	Backfire
Sunderland — Shpbldg, docks	–	–	–	–	G	G	G	G	G	G	G	Backfire
Durham — Phillips, steel, ind./urban	–	–	–	–	–	–	–	–	–	G	G	–
N. Tees, Seal Sands, Greatham — Oil ref., power stn (236 MW) chem. ind.	–	–	–	–	A	A	A	A	A	A	A	Backfire
Billingham — oil ref. (5000 kt/yr)	–	–	–	–	–	–	–	–	–	–	A	–
Tees Port, Redcar, Wilton — Oil ref. (with N. Tees 5200 kt/yr), oil termnl, chem. ind., steel, non-ferrous metals	–	–	–	–	A	A	A	A	A	A	A	Backfire
Barnard Castle — Chem. ind.	–	–	–	–	–	–	–	–	A	A	A	–
Eaglescliff — RN Depot (Polaris stores)	–	–	A	G	G	G	G	A	G	G	G	Backfire
Port Clarence — Port, chem. ind.	–	–	–	–	A	A	A	A	A	A	A	Badger
Stockton-on-Tees — Ind./urban, steel, Middlesbrough nrby	–	–	–	–	–	–	–	–	A	A	A	–
Aycliffe — Chem. ind. (& Bishop Auckland (steel))	–	–	–	–	–	–	–	–	A	A	A	Backfire
Darlington — Ind./urban	–	–	–	–	–	–	–	–	–	A	A	–
Tees Side Airport — Civil airport (rways 2400, 1500 m)	–	G	G	G	G	G	G	G	G	G	G	Backfire
Peterlee — Urban/ind.	–	–	–	–	–	–	–	–	–	A	A	–
Grid square SD												
Barrow-in-Furness — Nuc. sub. constr. & re-fit yard, Shpbldg, docks	–	–	G	G	G	G	G	G	G	G	G	SS11
Heysham — Nuc. power stn (AGR) (1320 MW)	–	–	–	–	G	G	G	G	G	G	G	Backfire
Blackpool Airport — Civil airport (rways 1900, 1400 m)	–	–	G	G	G	G	G	G	G	G	G	Backfire
Blackpool — Urban/ind.	–	–	–	–	–	–	–	–	–	–	A	–
Springfields — Nuc. fuel manuf. (BNFL)	–	–	G	G	G	G	G	A	G	G	G	Backfire
Fleetwood — Port, chem. ind., power stn (90 MW)	–	–	–	–	G	G	G	G	G	G	G	Backfire
Blackburn — Royal Ordnance Factory, power stn (72 MW), non-ferrous metals	–	–	–	–	–	–	A	A	A	A	A	Backfire
Chorley — Royal Ordnance Factory	–	–	–	–	–	–	A	G	A	A	A	Backfire
Preston — Fulwood Barracks, UK Army HQ (NW Dsrict), B.Ae.	–	–	A	A	A	A	A	A	A	A	A	Backfire
Bolton — Hawker Siddeley, Courtaulds	–	–	–	–	–	–	A	G	A	A	A	Backfire
Inskip — RN transmitter	–	–	–	A	A	A	A	A	A	A	A	SS20
Southport — Phillips, SRHQ, ind./urban	–	–	–	–	–	–	–	–	–	A	A	–
Wigan — B.Ae. Dynamics, Dunlop	–	–	–	–	–	–	A	–	A	A	A	–
M62/M61 — Motorway intersection	–	–	–	–	–	–	–	–	–	–	G	–
Burnley — Lucas, ind./urban	–	–	–	–	–	–	–	–	A	A	A	–
Barnoldswick — Aeroengines manuf.	–	–	–	–	–	–	–	–	A	A	A	–
Ulverston — Chem. ind.	–	–	–	–	–	–	–	–	A	A	A	–

Description	Included in attack											Weapon in H
	A	B	C	D	E	F	G	H	I	J	K	
Grid square SD — continued												
Rochdale — Ind./urban	—	—	—	—	—	—	—	—	—	A	A	—
Clitheroe — Chem. ind.	—	—	—	—	—	—	—	—	—	A	A	—
Oldham — Ind./urban	—	—	—	—	—	—	—	—	—	A	A	—
Woodvale — RAF (rways 1700, 1100, 1000 m)	—	—	G	G	G	G	G	G	G	G	G	SS20
Lancaster — Ind./urban	—	—	—	—	—	—	—	—	—	A	A	—
Skelmersdale — Ind./urban	—	—	—	—	—	—	—	—	—	A	A	—
Grid square SE												
Catterick — UK Army garrison RAF base nrby	—	—	G	G	G	G	G	G	G	G	G	SS20
Leeming — RAF & USAF (rways 2400, 1600, 1300 m)	D	D	D	D	D	D	D	D	D	D	D	SS20
Fylingdales — BMEWS, SOSUS(?)	A	A	A	A	A	A	A	D	A	A	A	SS20
Topcliffe — RAF (rways 2000, 1300, 1100 m)	—	G	G	G	G	G	G	G	G	G	G	SS20
Dishforth — RAF (rways 1900, 1400, 1400 m)	—	—	G	G	G	G	G	G	G	G	G	SS20
Linton-on-Ouse — RAF (rways 2000, 1400, 1300 m)	—	G	G	G	G	G	G	G	G	G	G	SS20
Menwith Hill — US NSA sat. control & intelligence centre	A	A	A	A	A	A	A	D	A	A	A	SS20
Forest Moor — RN receiver stn	—	—	A	A	A	A	A	—	A	A	A	—
Elvington — RAF (rway 3200 m)	—	G	G	G	G	G	G	G	G	G	G	SS20
Ferrybridge C — Power stn (2000 MW)	—	—	—	—	—	G	G	A	G	G	G	Backfire
Imphal, York — Barracks, HQ UK Army (NE Dist), Vickers nrby	—	—	A	A	A	A	A	A	A	A	A	Backfire
Drax — Power stn (1350 MW)	—	—	—	—	—	G	G	G	G	G	G	Backfire
Eggborough — Power stn (over 1000 MW)	—	—	—	—	—	G	G	G	G	G	G	Backfire
Leeds/Bradford — Civil airport (rways 1700, 1200 m)	—	—	G	G	G	G	G	G	G	G	G	Badger
Harrogate — Dunlop, ind./urban	—	—	—	—	—	—	—	—	—	A	A	—
Leeds — Royal Ordnance Factory, Vickers	—	—	—	—	—	—	A	A	A	A	A	Badger
Leeds/Pudsey — Ind./urban, steel	—	—	—	—	—	—	—	—	—	A	A	—
Huddersfield — Ind./urban, steel, power stn (56 MW)	—	—	—	—	—	—	—	—	—	A	A	—
Church Fenton — RAF (rways 1900, 1700 m)	—	—	G	G	G	G	G	G	G	G	G	SS20
Lindholme — RAF (rways 2000, 1400 m)	—	—	G	G	G	G	G	G	G	G	G	SS20
Thorpe Marsh — Power stn (1000 MW)	—	—	—	—	—	G	G	—	G	G	G	—
Doncaster — RAF HQ No. 1 group, power stn	—	—	G	G	G	G	G	G	G	G	G	SS11
Keighley — Ind./urban	—	—	—	—	—	—	—	—	—	—	A	—
Bradford — Ind./urban	—	—	—	—	—	—	—	—	—	A	A	—
Scunthorpe — Steel, chem. ind.	—	—	—	—	—	—	—	—	A	A	A	—
Castleford — Ind./urban, chem. ind. (Knottingley)	—	—	—	—	—	—	—	—	—	A	—	—
Dewsbury/Batley — Ind./urban, fertilizers	—	—	—	—	—	—	—	—	—	A	—	—
Halifax — Ind./urban	—	—	—	—	—	—	—	—	—	A	—	—
Wakefield — Ind./urban	—	—	—	—	—	—	—	—	—	A	A	—
Grid square TA												
Irton Moor — SIGINT centre	—	—	A	A	A	A	A	A	A	A	A	SS20
Staxton Wold — Radar (NADGE)	—	—	A	A	A	A	—	A	A	A		—
Humberside — Civil airport (rways 1500,1000 m)	—	—	—	G	—	—	—	—	—	—	—	—
Grimsby — Port, pharmaceuticals	—	—	—	—	G	G	G	G	G	G	G	Backfire
North Coates — RAF (rway 1400 m), air def. radar, surface-to-air missiles	—	G	G	G	G	G	G	D	G	G	G	SS20
Easington — N. Sea gas termnl	—	—	—	—	A	A	A	A	A	A	A	Backfire
Killingholme — Oil ref. (9400 kt/yr) & S. Killingholme oil ref. (6000 kt/yr), chem. ind.	—	—	—	—	A	A	A	A	A	A	A	Backfire
Immingham Dock — RN POL depot, fertilizers	—	—	G	G	G	G	G	G	G	G	G	Badger
Hull — Port, pharmaceuticals	—	—	—	—	G	G	G	G	G	G	G	Badger
Humber Bridge — Bridge (& non-ferrous metals)	—	—	—	—	—	G	G	—	G	G	G	—
Leconfield — USAF & RAF (rway 2470 m)	—	G	G	G	G	G	G	G	G	G	G	SS20
Scarborough — Ind./urban	—	—	—	—	—	—	—	—	—	—	A	—
Bridlington — Ind./urban	—	—	—	—	—	—	—	—	—	—	A	—

Description	Included in attack											Weapon in H
		A	B	C	D	E	F	G	H	I	J	K	

Grid square SH

Place	Description	A	B	C	D	E	F	G	H	I	J	K	Weapon in H
Llanbedr	RAF (rways 2500, 1500, 1450 m)	–	G	G	G	G	G	G	G	G	G	G	SS20
Transfynydd	Nuc. power stn (Magnox) (2 × 195 MW)	–	–	–	–	G	G	G	G	G	G	G	SS20
Wylfa	Nuc. power stn (Magnox) (2×460 MW)	–	–	–	–	G	G	G	G	G	G	G	SS20
Valley	RAF (rwys 2400, 1870, 1300 m)	–	D	D	D	G	G	G	G	G	G	G	SS11
Colwyn Bay	Ind./urban, non-ferrous metals	–	–	–	–	–	–	–	–	–	–	A	–

Grid square SJ

Place	Description	A	B	C	D	E	F	G	H	I	J	K	Weapon in H
Criggion	VLF radio commns with nuc. subs	–	A	A	A	A	A	A	A	A	A	A	SS20
Shawbury	RAF (rways 1900, 1400 m)	–	–	G	B	G	G	G	G	G	G	G	SS20
Capenhurst	Nuc. fuel enrichment plant	–	–	G	G	G	G	G	G	G	G	G	SS20
Chester	Ind./urban, non-ferrous metals	–	–	–	–	–	–	–	–	–	–	A	–
Crewe	Major rail junction, RR	–	–	–	–	–	G	G	G	G	G	G	SS11
Radway Green	Royal Ordnance Factory	–	–	–	–	–	–	G	A	G	G	G	SS4
Sealand	RAF maint. unit. (rway 1300 m)	–	–	–	G	–	–	–	–	–	–	–	–
Ternhill	RAF (rways 1000, 1000 m)	–	–	–	G	–	–	–	–	–	–	–	–
Rhydymwyn	Poss. central govt reserve HQ	–	G	G	G	G	G	G	G	G	G	G	SS20
Fenton	Chem. ind.	–	–	–	–	–	–	–	A	A	A	A	SS4
Eastham	Oil ref. (600 kt/yr)	–	–	–	–	A	A	A	A	A	A	A	Backfire
Shotton	Steel ind.	–	–	–	–	–	–	–	–	A	A	A	–
Ellesmere Port	Oil ref. (1500 kt/yr), chem. ind. Stanlow oil ref. (12300 kt/yr)	–	–	–	–	A	A	A	A	A	A	A	Backfire
Shrewsbury	Barracks, UK Army HQ (W. Mid. dist.)	–	–	A	A	A	A	A	G	A	A	A	SS11
Runcorn/Widnes	Mersey bridge, Fidlers Ferry power stn (1950 MW), chem. ind.	–	–	–	–	–	G	G	G	G	G	G	Backfire
Iron Bridge A & B	Power stn (1150 MW)	–	–	–	–	–	G	G	G	G	G	G	SS4
Liverpool–Birkenhead	USN termnl, port, chem. ind.	–	–	G	G	G	G	G	G	G	G	G	Backfire
Birkenhead/Port Sunlight	Port, ind./urban, power stn (197 MW)	–	–	–	–	–	–	–	–	–	–	A	–
Liverpool	Ind./urban, Plessey, drug. ind.	–	–	–	–	–	–	–	–	–	–	A	–
Speke Airport	Civil airport (rways 1900, 2 × 1500 m)	–	–	G	G	G	G	G	–	G	G	G	–
Speke Airport	Civil airport (rway 2900 m)	–	G	G	G	G	G	G	G	G	G	G	SS5
Featherstone	Royal Ordnance Factory	–	–	–	–	–	–	A	A	A	A	A	SS4
Burtonwood	Major US military stores, (prob. theatre nuc. weapons store)	G	G	K	K	K	K	K	B	K	K	K	SS4/SS11
Ringway Airport	Civil airport (rways 3000, 900 m)	–	G	K	G	G	G	G	B	G	G	G	SS4/SS5
Donnington	UK ordnance depot (occasional nuc. materials store)	–	G	G	G	G	G	G	G	G	G	G	SS20
Manchester	Patricroft Royal Ordnance Factory,	–	–	–	–	–	–	A	G	A	A	A	Backfire
	several military-related inds. (B.Ae., Hawker Siddeley, Dunlop, Ferranti, Phillips), steel, chem. ind., ind./urban	–	–	–	–	–	–	A	A	A	A	A	SS4
M6/M62	Motorway intersection	–	–	–	–	–	G	G	–	G	G	G	–
St Helens	Chem. ind., non-ferrous metals	–	–	–	–	–	–	–	–	A	A	A	–
Warrington	Chem. ind., ind./urban	–	–	–	–	–	–	–	–	A	A	A	–
Northwich	Chem. ind., ind./urban	–	–	–	–	–	–	–	–	A	A	A	–
Lostock	Chem. ind., ind./urban	–	–	–	–	–	–	–	–	A	A	A	–
Sandbach	Chem. ind., ind./urban	–	–	–	–	–	–	–	–	A	A	A	–
Macclesfield	Chem. ind., ind./urban	–	–	–	–	–	–	–	–	A	A	A	–
Stockport	Ind./urban	–	–	–	–	–	–	–	–	A	A	A	–

Description	A	B	C	D	E	F	G	H	I	J	K	Weapon in H
Grid square SJ — continued												
Kirkby — Ind./urban	—	—	—	—	—	—	—	—	—	A	A	—
Ruabon — Chem. ind., silicon	—	—	—	—	—	—	—	—	A	A	A	—
Wrexham — Ind./urban, steel	—	—	—	—	—	—	—	—	—	A	A	—
Stoke-on-Trent/ Newcastle-u-Lyme — Ind./urban, steel	—	—	—	—	—	—	—	—	—	—	A	—
Stafford — Ind./urban	—	—	—	—	—	—	—	—	—	—	A	—
Grid square SK												
Beeston — Chem. ind.	—	—	—	—	—	—	—	—	A	A	A	—
Mexborough — Heavy engineering	—	—	—	—	—	—	—	—	A	A	A	—
Rotherham — Steel, engineering, non-ferrous metals, power stn (69 MW)	—	—	—	—	—	—	—	A	A	A	A	Backfire
Sheffield — Ind./urban, chem. ind., steel	—	—	—	—	—	—	—	—	—	A	A	—
Derby — PWR for nuc. subs (RR), (& chem. ind., power stn (114 MW))	—	—	—	—	—	—	A	G	A	A	A	SS4
Nottingham — Royal Ordnance Factory, drug ind., electronics, power stns (214 MW)	—	—	—	—	—	—	A	A	A	A	A	Backfire
Ruddington — Major UK ordnance depot	—	—	G	G	G	G	G	G	G	G	G	SS11
Ratcliffe (Soare) — Power stn (2000 MW)	—	—	—	—	A	A	A	A	A	A	A	Backfire
Rugeley A & B — Power stn (1530 MW)	—	—	—	—	A	A	A	A	A	A	A	SS4
Lincoln — GEC	—	—	—	—	—	—	—	—	A	A	A	—
Newark — Electrical goods	—	—	—	—	—	—	—	—	A	A	A	—
Staveley/Bolsover — Chem. ind.	—	—	—	—	—	—	—	—	—	—	A	—
Burton-on-Trent — Ind./urban	—	—	—	—	—	—	—	—	—	—	A	—
Waddington — USAF & RAF (Vulcans, Tornados) (rway 2900 m)	D	D	D	D	D	D	D	D	D	D	D	SS20
Swinderby — RAF (rways 2000, 1400, 1300 m)	—	G	G	G	G	G	G	G	G	G	G	SS20
Bawtry — RAF strike cmnd centre	G	G	G	G	G	G	G	—	G	G	G	—
Scampton — USAF & RAF (Vulcans, Tornados) (rways 3200, 1500 m)	D	D	D	D	D	D	D	D	D	D	D	SS20
Syerston Newton — RAF (rways 1900, 1400, 1400 m)	—	G	G	G	G	G	G	G	G	G	G	SS20
Cranwell — RAF (rways 2200, 1500 m)	—	G	G	G	G	G	G	G	G	G	G	SS20
Cheadle — SIGINT centre (back-up for Cheltenham)	—	A	A	A	A	A	A	A	A	A	A	SSN5
Leicester — GEC, Dunlop, ind.	—	—	—	—	—	—	A	G	A	A	A	Backfire
Cottam — Power stn (1900 MW)	—	—	—	—	—	G	G	G	G	G	G	Backfire
High Marnham — Power stn (over 900 MW)	—	—	—	—	—	G	G	G	G	G	G	Backfire
Finningley — USAF & RAF (rway 2900 m)	D	D	D	D	D	D	D	G	D	D	D	SS20
Cottesmore — RAF (Tornados) (rways 2000, 1600, 1500 m)	—	G	G	G	G	G	G	D	G	G	G	SS20
E. Midlands Airport — Civil airport (rway 2450 m)	—	G	G	G	G	G	G	—	G	G	G	—
Mansfield — Ind./urban, steel	—	—	—	—	—	—	—	—	—	A	A	—
Mountsorrel — Aeroengines	—	—	—	—	—	—	—	—	—	A	A	—
Grid square TF												
Digby — RAF, SIGINT centre	—	—	A	A	A	A	A	A	A	A	A	SS20
Binbrook — RAF (Lightnings, Phantoms) (rway 2400 m)	—	D	G	G	G	G	G	G	G	G	G	SS20
Conningsby — RAF (Lightnings, Phantoms) (rways 3000, 1900, 1500, 1400 m)	D	D	D	D	D	D	D	G	D	D	D	SS20
Wittering — USAF & RAF (Harriers) (rway 2900 m)	—	D	D	D	D	D	D	D	D	D	D	SS20
Marham — USAF (B52), RAF (Vulcan, Victor K2) (rways 3000, 1900, 2100, 2000 m)	D	D	D	D	D	D	D	D	D	D	D	SS20
West Raynham — USAF (air def. missiles) (rway 1900 m)	—	G	G	G	G	G	G	G	G	G	G	SS20
Sculthorpe — USAF logistic support (rways 3100, 2000, 2000 m)	—	G	G	G	G	G	G	D	G	G	G	SS20

Description	A	B	C	D	E	F	G	H	I	J	K	Weapon in H
Grid square TF — continued												
Theddlethorpe — N. Sea gas termnl	–	–	–	–	A	A	A	A	A	A	A	Backfire
Watton — USAF signals/store (rway 1900 m)	–	–	G	G	G	G	G	G	G	G	G	SS19/1
Grid square TG												
Swanton Morely — RAF major depot (rway 1400 m)	–	–	G	G	G	G	G	G	G	G	G	SS20
Coltishall — USAF & RAF (Jaguar) (rway 2400 m)	G	G	G	G	G	G	G	D	G	G	G	SS20
Neatishead — RAF (air def.), radar, sector operations control	–	A	A	A	A	A	A	A	A	A	A	SS20
Norwich — Ind./urban, SRHQ, power stn (110 MW)	–	–	–	–	–	–	–	–	–	A	A	–
Horsham St Faith — Civil airport (rways 2 × 1900, 1400 m)	–	–	G	G	D	D	D	G	D	D	D	Fencer
Bacton — N. Sea gas termnl	–	–	–	–	–	G	G	G	G	G	G	Fencer
Grid square SM												
Brawdy — USN ASW (SOSUS) base	G	G	G	G	G	G	G	G	G	G	G	SS11
Brawdy — RAF (rways 2500, 1500, 1000 m)	–	G	G	G	G	G	G	G	G	G	G	SS11
Milford Haven & Angle Bay — Oil ref. (19100 kt/yr), chem. ind., oil termnl	–	–	–	–	A	A	A	A	A	A	A	SSN5
Fishguard — Oil termnl	–	–	–	–	A	A	A	–	A	A	A	–
Pembroke — Oil ref. (9000 kt/yr) pipeline, power stn (1920 MW)	–	–	–	–	A	A	A	G	A	A	A	SS4
Grid square SN												
Aberporth — RAF (rway 1000 m) missile testing	–	–	G	G	G	G	G	A	G	G	G	SS11
Clydach — Chem. ind., non-ferrous metals	–	–	–	–	–	–	–	–	–	A	A	–
Grid square SO												
Ebbw Vale — Steel, heavy ind.	–	–	–	–	–	–	–	–	A	A	A	–
Merthyr Tydfil — Ind./urban	–	–	–	–	–	–	–	–	–	A	–	–
Brecon — UK Army HQ (Wales)	–	–	G	G	G	G	G	G	G	G	G	SS11
Cheltenham — GCHQ (SIGINT centre), NSA	–	A	A	A	A	A	A	A	A	A	A	SS5
Worcester — Urban/ind.	–	–	–	–	–	–	–	–	–	A	–	–
Gloucester — Urban/ind.	–	–	–	–	–	–	–	–	–	A	–	–
Stourbridge — Urban/ind.	–	–	–	–	–	–	–	–	–	A	–	–
Clee Hill — Radar	–	–	A	A	A	A	A	–	A	A	A	–
Ashchurch — Major UK ordnance depot	–	–	A	A	A	A	A	A	A	A	A	SS4
Defford — NATO sat. commns (reserve to Oakhanger)	–	A	A	A	A	A	A	A	A	A	A	SS20
Pershore — RAF (rways 2450, 1500, 1400 m)	–	–	G	G	G	G	G	G	G	G	G	SS20
Staverton — Civil aiport	–	–	–	G	–	–	–	–	–	–	–	–
Wolverhampton — Several major MoD contractors, (Dunlop, Lucas, BL, Dowty Group, etc.), steel, tin	–	–	–	–	–	–	A	A	A	A	A	Backfire
Grid square SP												
Walsall — Non-ferrous metals, steel, power stn (195 MW), ind./urban	–	–	–	–	–	–	–	–	A	A	A	–
Birmingham Airport — Civil airport (rways 2400, 1400 m)	–	G	G	G	G	G	G	G	G	G	G	SS5
Birmingham — Major ind./urban (inc. MoD contractors), steel, non-ferrous metals, rail junction, etc.	–	–	–	–	–	–	A	A	A	A	A	Backfire
	–	–	–	–	–	–	–	G	G	G	G	Backfire
	–	–	–	–	–	–	–	–	–	A	A	–
M5/M6 — Motorway intersection	–	–	–	–	–	–	G	–	G	G	G	–
Coventry Airport — Civil airport	–	–	G	G	G	G	G	–	G	G	G	–
Coventry — RR, BL, Dunlop, non-ferrous metals, ferrous metals	–	–	–	–	–	–	A	G	A	A	A	Backfire
Rugby — VLF commns with nuc. subs	–	A	A	A	A	A	A	A	A	A	A	SS20
Rugby — Ind./urban	–	–	–	–	–	–	–	–	A	A	A	–
Barford St. John — US commns centre (annexe to Croughton)	–	A	A	A	A	A	A	A	A	A	A	SS20
Greatworth — RAF commns centre	–	–	–	G	–	–	–	–	–	–	–	–

Description	A	B	C	D	E	F	G	H	I	J	K	Weapon in H
Grid square SP — continued												
Croughton — US commns centre: AUTODIN switching centre, missile targeting (data on weather), CIA?	G	D	D	D	D	D	D	D	D	D	D	SS20
Nuneaton — Urban/ind.	–	–	–	–	–	–	–	–	–	A	A	–
Daventry — US microwave link, ballbearings	–	–	–	G	–	–	–	–	–	–	–	–
Brize Norton — USAF & RAF trnspt & dispersal base (rways 3000, 1800, 1200 m)	K	K	K	K	K	K	K	K	K	K	K	SS19/1 SS20
Upper Heyford — USAF (F111s) (rways 3800, 1600, 1500 m)	K	K	K	K	K	K	K	D	K	K	K	SS19/1
Bicester — UK ordnance depot, US store?	–	–	G	G	G	G	G	G	G	G	G	SS19/1
Wolverton — Heavy vehicles	–	–	–	–	–	–	–	–	–	A	A	–
Northampton — Ind./urban, Plessey	–	–	–	–	–	–	–	–	–	–	A	–
Bletchley — Ind./urban	–	–	–	–	–	–	–	–	–	–	A	–
Kettering — Ind./urban	–	–	–	–	–	–	–	–	–	–	A	–
Hanslope Park — Overseas commns, reserve SIGINT centre	–	–	A	A	A	A	A	A	A	A	A	Fencer
Stanbridge — RAF long-range radio	–	–	A	A	A	A	A	A	A	A	A	Fencer
Gawcott — Foreign Office commns centre	–	–	–	A	–	–	–	–	–	–	–	–
Leamington Spa — Ind./urban	–	–	–	–	–	–	–	–	–	A	A	–
Oxford — Ind./urban, BL	–	–	–	–	–	–	–	–	–	A	A	–
Cranfield — Airfield (rways 2000, 2 × 1400 m)	–	–	G	G	G	G	G	–	G	G	G	–
Grid square TL												
Thurleigh — RAE (rways 3000, 2200, 2200 m)	–	G	G	G	G	G	G	G	G	G	G	SS20
Lakenheath — USAF (F111s & B52s) (rways 3000, 2300, 2000 m)	D	D	D	D	D	D	D	D	D	D	D	SS19/1
Mildenhall — USAF (rways 3000, 1400, 1400 m), US European cmnd ('Silk Purse'), strategic air reconnaissance (U2s, TR1s), trnsprt)	D	D	D	D	D	D	D	D	D	D	D	SS19/1
Feltwell — US storage site	–	–	G	G	G	G	G	G	G	G	G	SS19/1
Hatfield — B.Ae. (rway 2000 m), Marconi	–	–	G	G	G	G	G	A	G	G	G	Fencer
Stevenage — B.Ae., GEC	–	–	–	–	–	–	A	A	A	A	A	SS4
Alconbury — USAF (rways 3600, 2000 m)	G	G	G	G	G	G	G	D	G	G	G	SS20
Upwood — USAF & RAF storage site	–	–	–	G	–	–	–	–	–	–	–	–
Molesworth — (Planned cruise missile base)	K	K	K	K	K	K	K	D	K	K	K	SS20
Cottesmore — RAF (rways 2000, 1600, 1500 m)	–	G	G	G	G	G	D	G	G	G	G	SS20
Wyton — RAF (rway 3000 m), strategic air reconnaissance, SIGINT centre	G	K	G	G	G	G	G	D	G	G	G	SS20
Waterbeach — Minor military installation	–	–	–	G	–	–	–	–	–	–	–	–
Teversham — civil airport (rway 2100 m), engineering ind. nrby	–	–	G	G	G	G	G	G	G	G	G	SS20
Brampton — CinC RAF support cmnd, joint air reconnaissance, US sat. cmmns	G	K	G	G	G	G	G	G	G	G	G	SS11
Luton Airport — Civil airport (rway 2300 m). B.Ae.	–	G	G	G	G	G	G	G	G	G	G	SS5
Chicksands — SIGINT centre, USAF electronic security cmnd for NSA, microwave link	–	A	A	A	A	A	A	A	A	A	A	SS20
Chelmsford — GEC–Marconi (missiles), ballbearings	–	–	–	–	–	–	A	A	A	A	A	Fencer
Stanstead — Civil airport (rway 3200 m)	–	G	G	G	G	G	G	G	G	G	G	SS5
Honington — RAF (Tornados, Buccaneers) (rway 2900 m)	G	G	G	G	G	G	G	G	G	G	G	SS20
Colchester — Barracks, Army HQ (E. Dist.), GEC	–	–	G	G	G	G	G	G	G	G		Blinder
Peterborough — Ind./urban	–	–	–	–	–	–	–	–	A	A	A	–
Barkway — US microwave link	–	–	A	–	–	–	–	–	–	–	–	–
Wethersfield — USAF base	D	D	D	D	D	D	D	G	D	D	D	SS20
Ridgewell — USAF store?	–	–	G	–	–	–	–	–	–	–	–	–
Dunton — Vehicles	–	–	–	–	–	–	–	–	–	A	A	–

Description	A	B	C	D	E	F	G	H	I	J	K	Weapon in H
Grid square TL — continued												
Bovingdon — US microwave link	–	–	–	A	–	–	–	–	–	–	–	–
Ware — Chem. ind., SRHQ	–	–	–	–	–	–	–	–	–	A	A	–
Whettlesford — Chem. ind.	–	–	–	–	–	–	–	–	A	A	A	–
Harlow — Urban/ind., drug ind.	–	–	–	–	–	–	–	–	–	–	A	–
Hitchin/Letchworth — Ind./urban, steel	–	–	–	–	–	–	–	–	–	–	A	–
Grid square TM												
Framlingham — USAF minor storage site	–	–	–	G	–	–	–	–	–	–	–	–
Wattisham — USAF & RAF fighter and missile air def. base (rway 2500 m)	–	G	G	G	G	G	G	G	G	G	G	SS20
Sizewell A — Nuc. power stn (Magnox) (2 × 195 MW)	–	–	–	–	G	G	G	G	G	G	G	Blinder
Bentwaters — USAF (rways 3600, 1300, 1300 m)	G	D	D	D	D	D	D	D	D	D	D	SS20
Martlesham Heath — AUTOVON switching centre (US worldwide military commns network)	–	G	G	G	G	G	G	A	G	G	G	SS20
Woodbridge — USAF (rway 3800 m)	D	D	D	D	D	D	D	D	D	D	D	SS20
Bawdsey — Air def. missile base	–	A	A	A	A	A	A	A	A	A	A	SS20
Harwich & Felixstowe — Ports	–	–	W	K	W	W	W	W	W	W	W	SS20
Bradwell — Nuc. power stn (Magnox) (2 × 150 MW)	–	–	–	–	G	G	G	G	G	G	G	SS4
Great Bromley — US microwave link	–	–	–	A	–	–	–	–	–	–	–	–
Lowestoft — Port	–	–	–	–	G	G	G	–	G	G	G	–
Ipswich — Ind./urban, fertilizers	–	–	–	–	–	–	–	–	A	A	A	–
Grid square SS												
Pontypool — Chem. ind., ind./urban	–	–	–	–	–	–	–	–	A	A	A	–
Llandarcy — Oil ref. (5500 kt/yr)	–	–	–	–	A	A	A	A	A	A	A	SS4
Swansea — Port	–	–	–	–	G	G	G	G	G	G	G	SS4
Chivenor — RAF (rway 2000 m)	–	–	G	G	G	G	G	G	G	G	G	SS20
Culmhead — SIGINT centre	–	A	A	A	A	A	A	A	A	A	A	SS20
Hartland Point — Radar	–	A	A	A	A	A	A	A	A	A	A	SS20
Burrington — Radar (civil)	–	A	A	A	A	A	A	–	A	A	A	–
Morwenstow — SIGINT centre, CIA sat. commns	–	A	A	A	A	A	A	A	A	A	A	SS20
Llanelli — Ind./urban, steel	–	–	–	–	–	–	–	–	–	A	A	–
Port Talbot — Port, ind./urban	–	–	–	–	G	G	G	–	G	G	G	–
Grid square ST												
Barry Island — Docks (prob. landing point for US reinforcements), chem. ind.	–	–	G	G	G	G	G	G	G	G	G	SS4
St Athan — RAF (rways 2000, 1100 m)	–	–	G	G	G	G	G	G	G	G	G	SS5
Cardiff — Docks, ind./urban	–	–	–	–	G	G	G	G	G	G	G	SS4
Cardiff — Royal Ordnance Factory (nuc. weapons construction)	–	G	G	G	G	G	G	A	G	G	G	SS4
Pontypridd — Ind./urban, chromium	–	–	–	–	–	–	–	–	–	A	A	–
Blackwood/Newbridge — Ind. urban	–	–	–	–	–	–	–	–	–	–	A	–
Newport — Steel works, docks, ind./urban	–	–	–	–	–	–	–	A	G	D	D	SS4
Caerwent — Major munitions store, prob. nuc. weapons store, chem. ind.	–	G	G	G	G	G	G	G	G	G	G	SS5
Berkeley — Nuc. power stn. (Magnox) (2 × 143 MW)	–	–	–	–	G	G	G	G	G	G	G	SS4
Oldbury A — Nuc. power stn (Magnox) (2 × 205 MW)	–	–	–	–	G	G	G	G	G	G	G	SS4
Severn Bridge — Bridge	–	–	–	–	–	G	G	G	G	G	G	SS4
Avonmouth — Docks, non-ferrous metals	–	–	–	–	–	G	G	G	G	G	G	SS4
Hawthorn — Prob. national govt wartime HQ, Wartime HQ UK Land Forces	G	G	G	G	G	G	G	G	G	G	G	SS19/2

	Description	A	B	C	D	E	F	G	H	I	J	K	Weapon in H
						Included in attack							
Grid square ST — continued													
Bristol	Ind./urban, chem. ind.	–	–	–	–	–	–	–	–	A	A	A	–
M4/M5	Motorway intersection	–	–	–	–	–	G	G	–	G	G	G	–
Bristol Airport	Civil airport (rways 2200, 1100 m)	–	G	G	G	G	G	G	G	G	G	G	SS5
Filton	RAF (rways 2600, 1200m), RR, B.Ae.	–	G	G	G	G	G	G	A	G	G	G	SS20
Yeovilton	RN cmnd (Fleet Air Arm)(Harriers) (rways 2400, 1500,1000 m)	–	D	D	D	D	D	D	D	D	D	D	SS20
Bridgwater	Royal Ordnance Factory	–	–	–	–	–	–	A	G	A	A	A	SS20
Hinckley Point	Nuc. power stns; A (Magnox) (2 × 230 MW), B(AGR) (2 × 660 MW)	–	–	–	–	G	G	G	G	G	G	G	SS5
Bunwell	Vickers	–	–	–	–	–	–	A	A	A	A	A	SS4
Weston-super-Mare	Westland Aircraft	–	–	–	–	–	–	A	–	A	A	A	–
Rampisham	PO commns centre (hardened)	–	–	–	G	–	–	G	G	G	G	G	SS20
Yeovil	Westland Aircraft	–	–	–	–	–	–	A	A	A	A	A	SS20
Kemble	RAF (rway 2000 m)	–	G	G	G	G	G	G	G	G	G	G	SS20
Chilmark	Prob. UK nuc. weapons store	G	G	G	K	G	G	G	G	G	G	G	SS11
Taunton	UK Army barracks, ind./urban	–	–	–	A	–	–	–	–	–	–	–	–
Chard	Westland Aircraft	–	–	–	–	–	–	A	–	A	A	A	–
Bath	Ind./urban	–	–	–	–	–	–	–	–	–	A	A	–
Grid square SU													
Lyneham	RAF trnspt & dispersal base (rways 2500, 1700, 1500 m)	–	D	D	D	D	D	D	D	D	D	D	SS20
Wroughton	RAF (rways 1500, 1200 m)	–	–	–	G	–	–	–	–	–	–	–	–
Middle Wallop	RAF (AAC) (rway 2000 m)	–	G	G	G	G	G	G	G	G	G	G	SS20
Netheravon	RAF	–	–	–	G	–	–	–	G	–	–	–	SS20
Fairford	USAF & RAF (rways 3900, 1900, 1400 m)	D	D	D	D	D	D	D	D	D	D	D	SS11/SS4
Oakhanger	UK 'Skynet' system, US sat. commns	–	A	A	A	A	A	A	A	A	A	A	SS20
Odiham	USAF & RAF (rway 1900 m)	–	D	D	D	D	D	D	D	D	D	D	SS20/SS4
Aldershot	UK Army HQ and barracks	–	–	A	A	A	A	A	A	A	A	A	SS20
Burghfield Common	UK nuc. weapons research & constr.	G	G	G	G	G	G	G	G	G	G	G	SS19/1
Bulford	UK Army HQ (SW Dist.)	–	–	G	G	G	G	G	G	G	G	G	SS20
Welford	Major USAF depot (incl. nuc. weapons)	K	K	K	K	K	K	G	K	K	K	K	SS19/1
High Wycombe	CinC UK strike cmnd (RAF) (nr Naphill)	K	K	K	K	K	K	K	K	K	K	K	SS19/1 SS11
High Wycombe	US cmnd centre (nr Daws Hill)	K	K	K	K	K	K	K	K	K	K	K	SS19/1 SS11
Greenham Common	Cruise missile base	K	K	K	K	K	K	D	K	K	K	K	SS19/1
Benson	USAF & RAF (rway 1900 m)	–	G	G	G	G	G	G	K	G	G	G	SS19/1 SS20
Abingdon	USAF & RAF (rways 2100, 1600 m)	G	G	D	D	D	D	D	K	D	D	D	SS19/1 SS20
Winkfield	US sat. tracking	–	–	–	A	–	–	–	–	–	–	–	–
Aldermaston	AWRE (nuc. weapons research & constr.)	G	G	G	G	G	G	G	G	G	G	G	SS20
Bracknell	Meterological Office	–	–	A	A	A	A	A	–	A	A	A	–
Farnborough	RAF (rways 2600, 1500, 1400 1100 m)	–	G	G	G	G	G	G	B	G	G	G	SS20
Didcot	Power stn (1840 MW)	–	–	–	–	–	G	G	G	G	G	G	SS4
Bramley	US munitions store	–	–	G	G	G	G	G	G	G	G	G	SS20
Reading	Commns, railway junction, ind./urban	–	–	–	G	–	–	–	–	G	G	G	–

Description	A	B	C	D	E	F	G	H	I	J	K	Weapon in H
Grid square SU — continued												
Boscombe Down — USAF & RAF (rways 3520, 2200, 1430 m)	D	D	D	D	D	D	D	D	D	D	D	SS20
Upavon — UK Army barracks	–	–	A	A	A	A	A	A	A	A	A	SS20
Portsmouth/Gosport — NATO & RN cmnd centre, Plessey, B.Sh., B.Ae., GEC, steel	–	G	G	G	G	G	G	G	G	G	G	SS19/1
Portsmouth/Langstone — Harbour, SRHQ, Plessey	–	–	–	–	G	G	G	G	G	G	G	SS4
Lee-on-Solent — USN, RN Fleet Air Arm	–	–	G	G	G	G	G	G	G	G	G	SS19/1
Hythe — US Marines fleet cmnd centre, Fawley oil ref., power stn (400 MW)	–	–	G	G	G	G	G	G	G	G	G	SS19/1
Marchwood — US Marines depot, power stn (450 MW)	–	–	G	G	G	G	G	A	G	G	G	SS19/1
Southampton — Ind./urban, Phillips	–	–	–	–	–	–	A	–	A	A	A	–
West Dean — Ordnance store	–	–	G	G	G	G	G	G	G	G	–	–
Wilton — UK Land Forces HQ (peacetime)	–	B	G	G	G	G	G	K	G	G	G	SS19/1 SS11
Swindon — Non-ferrous metals, Plessey	–	–	–	–	–	–	–	–	A	A	A	–
Slough — Ind./urban, steel, drug ind.	–	–	–	–	–	–	–	–	–	A	–	–
Christmas Common — US microwave link stn	–	–	–	A	–	–	–	–	–	–	–	–
Basingstoke — Urban/ind., SRHQ	–	–	–	–	–	–	–	–	–	A	A	–
Grid square TQ												
Staines — Ind./urban, gas emergency control	–	–	–	–	–	–	–	–	A	A	A	–
Guildford — Urban/ind.	–	–	–	–	–	–	–	–	–	A	–	–
Esher — Non-ferrous metals, B.Ae. nrby	–	–	–	–	–	–	–	–	–	A	–	–
Horsham — Drug ind., UKWMO sector control	–	–	–	–	–	–	–	–	–	A	–	–
Tonbridge — Ind./urban, non-ferrous metals	–	–	–	–	–	–	–	–	–	A	–	–
Stanmore — No. 11 Group air def.	–	G	G	G	G	G	G	G	G	G	G	SS11
Watford — Railway junction, RR	–	–	–	–	–	–	–	–	G	G	–	–
Northwood — Major NATO cmnd centre, RN Command, Polaris exec.	G	G	G	G	G	G	G	G	G	G	G	SS19/2
Biggin Hill — RAF (rways 2000, 1000, 900 m)	–	G	G	G	G	G	G	G	G	G	G	SS5
Heathrow — Civil airport (rways 4200, 3900, 2300 m)	–	G	G	G	G	G	D	G	G	G	G	SS19/1
West Drayton — Air def. data centre	–	A	A	A	A	A	A	–	A	A	A	–
Grosvenor Square, London — USN HQ (6th Fleet), SULSO intelligence and commns centre	G	G	G	G	G	G	G	K	G	G	G	SS19/1 SS20
Northolt — USAF & RAF commns (rway 1800, 1500m)	–	–	G	G	G	G	G	G	G	G	G	SS20
Hillingdon — US commns centre (2nd AUTOVON centre after Martlesham Heath)	–	–	A	A	A	A	A	A	A	A	A	SS20
Enfield — Royal Ordnance Factory	–	–	–	–	–	–	A	A	A	A	A	SS4
Hendon/Wembley — Ordnance depot, non-ferrous metals	–	–	A	A	A	A	A	A	A	A	A	SS4
Whitehall — UK govt (MoD, etc.)	G	G	G	G	G	G	G	K	G	G	G	SS19/1
Croydon — Railway junction	–	–	–	–	–	–	–	–	A	A	A	–
Clapham — Railway junction	–	–	–	–	–	–	–	–	G	G	G	–
City of London — Bank of England, gold reserves, financial and commercial centre	–	–	–	–	G	G	G	G	G	G	G	SS19/1
Weybridge — Plessey, B. Ae.	–	–	–	–	–	–	G	G	G	G	G	SS4
Catford — Ind./urban	–	–	–	–	–	–	–	–	–	A	A	–
Romford/Ilford — Plessey, non-ferrous metals	–	–	–	–	–	–	–	–	–	A	–	–
Kenley — RAF (rways 1100, 800 m)	–	–	–	G	–	–	–	–	–	–	–	–
Chatham — RN base, NADGE radar, docks	–	G	G	G	G	G	G	G	G	G	G	SS11
Gatwick — Civil airport (rway 2900 m)	–	D	G	G	G	G	D	D	G	G	G	SS11

Description	A	B	C	D	E	F	G	H	I	J	K	Weapon in H
Grid square TQ — continued												
Dunsfold — Airfield (rways 2350, 2 × 1430 m)	–	G	G	G	G	G	G	–	G	G	G	–
Basildon — GEC, ind./urban	–	–	–	–	–	–	–	–	A	A	A	–
Shellhaven — Oil ref. (8500 kt/yr)	–	–	–	–	A	A	A	A	A	A	A	Fencer
Coryton — Oil ref. (9500 kt/yr)												
Canvey Island — Liquefied gas storage, oil ref.												
Isle of Grain — Oil ref. (10400 kt/yr), chem. ind., steel (Sheerness)	–	–	–	–	A	A	A	A	A	A	A	Fencer
Tilbury — Docks, Tilbury A & B power stns (1548 MW), W. Thurrock power stn (1240 MW) nrby	–	–	–	–	G	G	G	G	G	G	G	Fencer
Victoria & Albert Docks, London — Power stns, switching stns	–	–	–	–	G	G	A	G	G	G	G	Fencer
West Malling — RAF (rway 1800 m)	–	–	G	G	G	G	G	G	G	G	G	SS20
Southend — Urban/ind., civil airport	–	–	–	–	–	–	–	–	–	–	A	–
Eastcote — USAF facility	–	–	–	A	–	–	–	–	–	–	–	–
Coldblow Lane — USAF microwave link stn	–	–	–	A	–	–	–	–	–	–	–	–
East Grinstead — CEGB emergency control, EMI	–	–	–	–	–	–	–	–	A	A	A	–
Gillingham — Ind./urban	–	–	–	–	–	–	–	–	A	A	A	–
Newhaven — Port	–	–	–	–	G	G	G	–	G	G	G	–
Shoreham — Docks, pharmaceuticals (Worthing)	–	–	G	G	G	G	G	G	G	G	G	SS4
Hastings — Minor port	–	–	–	–	–	–	–	–	–	–	A	–
Brighton — Non-ferrous metals	–	–	–	–	–	–	–	–	–	A	A	–
Grid square TR												
Folkestone — Port	–	–	G	G	G	G	G	G	G	G	G	SS20
Ramsgate — Port	–	–	–	–	–	–	G	–	–	–	–	SS20
Dover — Port, Swingate commns, SRHQ	–	–	G	G	G	G	G	G	G	G	G	SS20
Manston — RAF (rways 2900, 2000 m)	–	G	G	G	G	G	G	G	G	G	G	SS20
Canterbury — Urban	–	–	–	–	–	–	–	–	–	–	A	–
Dungeness — Nuc. power stns: A (Magnox) (2 × 205 MW), B (AGR) (2 × 607 MW)	–	–	–	–	G	G	G	G	G	G	G	SS20
Grid square SW												
St Mawgan — USN & RN ASW base (Nimrod) (rways 3000, 2000, 1500 m) USN & RN nuc. weapons store	G	G	D	D	D	D	D	T	D	D	D	SS20
Portreith — Air def. centre, radar	–	–	A	A	A	A	A	G	A	A	A	SS11
Grid square SX												
Exeter — Railway junction, commns link to SW	–	–	–	–	–	–	·	G	–	G	G	SS20
Plymouth — Major NATO & RN naval cmnd centre, power stn	G	G	G	G	G	G	G	G	G	G	G	SS11
Devonport — RN dockyard (hunter-killer subs re-fit)	–	G	G	G	G	G	G	B	G	G	G	SS11/SS4
Torbay — Minor port	–	–	–	–	–	–	–	–	–	–	A	–
Grid square SY												
Winfrith — UKAEA nuc. power stn (92 MW)	–	–	–	–	G	G	G	G	G	G	G	SS4
Exeter Airport — Civil airport (rways 1900, 1400 m)	–	–	G	G	G	G	G	G	G	G	G	SS20
Portland — RN base, Defence Research Establishment (incl. chem. weapons?)	–	W	W	W	W	W	W	W	W	W	W	SS11
Grid square SZ												
Poole — US Marines supply depot, power stn, docks, Plessey	–	–	G	G	G	G	G	G	G	G	G	SS4
Hurn — Bournemouth civil airport (rways 1900, 1500, 1200 m) (& B.Ae. & Westland)	–	–	G	G	G	G	G	G	G	G	G	SS4
Ventnor — Civil radar	–	–	A	A	A	A	A	–	A	A	A	–
Christchurch — Radar, commns (minor)	–	–	–	–	–	–	–	–	–	–	A	–

ABBREVIATIONS

AAC	Army Air Corps
Ace High	Over-the-horizon radar system capable of covering Soviet airspace (cf. NADGE)
ASW	anti-submarine warfare
AUTODIN	Worldwide computer link-up network for the US military
AUTOVON	Worldwide automatic phone network for the US military
AWRE	Atomic Weapons Research Establishment
B.Ae.	British Aerospace
BL	British Leyland
BMEWS	Ballistic missile early warnings system
BNFL	British Nuclear Fuels Ltd
B.Sh.	British Shipbuilders
CEGB	Central Electricity Generating Board
CIA	Central Intelligence Agency, USA
CinC	Commander-in-Chief
COMMAIR	Air Command
GCHQ	General Communications Headquarters; main UK signals intelligence centre (at Cheltenham)
kt/yr	kilotonnes per year
MoD	Ministry of Defence
Mt	megatons
MW	megawatts
NADGE	NATO Air Defence Ground Environment; system of long-range radars able to cover all Western European airspace (cf. Ace High)
NATO	North Atlantic Treaty Organisation
NSA	National Security Agency, USA
NSHEB	Northern Scotland and Hebrides Electricity Board
nuc.	nuclear
PO	post office
POL	petrol, oil and lubricants
PWR	pressurized water reactor
RAE	Royal Aircraft Establishment
RAF	Royal Air Force
RN	Royal Navy
RR	Rolls-Royce
rway	runway
sat.	satellite
SIGINT	Signals Intelligence; the reception and analysis of foreign communications and other electronic transmissions for intelligence purposes
SOSUS	Sound Surveillance System (for anti-submarine warfare)
SRHQ	Sub-Regional Headquarters; intended to be the effective level of government in the aftermath of nuclear attack
SSEB	Southern Scotland Electricity Board

UKAEA	United Kingdom Atomic Energy Authority
UKWMO	United Kingdom Warning and Monitoring Organisation
USAF	United States Air Force
USN	United States Navy
VLF	Very low frequency (radio communications)

Appendix 2

Methods for calculating thermal radiant exposure levels

Glasstone and Dolan (*Effects of Nuclear Weapons*, pp. 316–22) provide empirically-determined equations for estimating radiant exposure levels. The radiant exposure, or more explicitly the thermal energy received per unit area normal to the direction of propagation at a given distance from the explosion is

$$Q_i = 3.07fWr/D^2 \tag{1}$$

where

Q_i is the radiant exposure in calories per cm^2 for location i,
f is the proportion of the explosive energy that is converted into thermal radiation,
W is the explosive yield in kilotons,
r is the fraction of the radiation that is transmitted, and depends on atmospheric conditions, and
D is the slant distance from the explosion in miles.

Approximate values for f and r have been determined from measurements made at a large number of weapons tests. The parameter r can be expressed as an exponential function of distance from ground zero, as shown in figure 7.98 (p. 318) in Glasstone and Dolan. The parameter f is tabulated against height of burst in table 7.101 (p. 319) and can be set at 0.18 for a groundburst and 0.35 for an airburst (table 7.88, p. 313). An operational version of equation (1) takes the form

$$Q_i = 3.07fWa \; \exp(-bd_i)/(d_i^2 + h^2) \tag{2}$$

where

d_i is the distance from ground zero in miles,
h is the height of the explosion in feet, and
a, b and f are constants which depend on the height of the explosion.

Appendix 3

Method for deriving shapes and sizes of idealized fallout plumes

Glasstone and Dolan (*Effects of Nuclear Weapons*, table 9.93, p. 430) give equations for determining the major and minor axes of a series of ellipses, each representing a different unit-time reference dose-rate, as a function of energy yield of explosion. Eight reference dose-rates are given covering the range 1 to 3,000 rads/hr. This is extended by extrapolation to include 5,000, 7,000 and 9,000 rads/hr. The foci of the ellipses are adjusted to give the correct downwind distance and area upwind of ground zero (approximating the specified width at ground zero). For example, the 300 rads/hr dose-rate ellipse has a downwind distance of $7.24W^{0.45}$ km, a maximum width of $0.21W^{0.66}$ km, and a ground-zero width of $0.32W^{0.48}$ km, where W is the yield in kilotons. These dimensions assume an average effective wind speed of 24 km/hr. Corrections to the major axis can be made for other wind speeds using a correction factor given in Glasstone and Dolan, pp. 430–2. The fission fraction of 0.5 and the ground roughness factor of 0.7 are used to modify the unit-time reference dose-rates. The resulting corrected ellipse dimensions for selected yields are given in table 6.6.

The ellipses must then be oriented to the National Grid depending on wind direction. All 1 km grid-squares which contain injured or uninjured survivors of heat and blast effects are examined in order to estimate accumulated doses. It is necessary to determine between which, if any, of the ellipses each grid-square is located. A unit-time reference dose-rate is then obtained by interpolation.

Appendix 4

Modelling the build-up and radioactive decay
of fallout

The 'time of arrival' of the fallout at any chosen grid-square downwind of a groundburst, can be determined from the wind speed, allowing for the radius of the stabilized cloud (see Glasstone and Dolan, *Effects of Nuclear Weapons*, fig. 2.16, p. 34).

For modelling the processes of build-up and radioactive decay of fallout thereafter, we have followed a method due to Bentley ('Casualty assessment' pp. 8–10) in which both build-up and decay are approximated linearly. These are illustrated in fig. A4.1, in which TOA is the 'time of arrival', TOC is the 'time of completion' and TOM is the 'time of maximum' dose-rate. Bentley considers that there is evidence to suggest that the ratio of TOA to TOM may vary between 1.1 and 5. The model which he uses is based on the assumption that

$$TOM = 1.2 \ TOA$$

which is within the extreme values but allows a rapid build-up as a conservative measure. The time of completion TOC is assumed to be proportional to the build-up time. Bentley uses

$$TOC = TOM + 0.5(TOM - TOA)$$

This is a somewhat arbitrary model which lacks any interpretation in terms of the physics of the situation. (Compare for example that used by Greene et al., *London after the Bomb* Appendix 2 pp. 104–7.) But it has the virtue of simplicity, and it appears that the errors it causes are of little significance for accumulated doses measured over long periods. Once fallout is complete, the remaining accumulated dose for any period of time can be determined by interpolation from a graph given in Glasstone and Dolan, fig. 9.20, p. 395. Some grid-squares will receive doses from several bombs, in which case the accumulated doses are summed — the assumption being that all the bombs detonate within a short time of each other. The calculations are repeated for all groundbursts, so that total accumulated radiation doses can be computed for each populated grid-square, for a fixed time interval. We use a 14 day period.

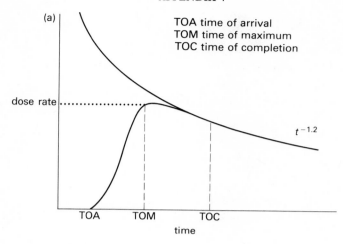

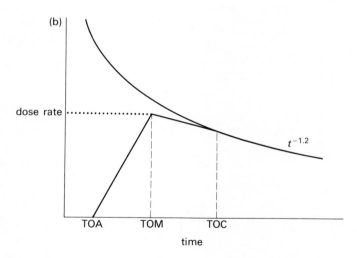

Figure A4.1 (a) Typical form of actual dose-rate build-up and decay curves; (b) Build-up and decay approximated linearly for modelling purposes.
Source: Bentley, 'Casualty assessment', fig. 6, p. 9.

Appendix 5

Casualties in Attacks A to K, by county, calculated as percentages of the pre-attack population

The tables show deaths; serious injuries; and overall casualty rate (deaths plus injuries). These results can be related to Home Defence Regions by reference to the map of figure 10.1, since the regions (or zones in Scotland) are all made up of groups of counties.

APPENDIX 5

Casualty rate

COUNTY	A	B	C	D	E	F	G	H	I	J	K
Scotland											
Borders	0.35	0.07	0.03	0.01	0.0	0.00	0.00	0.13	0.01	26.93	26.93
Central	0.00	0.87	5.83	49.47	54.81	46.39	65.50	86.88	73.40	77.72	94.82
Dumfries & Galloway	0.00	0.0	7.79	9.02	9.13	9.05	9.05	12.75	9.14	9.14	40.77
Fife	34.62	48.66	48.90	58.85	88.56	90.05	90.05	93.13	90.34	90.34	90.35
Grampian	4.47	15.75	17.88	52.30	64.13	64.69	64.69	64.32	64.85	64.85	64.89
Highland	0.00	0.11	12.88	23.72	3.65	3.66	3.66	6.45	3.70	3.70	31.01
Lothian	0.32	17.09	12.84	52.48	33.57	83.01	82.01	86.11	89.72	91.79	92.85
Strathclyde	6.08	17.88	29.90	52.41	64.84	54.23	74.04	90.11	68.60	68.60	80.98
Tayside	5.92	25.32	25.70	30.86	64.84	68.48	68.48	67.19	68.60	68.60	80.98
Islands	15.57	17.16	17.84	21.08	23.74	23.86	23.86	23.82	23.89	23.89	23.92
East Anglia											
Cambridgeshire	52.18	69.00	95.81	96.19	97.01	97.01	97.83	94.24	94.44	99.45	89.45
Norfolk	9.53	15.58	45.42	46.14	72.15	72.15	72.86	56.64	75.45	80.18	82.39
Suffolk	10.10	38.10	48.10	48.25	72.21	72.21	72.21	54.27	80.80	80.80	81.21
East Midlands											
Derbyshire	0.00	29.43	32.44	29.98	34.19	41.44	60.53	75.58	70.39	77.71	89.93
Leicestershire	8.76	15.89	30.69	18.93	31.59	35.94	88.58	83.41	88.95	91.12	92.92
Lincolnshire	34.91	56.29	55.75	57.25	61.30	67.78	68.20	68.27	76.99	77.06	77.06
Northamptonshire	18.00	24.65	47.00	48.46	48.32	54.48	54.20	64.62	61.40	59.16	97.73
Nottinghamshire	0.26	40.51	85.16	83.25	85.61	90.14	91.96	86.24	95.44	97.21	97.35
North											
Cleveland	0.03	22.04	62.06	62.02	97.42	98.69	98.75	98.41	98.83	99.05	79.15
Cumbria	0.00	21.56	38.57	41.58	53.74	70.92	70.70	71.49	79.27	99.66	79.68
Durham	0.02	21.56	27.14	27.04	30.64	32.72	45.60	74.09	74.70	84.25	85.48
Northumberland	5.35	41.15	41.84	41.43	42.81	41.72	73.66	74.39	73.71	73.73	74.12
Tyne & Wear	0.00	19.62	20.52	20.36	48.52	61.14	98.37	98.63	98.44	99.40	99.55
North West											
Cheshire	14.21	23.28	41.60	36.39	51.19	74.36	77.06	83.11	94.77	96.12	96.92
Greater Manchester	7.76	55.69	56.02	55.86	58.86	80.30	97.16	98.22	99.26	99.97	99.97
Lancashire	9.38	24.48	73.35	62.55	76.39	98.46	95.64	99.04	99.54	99.95	99.95
Merseyside	7.45	64.18	99.14	96.64	99.70	100.00	100.00	99.04	100.00	100.00	100.00
South East											
Bedfordshire	73.16	96.64	92.24	92.33	95.19	95.20	95.66	99.91	97.71	99.00	99.01
Berkshire	29.62	63.20	77.24	88.83	82.04	82.69	83.38	58.51	93.95	94.51	98.21
Buckinghamshire	50.15	69.52	87.75	91.53	91.34	91.75	91.95	87.52	93.45	98.61	99.67
East Sussex	0.00	0.00	26.30	26.30	13.70	13.70	13.20	0.26	15.96	47.95	65.83
Essex	5.77	11.63	23.06	25.20	74.95	74.95	79.34	83.77	83.60	83.68	98.18
GLC	56.93	75.53	84.18	73.12	88.49	88.01	94.77	90.60	96.38	98.54	98.41
Hampshire	0.50	26.94	73.10	73.12	82.01	82.01	85.27	84.61	85.70	89.54	92.00
Hertfordshire	94.28	93.92	97.67	98.40	99.82	99.82	99.91	99.60	99.92	89.94	99.94
Isle of Wight	0.0	0.03	26.08	26.08	26.09	26.09	26.96	12.08	26.96	26.96	27.04
Kent	53.35	21.14	33.28	37.38	42.81	42.81	42.82	44.29	48.93	50.00	67.76
Oxfordshire	1.12	62.49	74.76	79.70	75.52	83.97	83.48	89.94	88.05	99.47	89.47
Surrey	0.0	34.49	37.60	37.74	36.97	36.97	59.48	57.96	67.98	68.04	88.29
West Sussex	0.0	12.16	32.22	32.22	20.31	20.31	20.31	19.15	23.16	29.85	37.91

Casualty rate — continued

COUNTY	A	B	C	D	E	F	G	H	I	J	K
South West											
Avon	7.63	47.17	47.17	47.83	47.89	55.23	63.11	56.77	87.33	93.58	93.34
Cornwall	11.20	12.04	16.83	16.83	16.83	16.83	16.83	23.05	16.83	16.83	16.83
Devon	27.17	25.03	33.31	33.31	33.31	33.31	33.39	42.12	33.39	48.62	62.58
Dorset	71.00	15.69	42.07	42.78	47.46	47.46	48.19	72.41	48.19	48.19	74.96
Gloucestershire	71.16	83.32	83.43	83.83	97.57	97.80	97.46	96.92	97.06	97.06	98.10
Somerset	0.03	6.74	8.76	22.16	12.08	12.08	27.49	25.23	27.50	29.15	29.15
Wiltshire	33.15	44.01	49.57	67.05	54.84	58.71	58.74	85.89	76.61	78.31	78.31
West Midlands											
Hereford & Worcester	8.08	32.52	20.63	21.82	50.92	62.13	62.61	61.00	67.31	68.06	83.96
Salop	0.00	26.26	41.80	42.93	48.43	69.63	70.30	64.26	75.21	74.76	76.65
Staffordshire	0.00	24.47	19.56	20.72	33.94	62.38	92.08	95.98	96.97	96.68	99.60
Warwickshire	7.07	46.16	84.47	64.02	85.29	85.56	88.77	87.96	89.11	90.70	90.71
West Midlands	0.10	22.07	28.53	31.18	38.76	44.72	96.34	98.60	94.94	99.70	99.76
Yorkshire & Humberside											
Humberside	0.85	13.23	25.40	47.57	79.07	96.12	96.12	95.50	97.77	97.68	97.78
North Yorkshire	5.82	11.20	57.65	57.27	59.35	77.41	77.45	79.33	81.74	81.91	92.74
South Yorkshire	4.61	6.79	16.84	16.01	17.23	19.42	21.11	90.53	92.95	97.36	98.44
West Yorkshire	0.00	0.47	16.21	16.34	17.79	26.61	60.87	61.15	64.82	99.02	99.90
Wales											
Clwyd	0.00	15.73	17.82	7.97	20.29	20.29	20.29	10.09	52.62	60.12	71.68
Dyfed	1.69	32.48	11.51	1.51	25.40	25.40	25.40	28.05	27.85	50.11	50.11
Gwent	0.00	36.23	13.43	13.43	56.42	56.42	56.42	92.37	95.22	98.29	0.83
Gwynedd	0.00	7.09	6.89	8.89	10.40	10.40	10.40	10.68	10.46	10.40	24.56
Mid Glamorgan	0.00	13.56	8.45	6.45	11.47	11.47	11.47	48.73	18.40	63.07	74.24
Powys	0.00	8.66	10.83	10.83	27.00	27.00	27.00	30.51	53.05	54.11	56.14
South Glamorgan	0.00	65.61	61.97	61.97	65.71	95.71	95.71	99.56	85.71	92.81	96.81
West Glamorgan	0.00	0.00	0.00	0.00	87.69	87.69	87.69	84.32	87.74	92.98	93.18

Seriously injured

COUNTY	A	B	C	D	E	F	G	H	I	J	K
Scotland											
Borders	0.00	0.00	0.00	0.01	0.00	0.00	0.00	0.13	0.01	8.13	8.13
Central	0.33	0.79	2.91	5.09	23.11	20.44	20.25	2.07	0.05	18.20	12.20
Dumfries & Galloway	0.00	0.00	0.72	1.87	1.95	1.95	1.95	1.89	1.95	1.95	6.51
Fife	4.10	8.42	8.46	10.39	20.53	19.95	19.95	21.62	18.97	18.97	18.97
Grampian	2.04	4.58	8.04	12.87	6.11	6.02	6.02	6.03	5.97	5.98	5.97
Highland	0.00	0.98	0.98	4.87	1.22	1.22	1.27	3.67	1.27	1.27	4.50
Lothian	0.32	10.56	10.51	22.60	16.88	14.20	14.25	13.15	8.37	8.37	8.37
Strathclyde	2.68	13.53	16.74	13.00	8.03	20.57	15.37	13.75	8.39	3.39	3.11
Tayside	2.36	11.50	11.48	13.00	3.95	25.42	15.37	7.31	5.43	5.43	4.11
Islands	6.27	7.42	7.45	7.48	12.01	12.02	12.02	11.55	12.02	12.02	12.03
East Anglia											
Cambridgeshire	28.66	27.30	21.09	20.15	19.11	19.10	18.61	27.84	6.33	6.31	6.31
Norfolk	4.26	8.26	21.96	20.68	22.86	22.86	23.35	16.52	24.69	24.44	24.73
Suffolk	3.18	15.54	13.84	14.31	17.29	17.29	17.29	20.57	6.06	6.06	6.17
East Midlands											
Derbyshire	0.00	20.20	21.75	20.43	22.83	24.82	12.59	18.90	16.92	16.23	9.54
Leicestershire	8.72	25.88	12.61	11.35	13.17	15.48	10.43	13.87	10.18	5.64	6.84
Lincolnshire	17.11	25.77	26.55	27.27	23.05	27.99	28.43	34.18	33.53	23.85	23.85
Northamptonshire	8.10	12.21	26.61	26.55	27.74	29.90	29.82	34.98	33.53	34.44	34.44
Nottinghamshire	0.24	17.20	16.25	16.32	14.14	14.06	10.02	9.66	9.39	4.31	4.25
North											
Cleveland	0.03	7.09	12.96	12.96	2.71	1.61	1.49	2.16	1.40	1.43	1.32
Cumbria	0.02	0.00	11.19	12.40	0.92	13.28	13.29	11.98	0.39	9.21	9.23
Durham	3.09	11.00	12.08	12.07	10.20	11.20	16.20	16.98	15.51	6.79	7.00
Northumberland	3.09	14.79	14.88	14.88	15.16	4.38	16.73	3.21	12.74	2.75	2.92
Tyne & Wear	0.00	9.82	10.44	10.45	15.98	20.51	2.24	2.00	2.20	1.22	1.02
North West											
Cheshire	4.87	9.22	14.06	12.23	15.13	12.21	11.19	16.75	4.88	4.88	3.44
Greater Manchester	2.04	14.55	14.52	13.76	15.40	18.22	15.79	2.55	2.08	4.07	0.06
Lancashire	6.80	16.85	11.48	10.88	7.93	12.35	8.24	4.25	1.49	0.16	0.13
Merseyside	4.01	22.46	3.20	5.57	2.03	0.89	0.89	1.61	0.89	0.06	0.04
South East											
Bedfordshire	38.10	16.39	15.44	15.45	16.54	16.54	16.60	15.32	17.06	14.20	14.09
Berkshire	9.78	24.19	22.46	16.99	22.12	22.02	21.54	26.90	8.94	8.70	4.10
Buckinghamshire	17.00	20.64	23.80	20.61	26.05	24.02	24.10	6.24	13.76	5.00	5.70
East Sussex	2.93	6.96	9.82	8.32	1.15	1.15	8.00	10.70	6.65	6.23	6.92
Essex	12.47	17.39	13.36	11.64	13.15	13.15	11.58	10.58	11.18	11.22	10.12
GLC	0.31	10.01	13.12	10.12	7.89	7.89	15.38	9.71	14.59	14.12	3.24
Hampshire	4.16	8.50	15.58	17.28	7.14	7.14	7.15	1.71	7.15	5.16	5.72
Hertfordshire	0.00	0.03	15.29	17.68	17.89	2.188	7.247	1.65	17.87	1.07	1.02
Isle of Wight	0.00	3.95	4.58	17.28	15.22	17.22	17.22	1.71	17.87	17.87	17.88
Kent	20.77	20.01	25.02	6.22	25.37	12.73	12.73	10.16	7.87	8.50	13.91
Oxfordshire	1.11	0.75	28.89	23.86	28.17	8.17	8.17	10.81	9.81	13.50	10.07
Surrey	0.00	20.01	4.58	10.09	4.39	4.39	4.39	10.06	13.50	13.50	13.35
West Sussex	0.00	1.16	10.09	10.09	4.39	4.39	4.39	5.45	6.07	8.47	9.35

Seriously injured — continued

COUNTY	A	B	C	D	E	F	G	H	I	J	K
South West											
Avon	6.35	18.48	18.48	18.60	18.02	20.37	21.19	18.52	11.43	7.62	7.53
Cornwall	3.52	2.80	3.07	3.07	3.07	3.07	3.07	6.83	3.07	3.07	3.07
Devon	2.44	3.59	4.77	4.77	4.77	4.77	4.77	5.81	4.77	4.98	7.99
Dorset	0.00	2.31	15.80	16.09	17.32	17.32	17.62	11.82	17.62	17.62	18.94
Gloucestershire	22.74	11.09	11.11	10.93	7.78	7.19	6.92	6.63	6.90	6.90	3.96
Somerset	0.03	4.46	6.05	7.32	8.60	8.60	6.97	8.42	9.08	11.63	11.63
Wiltshire	15.57	17.40	17.77	17.68	20.06	22.18	22.19	11.26	13.14	12.92	12.92
West Midlands											
Hereford & Worcester	6.85	14.85	11.47	12.55	34.13	35.77	35.97	34.85	40.46	34.40	16.71
Salop	0.00	10.46	13.17	13.94	11.77	12.88	12.64	8.59	14.12	14.26	13.73
Staffordshire	0.00	14.51	12.78	13.82	21.24	30.08	12.85	4.55	14.05	3.85	10.23
Warwickshire	6.88	11.19	12.66	16.53	21.88	12.92	10.15	12.58	8.85	9.11	9.03
West Midlands	0.10	10.36	13.70	16.93	22.97	28.75	6.01	1.94	9.25	1.98	0.36
Yorkshire & Humberside											
Humberside	0.81	8.21	14.64	21.79	9.12	5.69	5.68	9.62	4.43	4.45	3.66
North Yorkshire	4.28	8.29	13.25	12.93	13.76	16.01	17.26	19.59	17.64	12.06	10.05
South Yorkshire	2.48	3.54	3.98	3.64	4.29	2.94	4.60	11.55	8.91	4.65	2.73
West Yorkshire	0.00	0.41	9.11	9.15	9.26	12.08	14.99	14.41	15.30	3.66	0.60
Wales											
Clwyd	0.00	5.02	5.72	4.88	5.81	5.81	5.81	6.30	13.76	4.42	7.54
Dyfed	0.71	1.07	0.51	0.51	5.86	5.86	5.86	7.24	8.04	12.20	12.20
Gwent	0.00	11.78	5.72	5.72	23.55	23.54	23.54	10.73	7.62	4.83	1.27
Gwynedd	0.00	2.90	2.98	2.98	3.11	3.11	4.38	3.13	3.11	3.11	8.07
Mid Glamorgan	0.00	2.82	2.89	2.89	4.38	4.38	4.38	10.43	10.43	20.52	15.31
Powys	0.00	6.73	3.21	3.21	6.33	6.33	6.33	10.58	7.96	7.76	6.46
South Glamorgan	0.00	13.65	16.32	16.32	2.94	2.94	2.94	10.48	2.94	2.46	2.44
West Glamorgan	0.00	0.00	0.00	0.00	8.86	8.86	8.86	11.59	8.91	7.19	7.37

Deaths

COUNTY	A	B	C	D	E	F	G	H	I	J	K
Scotland	0.00	0.00	0.00	0.00	0.00	0.00	0.00	0.00	0.00	18.80	18.80
Borders	0.00	0.00	2.82	0.38	31.70	44.96	45.25	64.81	54.10	59.52	59.52
Central	0.00	0.00	6.87	7.15	7.09	7.10	7.10	10.86	7.19	7.19	34.62
Dumfries & Galloway	26.52	40.44	40.44	48.46	48.03	70.02	70.10	70.51	71.37	71.37	71.38
Fife	28.42	11.17	1.91	39.43	58.03	58.07	58.67	58.29	58.88	71.88	58.29
Grampian	0.00	0.01	1.91	18.85	2.43	2.43	2.43	2.61	2.43	2.43	26.50
Highland	3.40	7.135	7.14	22.78	54.54	67.66	67.81	73.30	83.34	83.73	83.73
Lothian	3.56	5.135	22.96	22.78	25.54	33.66	59.19	83.36	84.34	88.73	89.74
Strathclyde	6.30	13.82	14.22	17.86	25.89	63.11	63.11	59.89	63.17	63.17	76.87
Tayside		9.74	10.39	13.60	11.73	11.84	11.84	12.27	11.87	11.87	11.89
Islands											
East Anglia											
Cambridgeshire	23.52	41.69	74.72	76.05	77.91	77.91	79.22	66.40	93.11	93.14	93.14
Norfolk	5.27	27.32	23.46	23.47	49.30	49.30	49.51	40.12	50.76	55.74	57.66
Suffolk	6.91	22.57	34.26	33.95	54.91	54.91	54.91	33.70	74.74	74.74	75.04
East Midlands											
Derbyshire	0.00	9.23	10.69	9.55	11.35	16.63	47.93	56.69	53.47	61.48	80.39
Leicestershire	0.03	7.01	18.08	7.58	18.42	20.25	78.46	59.54	78.82	85.49	86.28
Lincolnshire	17.80	36.52	29.00	29.98	33.24	39.00	40.29	42.09	53.01	53.21	53.21
Northamptonshire	9.91	12.43	20.39	29.91	29.58	24.67	24.68	29.64	27.88	24.72	90.85
Nottinghamshire	0.03	23.31	68.91	66.92	69.47	76.07	61.94	76.58	86.05	92.90	93.10
North											
Cleveland	0.00	14.95	49.10	49.06	94.71	97.08	97.25	96.25	97.44	97.62	97.83
Cumbria	0.00	10.56	27.88	36.18	42.78	57.63	57.63	59.51	69.88	70.45	70.45
Durham	2.53	26.35	15.06	14.97	20.44	21.83	29.38	57.91	59.19	70.45	78.49
Northumberland	0.00	9.80	10.08	26.55	27.65	67.34	70.92	70.98	70.90	70.45	71.20
Tyne & Wear				26.90	32.54	40.23	96.13	96.63	96.25	98.18	98.53
North West											
Cheshire	9.34	14.06	27.54	24.16	36.06	62.15	65.87	66.36	89.88	91.64	93.48
Greater Manchester	5.72	41.14	41.49	42.10	44.45	61.58	91.38	95.67	97.17	99.90	99.92
Lancashire	2.56	7.63	65.94	51.68	68.46	71.10	87.40	94.91	99.06	99.79	99.26
Merseyside	3.44	41.72	65.94	91.07	97.67	99.10	99.11	97.43	99.11	99.94	—
South East											
Bedfordshire	35.07	80.25	76.80	76.88	78.65	78.65	79.05	84.59	80.65	84.80	84.92
Berkshire	20.84	39.01	55.15	71.84	69.78	60.79	61.45	32.19	85.01	85.81	94.11
Buckinghamshire	33.15	48.90	64.18	70.92	69.59	69.73	78.55	67.62	83.70	89.11	93.07
East Sussex	30.30	4.67	17.93	17.93	8.59	8.81	8.59	0.02	83.31	41.72	58.92
Essex	2.84	58.14	70.81	13.91	61.80	61.80	68.06	85.41	72.42	72.86	76.07
GLC	44.19	16.93	62.99	74.82	74.87	74.87	89.55	74.90	72.78	72.86	95.17
Hampshire	20.12	85.41	64.08	63.09	97.87	97.87	78.55	97.89	78.55	84.38	86.28
Hertfordshire	90.12	0.00	8.80	9.80	8.81	98.21	98.66	1.39	98.82	98.93	98.93
Isle of Wight	0.00	17.19	8.80	56.48	30.59	35.59	9.10	34.11	9.10	9.10	9.15
Kent	0.00	42.68	49.74	28.87	50.15	71.00	35.59	78.88	41.16	41.49	54.45
Oxfordshire	32.57	25.74	28.71	28.80	28.80	28.80	71.00	47.15	54.48	79.39	79.39
Surrey	0.01	10.99	22.13	22.13	15.92	15.92	47.19	13.71	54.48	54.54	74.91
West Sussex	0.00						15.92		17.09	21.37	28.57

Deaths — continued

COUNTY	A	B	C	D	E	F	G	H	I	J	K
South West											
Avon	1.28	28.69	28.69	29.23	29.87	34.86	41.93	38.26	75.90	85.96	85.81
Cornwall	7.68	9.23	13.76	13.76	13.76	13.76	13.76	16.21	13.76	13.76	13.76
Devon	24.73	21.44	28.27	28.69	28.54	28.54	28.63	36.31	28.63	41.64	54.60
Dorset	48.00	13.32	26.27	26.69	30.14	30.14	30.58	60.59	30.58	30.58	56.02
Gloucestershire	48.42	72.22	72.33	89.89	89.79	90.61	91.03	92.28	91.06	91.06	94.14
Somerset	0.00	2.28	2.72	14.83	3.49	3.49	17.52	16.81	17.52	17.52	17.52
Wiltshire	17.58	26.61	31.80	49.37	34.78	36.52	36.55	74.63	63.46	65.39	65.39
West Midlands											
Hereford & Worcester	1.23	17.67	9.15	9.27	16.79	26.36	26.64	26.16	26.85	33.67	67.25
Salop	0.00	15.80	28.63	28.99	36.66	36.75	57.66	55.67	61.09	60.50	64.92
Staffordshire	0.00	9.96	6.79	6.90	32.70	32.30	79.24	91.43	92.91	92.83	98.67
Warwickshire	0.18	34.97	71.81	47.49	72.41	72.64	79.62	75.38	80.26	81.00	81.68
West Midlands	0.00	11.71	14.83	14.25	15.79	15.97	90.23	96.66	85.69	97.72	99.39
Yorkshire & Humberside											
Humberside	0.05	5.02	10.76	25.78	69.95	90.43	90.44	85.88	93.34	93.23	94.12
North Yorkshire	1.54	4.91	44.39	44.44	45.58	61.40	62.19	59.75	64.05	78.74	82.69
South Yorkshire	2.13	3.25	12.86	12.37	12.93	12.48	16.51	78.98	88.05	92.71	95.71
West Yorkshire	0.00	0.06	12.11	17.19	18.53	14.53	45.89	46.75	49.52	95.36	99.30
Wales											
Clwyd	0.00	10.71	12.10	3.08	14.48	14.48	14.48	3.79	38.87	55.70	64.14
Dyfed	0.98	21.41	21.41	11.00	19.54	19.54	19.44	20.84	19.82	37.90	37.90
Gwent	0.00	24.45	7.71	7.71	32.87	32.88	32.88	81.64	87.60	93.45	98.16
Gwynedd	0.00	4.19	3.91	3.11	7.29	7.29	7.29	7.55	7.26	42.50	16.48
Mid Glamorgan	0.00	10.74	5.55	5.55	7.00	7.00	7.00	37.88	38.00	46.34	58.93
Powys	0.00	1.94	5.65	5.62	2.67	2.67	2.67	10.07	40.08	49.35	49.68
South Glamorgan	0.00	51.94	45.65	45.65	22.77	92.77	92.87	99.07	92.77	94.35	94.37
West Glamorgan	0.00	0.00	0.00	0.00	78.83	78.83	78.83	72.73	78.83	85.79	85.81

Appendix 6

Approximations of Home Office blast casualty rates used in the authors' replica of the Home Office computer model

The data are approximated from curves given in 'Exercise ARC' (see figure 9.1), and from values incorporated in the Home Office 'Weapons effects computers' issued to civil defence workers. The chosen overpressure ranges are defined so as to achieve the best fit to the 'Exercise ARC' curves in each case. Those counted as 'trapped' are assumed to be killed.

Airbursts

Overpressure range (psi)	% killed	% seriously injured
Greater than 10.2	60	6.1
8.0 to 10.2	49	7
5.7 to 8.0	41.5	7
3.8 to 5.7	9	5.5
1.5 to 3.8	0	2

Groundbursts of yields 0.2 megatons and below

Overpressure range (psi)	% killed	% seriously injured
Greater than 25.5	99	0.3
6.4 to 25.5	55	6.5
2.9 to 6.4	7	5
1.6 to 2.9	0	1.2

Groundbursts of yields 0.5 megatons and above

Overpressure range (psi)	% killed	% seriously injured
Greater than 58.0	100	0
10.3 to 58.0	85.5	3.8
6.4 to 10.3	49	7
3.6 to 6.4	11.5	6
2.4 to 3.6	0	3.2
1.6 to 2.4	0	0.6

Notes

CHAPTER 1   INTRODUCTION

1 A. Haines, 'Possible consequences of a nuclear attack on London' in E. Chivian, S. Chivian, R. J. Lifton and J. E. Mack (eds), *Last Aid*, Freeman, San Francisco 1983, pp. 163–72; A. Qasrawi, F. Wellhoefer, F. Steward, *Ground Zero: The Short-term Effects of a Nuclear Attack on the West Midlands*, Scientists against Nuclear Arms, Milton Keynes 1982.
2 O. Greene, B. Rubin, N. Turok, P. Webber, G. Wilkinson, *London after the Bomb*, Oxford University Press, Oxford 1982.
3 M. Clarke, *The Nuclear Destruction of Britain*, Croom Helm, London 1982; P. Goodwin, *Nuclear War: The Facts on Our Survival*, Ash and Grant, London 1981.
4 S. F. J. Butler, 'Scientific advice in home defence' in F. Barnaby and G. Thomas (eds), *The Nuclear Arms Race – Control or Catastrophe?* Frances Pinter, London 1982, pp. 135–63.
5 P. R. Bentley, 'Blast overpressure and fallout radiation dose models for casualty assessment and other purposes', Home Office Scientific Research and Development Branch, London April 1981; revised December 1981.
6 Butler, 'Scientific advice'.
7 S. Glasstone and P. J. Dolan (eds), *The Effects of Nuclear Weapons*, US Department of Defense and US Department of Energy, 3rd edn 1977; published in UK by Castle House, Tunbridge Wells 1980.
8 S. Openshaw and P. Steadman, 'On the geography of a worst case nuclear attack on the population of Britain', *Political Geography Quarterly* 1, 1982, pp. 263–78; S. Openshaw and P. Steadman, 'Predicting the consequences of a nuclear attack on Britain: models, results, and implications for public policy', *Environment and Planning C: Government and Policy* 1, 1983 pp. 205–28; P. Steadman, 'The bomb: worse than government admits', *New Scientist* 90, 1981 , pp. 769–71.
9 British Medical Association (BMA) Board of Science and Education, *The Medical Effects of Nuclear War*, Wiley, Chichester 1983.
10 Ibid., p. 121.
11 *The Times*, 7 March 1983.
12 Home Office and Central Office of Information, *Protect and Survive*, HMSO, London 1980.
13 *The Times*, 7 March 1983.

CHAPTER 2   NUCLEAR STRATEGIES

1 Formalized by President Nixon in *National Security Decision Memorandum* 242 (NSDM 242) 17 January 1974.
2 Harold Brown, Convocation speech, 97th Naval War College Class, Rhode Island, 20 August 1980.
3 Robert McNamara, University of Michigan, Ann Arbor, 16 June 1967.
4 The SIOP target list has grown steadily, from about 70 targets in 1949 to about 40,000 in the SIOP-5 plan, which was introduced in 1976. SIOP-5 included over 15,000 industrial and economic targerts and more than 20,000 military targets. This was superseded in 1982 by SIOP-6, which provides more limited attack options and improved retargeting and attack assessment facilities. it is not known whether it also includes more targets than SIOP-5. See P. Rogers and W. Arkin, *Bulletin of the Atomic Scientists*, April 1983, p. 9; D. Ball, 'Déjà vu: the return to counterforce in the Nixon administration' in R. O'Neill (ed.), *The Strategic Nuclear Balance: An Australian Perspective*, Australian National University, Canberra 1975; D. Ball, 'US strategic forces: how would they be used?', *International Security* 7(3), 1982/83, pp. 31–60.
5 As outlined by Brown, Convocation speech.
6 R. Scheer, *With Enough Shovels: Reagan, Bush and Nuclear War*, Secker and Warburg, London 1982, p. 10.
7 C. Weinberger, US Secretary of Defense, *New York Times*, 30 May 1982; quoted in A. Suddaby, *American Nuclear Issues*, Longmans, London 1982, p. 17.
8 US Department of Defense, *Fiscal Year 1984–88 Defense Guidance;* quoted in Suddaby, *American Nuclear Issues*, p. 17.
9 J. Schlesinger quoted in A. Suddaby, *Deterrence and Defence in Nuclear War*, Longmans, London 1982, p. 12.
10 Scheer, *With Enough Shovels*, p. 12.
11 Brown, Convocation speech.
12 H. Kissinger, 'NATO: The Next Thirty Years', Brussels 1 September 1979, an edited text reproduced in *Survival* 21(6), 1979, pp. 264–8.
13 J. Snyder, *The Soviet Strategic Culture: Implications for Limited Nuclear Operations*, R-2154-AF, Rand Corporation, Santa Monica, September 1977.
14 Major General V. Zemskov in J. D. Douglass, Jr, and A. M. Hoeber (eds), 'Selected Readings from Military Thought 1963–73', *Studies in Communist Affairs*, vol. 5, part II, United States Air Force, US Government Printing Office, Washington, DC 20402, n.d., p. 53; see also p. 48.
15 L. I. Brezhnev, 'Reply to the Japanese writers' in *Press Bulletin*, Permanent Mission of the Soviet Union, Geneva, 1 March 1982; quoted in D. Frei, *Risks of Unintentional Nuclear War*, Croom Helm, London 1983, p. 69. See also L. I. Brezhnev, *The Guardian*, 30 August 1980; quoted in D. Ball, *Can Nuclear War be Controlled?*, Adelphi Paper 169, International Institute for Strategic Studies, London 1981.
16 G. A. Arbatov, Director of the Institute of US and Canadian Studies of the Soviet Academy of Sciences, in *Survival* 16(3), 1974, pp. 133–4.
17 D. F. Ustinov, Soviet Minister of Defence, *Against the Arms Race and the*

Threat of War, Novosti, Moscow 1980. See also G. A. Arbatov, 'The strategy of nuclear madness', *Coexistence* 18(2), pp. 162–4, quoted in Frei, *Risks of Unintentional Nuclear War*, p. 94; L. I. Brezhnev, *Pravda* 21 October 1981, quoted in Frei, *Risks of Unintentional Nuclear War*, p. 94.

18 D. F. Ustinov, quoted in Frei, *Risks of Unintentional Nuclear War*, p. 94.

19 A. Grigoryants, *Izvestia*, 2 February 1974; quoted in B. J. Lambeth, *Selective Nuclear Operations and Soviet Strategy*, Paper P5502, Rand Corporation, Santa Monica 1975, p. 12.

20 G. Trofimento, 'Problems of peace and security in Soviet-American relations', *SShA: Ekonomika, Politika, Ideologika*, 9 September 1974; see Lambeth, *Selective Nuclear Operations*, p. 12.

21 *Soviet Military Thought* (Translation of 'Officers' Library' series of seventeen books, 1964 to 1972), United States Air Force, 1973.

22 Marshal V. D. Sokolvsky et al., *Soviet Military Strategy*, Prentice-Hall, Englewood Cliffs NJ 1962.

23 A. A. Sidorenko, *The Offensive: Characteristic Features of the Offensive in a Nuclear War*, published as *The Basic Offensive (A Soviet View)* in the series *Soviet Military Thought* No. 1, United States Air Force 1973; V. Ye. Savkin, *Basic Principles of Operational Art and Tactics (A Soviet View)* in *Soviet Military Thought* No. 4, United States Air Force 1974. There are a number of other important Soviet military books in the USAF translation series; see J. D. Douglass Jr, *Soviet Military Strategy in Europe*, Pergamon, Oxford 1980, preface, note 5.

24 J. D. Douglass Jr and A. M. Hoeber (eds), 'Selected readings from Military Thought 1963–73', *Studies in Communist Affairs* vol. 5 parts I and II, United States Air Force, US Government Printing Office, Washington DC 20402, n.d.

25 See for instance the prepared statement of the Soviet delegation, SALT negotiations, 18 November 1969; quoted in R. Garthoff, 'Mutual deterrence and strategic arms', *International Security* 3(1), 1978, p. 126. See also N. I. Krylov, Commander-in-Chief, Strategic Missile Forces, quoted in Garthoff, ibid., p. 127.

26 General N. A. Talenskii, 'The late war: some reflections', *Mezhdunarodnaya zhizn (International Affairs)*, 5 May 1965, p. 23; quoted in Snyder, *Soviet Strategic Culture*. See also B. J. Lambeth, *Risk and Uncertainty in Soviet Deliberations about War*, R-2687-AF, Rand Corporation, Santa Monica 1981, p. 2.

27 See, for instance, T. Wolfe, *The SALT Experience*, Ballinger, Boston 1979, p. 111ff.

28 B. J. Lambeth, 'Uncertainties for the Soviet war planner', *International Security* 7(3), 1982/83, p. 141.

29 See, for example, L. I. Brezhnev, *Pravda* 14 June 1975; quoted in Garthoff, 'Mutual Deterrence', p. 139.

30 J. Erickson, 'The Soviet view of deterrence: a general survey', *Survival* 24(6), 1980, p. 244.

31 Marshal Moskalenko quoted in Ball, *Can Nuclear War be Controlled?*, p. 31.

32 N. A. Lomov (ed.), *Scientific-Technical Progress and the Revolution in Military Affairs (A Soviet View)* in *Soviet Military Thought* No. 3, United States Air Force 1974, p. 147 (our emphasis).

33 B. Byely (ed.), *Marxism-Leninism on War and Army (A Soviet View)* in *Soviet Military Thought* No. 2, United States Air Force 1974, pp. 9–10; quoted in Ball, *Can Nuclear War be Controlled?*, p. 31 (our emphasis).

34 Marshall N. I. Krylov, 'The nuclear missile shield', *Voyennaya Mysl'* 11 November 1967, p. 20; quoted in Garthoff, 'Mutual deterrence', p. 127.

35 Erickson, 'The Soviet view of deterrence', p. 244.

36 Savkin, *Basic Principles of Operational Art*, P. 173; quoted in Clarke, *Nuclear Destruction of Britain*, p. 120. See also Colonel M. Shirikov quoted in Ball, *Can Nuclear War be Controlled?*, p. 31.

37 Marshal A. A. Grechko, *The Armed Forces of the Soviet State (A Soviet View)* in *Soviet Military Thought* No. 12, United States Air Force 1977; quoted in Ball, *Can Nuclear War be Controlled?*, p. 31.

38 Major General V. Zemskov, *Voyennaya mysl'* 7 July 1969, translated in *Studies in Communist Affairs* vol. 5, part II, p. 49. See also Sidorenko, *The Offensive*, pp. 89 and 111; quoted in Douglass *Soviet Military Strategy in Europe*, pp. 70 and 28.

39 Savkin, *Basic Principles of Operational Art*, p. 126; quoted in Clarke, *Nuclear Destruction of Britain*, p. 111.

40 S. S. Lototskii, *Armya Sovetskaya*, 1969; quoted in Clarke, *Nuclear Destruction of Britain*, p. 111.

41 Major General V. Reznichenko, *Taktika [Tactics]*, Voyenizdat, Moscow 1966, quoted in Douglass, *Soviet Military Strategy in Europe*, p. 72; see also Sokolovsky, *Soviet Military Strategy*, pp. 291–2.

42 I. M. Nikishin and B. A. Veudensky, *Long Distance Movement of Small Units*, Moscow 1967 (translation US Army OACS(1), No. J-8454, 1970); quoted in Douglass, *Soviet Military Strategy in Europe*, p. 90.

43 'The task, important for all' (editorial), *Voyennyi Vestnik* (Military Herald), 6 June 1967 [translated H. F. Scott]; quoted in Douglass, *Soviet Military Strategy in Europe*, p. 83.

44 Sidorenko, *The Offensive*, p. 61; quoted in Douglass, Soviet Military Strategy in Europe, p. 83.

45 Sidorenko, *The Offensive*, p. 114.

46 Lambeth, *Selective Nuclear Operations*, pp. 9–10.

47 See, for instance, J. Erickson, *Soviet Military Power*, Royal United Services Institute, London 1971, p. 68.

48 Ball, *Can Nuclear War be Controlled?*, p. 34.

49 Lambeth, *Selective Nuclear Operations*, p. 10.

50 Ibid., p. 10.

51 Ibid., p. 20.

52 See, for instance, L. Goure, F. D. Kohler, M. L. Harvey, *The Role of Nuclear Forces in Current Soviet Strategy*, Center for Advanced International Studies, University of Miami 1974, pp. 107–10.

53 For a more detailed discussion see Snyder, *Soviet Strategic Culture*, p. 32ff.

54 A. Enthoven and W. Smith, *How Much is Enough? Shaping the Defense Program 1961–69*, Harper and Row, New York 1971; quoted in Snyder, *Soviet Strategic Culture*, p. 32. See also Ball, *Can Nuclear War be Controlled?*, p. 34.

55 Stockholm International Peace Research Institute, *World Armaments and Disarmament, SIPRI Yearbook 1983*, Taylor and Francis, London 1983, pp. 48, 49.

56 Ibid., p. 46.

CHAPTER 3   POSSIBLE NUCLEAR WARS

1 Home Office Scientific Advisory Branch, *Training Manual for Scientific Advisers*, Home Office, London 1977, paras 1.20 and 1.14, n.p.
2 Lord Renton (President), N. Thorne MP (Chair), Lord Mottistone (Vice-Chair), *The Times*, 24 March 1983, quoted in *Hansard*, 24 March 1983, p. 1088.
3 Report of the Independent Commission on Disarmament and Security Issues (O. Palme, Chair), *Common Security: A Programme for Disarmament*, Pan Books, London 1982, p. 46. Since 1945 officials in the US government have formally considered the use of nuclear weapons 20 times. (D. Ball, 'US strategic forces: how would they be used?', *International Security* 7(3), 1982/83, p. 41.) Because the USSR and the other nuclear weapons states are more secretive than the US, it is harder to obtain reliable information for these countries. The estimate of 10 occasions when they considered or threatened the use of nuclear weapons could be an underestimate.
4 J. Steinbruner, 'An assessment of nuclear crises' in F. Griffiths and J. C. Polanyi (eds), *The Dangers of Nuclear War*, University of Toronto, Toronto 1979, pp. 34–49; see p. 40.
5 R. Kennedy, *13 Days*, Macmillan, London 1968; quoted in S. Britten, *The Invisible Event*, Menard Press, London 1983, p. 35.
6 For more details see, for instance, J. Steinbruner, 'An Assessment of nuclear crises', or B. M. Blechman and D. M. Hart, 'The political utility of nuclear weapons: the 1973 Middle East crisis', *International Security* 7(1), 1982, pp. 132–56.
7 B. M. Blechman and D. M. Hart, 'The political utility of nuclear weapons', p. 145.
8 Ibid., p. 146.
9 Ibid., p. 137.
10 Ibid., p. 137.
11 C. Weinberger, Secretary of Defense, *Department of Defense Annual Report, Fiscal Year 1983*, US Government Printing Office, Washington 1982, chapter III–21; quoted in B. Posen, 'Inadvertent nuclear war? Escalation and NATO's Northern flank', *International Security* 7(1), 1982, pp. 28–54.
12 J. Steinbruner, 'An assessment of nuclear crises', p. 38.
13 Cruise missiles are defined as pilotless warhead carriers supported aerodynamically like aeroplanes. They are not a new invention. The V-1 'buzzbomb' of World War II was a very crude cruise missile. The type referred to here was a clumsy, inaccurate and relatively short-ranged missile. It is therefore not to be confused with the modern US cruise missile, which is vastly more capable.
14 Posen, 'Inadvertent nuclear war?', p. 31, footnote 5.
15 Ibid., p. 34.
16 Vice Admiral Kaufman, US Congress and Senate Committee on Armed Services, *Hearings on Department of Defense Appropriations for Fiscal Year 1978*, US Government Printing Office, Washington 1977, p. 6699; quoted in Posen, 'Inadvertent Nuclear War?', p. 41.
17 Posen, 'Inadvertent Nuclear War?'

18 Vice Admiral Doyle, US Congress and Senate Committee on Armed Services, *Hearings on Department of Defense Appropriations for Fiscal Year 1977*, US Government Printing Office, Washington 1976, p. 6609; quoted in Posen, 'Inadvertent Nuclear War?', p. 41.

19 US Congress and Senate Committee on Armed Services, *Hearings on Department of Defense Appropriations for Fiscal Year 1980*, US Government Printing Office, Washington 1979, p. 1292; quoted in Posen, 'Inadvertent Nuclear War?', p. 40.

20 Estimated from International Institute for Strategic Studies, *The Military Balance 1982–1983*, IISS, London 1982, table 5, p. 124.

21 Ibid., p. 132.

22 An estimate from *The Military Balance 1982–1983*; SIPRI, *World Armaments and Disarmament: SIPRI Yearbook 1982*, Taylor and Francis, London 1982; and D. Smith, *The Defence of the Realm in the 1980s*, Croom Helm, London 1980, pp. 90–1.

23 C. Donnelly, 'Soviet tactics for overcoming NATO anti-tank defenses', *International Defense Review* 12, 1979, p. 1099; quoted in J. Mearsheimer, 'Why the Soviets can't win quickly in Central Europe', *International Security* 7(1), 1982, p. 29, footnote 65.

24 J. D. Douglass Jr, *Soviet Military Strategy in Europe*, Pergamon, New York 1980, pp. 91–2, and 111–12. Douglass quotes a number of Soviet military sources to support his description.

25 See, for instance, J. Mearsheimer, 'Why the Soviets can't win quickly'.

26 Reported in *CounterSpy*, December 1982–February 1983, pp. 40–3, which includes extracts from the new *US Army Field Manual FM 100–5*, August 1982. See also *US News and World Report*, 20 September 1982, pp. 59–62.

27 It has been reported that the British and German armed forces are changing their own strategies in accordance with the 'Air-Land Battle' strategy, and that the 'Wintex 1983' NATO exercise was also played out according to the new strategy; J. Connell, *The Sunday Times*, 13 March 1983.

28 J. Record, 'Theatre nuclear weapons; begging the Soviet Union to pre-empt', *Survival*, September/October 1977, p. 208.

29 Ibid.

30 *US Army Field Manual FM 100–5*, July 1976, Headquarters Department of the Army, Washington, 1 July 1976, pp. 10–19.

31 Earl Mountbatten of Burma, speech on the occasion of the award of the Louise Weiss Foundation Prize to the Stockholm International Peace Research Institute in Strasbourg, 11 May 1979.

32 Field Marshal Lord Carver, *Hansard*, House of Lords, 23 April 1980, p. 834.

33 As quoted in Lord Zuckerman, *Nuclear Illusion and Reality*, Collins, London 1982, pp. 70–2.

34 Palme Commission, *Common Security*, pp. 44–5.

35 G. Prins (ed.), *Defended to Death*, Penguin, Harmondsworth 1983, pp. 214–18.

36 As suggested in P. Jabber, 'A nuclear Middle East: infrastructure, likely military postures, and prospects for strategic stability' in M. Leitenberg and G. Sheffer (eds), *Great Power Intervention in the Middle East*, Pergamon, New York 1979, p. 92; quoted in D. Frei, *Risks of Unintentional Nuclear War*, Croom Helm, London 1983, p. 171.

37 R. Forsberg, 'A bilateral nuclear weapon freeze', *Scientific American* 247, Nov. 1982, p. 57.

38 O. Wilkes, chapters 7 and 8 in SIPRI, *World Armaments and Disarmament: SIPRI Yearbook 1979*, Taylor and Francis, London 1979.

39 B. Jasani (ed.), *Outer Space – A New Dimension of the Arms Race*, SIPRI, Taylor and Francis, London 1982, pp. 167–83.

40 D. Ball, *Can Nuclear War be Controlled?*, Adelphi Paper No. 169, International Institute for Strategic Studies, London 1981, pp. 9–26.

41 It has been reported that the US plans to instal some Pershing II missiles in Alaska; *The Observer*, 3 April 1983.

42 P. Pringle and W. Arkin, *SIOP: Nuclear War from the Inside*, Sphere, London 1983.

43 SIPRI, *World Armaments and Disarmament: SIPRI Yearbook 1977*, Taylor and Francis, London 1977, pp. 52–85.

44 Controller General of the United States, *NORAD's Missile Warning System: What Went Wrong?*, Report to the Chairman, Committee on Government Operations, House of Representatives, MASAD-81-30, US General Accounting Office, Washington 15 May 1981.

45 SIPRI, *World Armaments and Disarmament: SIPRI Yearbook 1981*, Taylor and Francis, London 1981, p. 261.

46 J. Muller, 'On accidental nuclear war', *Newsweek*, 8 March 1982, p. 4.

47 L. J. Dumas, 'Human fallibility and weapons', *Bulletin of the Atomic Scientists* 36(9), 1980, p. 16.

48 Ibid., p. 16.

49 S. Britten, *The Invisible Event*, Menard Press, London 1983, p. 41.

50 Ibid, p. 19.

51 N. Calder, *Nuclear Nightmares: An Investigation into Possible Wars*, Penguin, Harmondsworth 1979, p. 96.

52 H. Kissinger, *Time*, 15 October 1979; quoted in Frei, *Risks of Unintentional War*, p. 113.

53 Ball, *Can Nuclear War be Controlled?*, p. 28.

54 US Office of Technology Assessment, *The Effects of Nuclear War*, Croom Helm, London 1980.

55 This is the scenario presented by General Sir John Hackett and six collaborators in their book *The Third World War: A Future History*, Sidgwick and Jackson, London 1978. In their story, escalation is avoided. But this involves quite fantastic wishful thinking on the part of the authors.

The news of the obliteration of Minsk spreads 'like wildfire' and triggers a spontaneous nationalist rebellion which sweeps through the USSR and Eastern Europe. In the Kazakh Soviet Socialist Republic in the far east, for instance, 'enthusiastic crowds [fill] the streets with banners', while their local supreme soviet proclaims secession from the Soviet Union. The area's military commander 'unaccustomed to taking local initiatives', takes himself and most of his garrison off to the Chinese frontier. Popular democratic movements spring up everywhere. The Polish government declares its withdrawal from the Warsaw Pact, after secretly obtaining assurances from London that the allies will airlift food supplies to Poland.

Meanwhile, a secret network of Ukrainian nationalists, who have succeeded in penetrating the KGB, join forces with sections of the Army. They arrange a fatal 'motor accident' for the KGB chief, so that one of them, Duglenko, can replace him on the Politburo. Duglenko then shoots the President, leads a successful coup, assumes effective command and control over the armed forces, and sues for peace with NATO. Finally, a number of independent republics were formed, anxious to establish friendly relations with the West. (See their chapter 26.)

The implausibility of all this, and particularly of it all occurring before the Politburo or military command got around to 'pushing the button', scarcely needs emphasizing.

CHAPTER 4   SOVIET WEAPONS AND THEIR TARGETS

1 The Stockholm International Peace Research Institute (SIPRI) *Yearbook* has been published each year since 1968.
2 Each year the London-based International Institute of Strategic Studies (IISS) publishes *The Military Balance*, an annual quantitative assessment of the military power and defence expenditure of countries throughout the world.
3 For instance, US Office of the Joint Chiefs of Staff, *United States Military Posture for 1983*, Washington DC 1982; US Department of Defense, *Authorization for Appropriations for Fiscal year 1984*, Hearings before the Senate Armed Services Committee, US Government Printing Office, Washington DC 20402, 1983, US Department of Defense, *Annual Report Fiscal Year 1983*, US Government Printing Office, Washington DC 20402, 1982.
4 US State Department, *'Gist' article on INF*, United States Information Service, 19 May 1983.
5 R. Berman and J. Baker, *Soviet Strategic Forces*, Brookings Institution, New York 1982, p. 15; R. Garthoff, 'The Soviet SS-20 Decision', *Survival* May/June 1983, pp. 110–19.
6 P. Rogers, private communication.
7 *Flight International*, 5 February 1983, p. 318.
8 US State Department, *'Gist' article on INF*.
9 SIPRI Yearbook 1982, p.10.
10 R. Garthoff, 'Brezhnev's opening: the INF tangle', *Foreign Policy*, 41, Winter 1980–81, and Berman and Baker, *Soviet Strategic Forces*, pp. 20 and 112.
11 *SIPRI Yearbook 1982*, p. 13.
12 See, for instance, Major General Kh. Dzhelaukhov, *Voyennaya mysl'*, (Military Thought), no. 2, February 1966, in 'Selected Readings from Military Thought 1963–1973', J. D. Douglass Jr and A. Hoeber (eds), *Studies in Communist Affairs*, vol. 5, part 1, part III, United States Air Force 1982.
13 The number of free-fall nuclear bombs on the backfire bomber is sometimes quoted to be three.
14 This is the figure given in the *SIPRI Yearbook 1982*, table 1.4, p. 18. There is apparently some disagreement about the combat range of the 'Blinder' since, in the IISS's *Military Balance 1982/83*, p. 136, the range is quoted to be 3,100 km.
15 Since the 'Blinder' and 'Fencer' bombers are comparatively short-ranged,

we assume that no more than one quarter of them are allocated to targets in the UK.

16 See, for instance: Home Office and Central Office of Information, *Domestic Nuclear Shelters: Technical Guidance*, HMSO, London 1981: S. F. J. Butler, 'Scientific Advice in Home Defence' in C. Barnaby and G. Thomas (eds), *The Nuclear Arms Race: Control or Catastrophe*, Frances Pinter, London 1982; Introduction to the Home Office Scientific Advisory Branch, *Training Manual for Scientific Advisers*, Home Office, London 1977. Over the last two years the Home Office's estimate of a 200-megaton attack seems to have been substantially reduced. No explanation for this has been offered by the Home Office.

17 A. G. Enthoven and K. Wayne Smith, *How Much is Enough?*, Harper and Row, New York 1971, p. 207; quoted by A. Katz, *Life after Nuclear War*, Ballinger, Cambridge Mass. 1982, p. 317.

18 See, for instance, B. R. Hollis, *United Kingdom Airfield Register*, Newport Pagnell, Bucks 1980.

19 P. Rogers, 'Possible Nuclear Attack Scenarios on Britain' in M. R. Dando and B. R. Newman (eds), *Nuclear Deterrence: Implications and Policy Options for the 1980s*, Castle House, Tunbridge Wells 1982, pp. 137–45.

20 D. Campbell, *War Plan UK*, Burnett Books, London 1982, p. 264.

21 Colonel M. Shirikov, 'Military Geography at the Present Stage', *Voyennaya mysl'*, No. 11, November 1966, in 'Selected Readings from Military Thought 1963–1973', *Studies in Communist Affairs*, vol. 5, part 1, p. 134.

22 See, for instance, Katz, *Life after Nuclear War*, p. 117 and D. Ball, 'US Strategic Forces: How Would They Be Used?', *International Security* 7(3), 1982/83, p. 53.

23 Ball, 'US Strategic Forces: How Would They Be Used?', p. 53, footnote 62.

24 See, for example, Shirikov, 'Military Geography at the Present Stage', p. 135.

25 Ministry of Defence, *Statement on the Defence Estimates 1981*, part 1, Cmnd. 8212-I, HMSO, London 1981, p. 49.

26 Ibid., p. 44.

27 From an article in *Voyennaya mysl'*, quoted in Campbell, *War Plan UK*, pp. 420–1.

28 Central Electricity Generating Board (CEGB), *Annual Report and Accounts 1981–82*, p. 12.

29 The Electricity Council, *Handbook of Electricity Supply Statistics*, 1982 edn. pp. 5–6; CEGB, *Statistical Yearbook 1978–79*, pp. 6–8.

30 CEGB, *Annual Report and Accounts 1981–82*, p. 12.

31 Katz, *Life after Nuclear War*, pp. 95, 114 and 117.

32 See, for instance, OTA, *The Effects of Nuclear War*, Croom Helm, London 1980, p. 64ff. for an analysis of the devastating effect on the US economy of an attack of 10 SS18 missiles.

33 Glasstone and Dolan, *The Effects of Nuclear Weapons*, pp. 38–9.

34 Campbell, *War Plan*, p. 427.

36 J. Romm and K. Tsipis, *Analysis of Dense Pack Vulnerabilities*, Program in Science and Technology for International Security, Report 8, Dept of Physics, Massachusetts Institute of Technology, Cambridge Mass. November 1982.

37 IISS, *The Military Balance 1982/83*, p. 136.

CHAPTER 5   PATTERNS OF NUCLEAR ATTACK

1 Colonel A. A. Sidorenko, *The Offensive: Characteristic Features of the Offensive in a Nuclear War*; quoted in M. Clarke, *The Nuclear Destruction of Britain*, Croom Helm, London 1982, p. 109.

2 See Clarke, *Nuclear Destruction of Britain*, p. 137, where he suggests the optimum time to be between 8.00 am and midday. The advantage of catching US and NATO staff based in West Germany and the UK unawares would also tend to favour as early a European time as possible.

3 See, for instance, Home Office Emergency Services Circular ESI/1981, *Civil Defence Review*, Home Office, London 1981.

4 D. Smith, *Defence of the Realm in the 1980s*, Croom Helm, London 1980, p. 89.

5 SIPRI, *World Armaments and Disarmament: SIPRI Yearbook 1982*, Taylor and Francis, London 1982, p. 320.

6 Clarke, *Nuclear Destruction of Britain*, p. 160.

7 *The Observer*, 24 April 1983.

8 D. Campbell, *New Statesman*, 18 July 1980; *New Statesman*, 31 October 1980; *New Statesman*, 24 September 1982; *War Plan UK: The Truth about Civil Defence in Britain*, Burnett Books, London 1982.

9 B. R. Hollis, *United Kingdom Airfield Register*, Newport Pagnell, Bucks 1980.

10 P. Laurie, *Beneath the City Streets*, Penguin, London 1970.

11 P. Rogers, 'Possible nuclear attack scenarios on Britain' in M. R. Dando and B. R. Newman (eds), *Nuclear Deterrence: Implications and Policy Options for the 1980s*, Castle House, Tunbridge Wells 1982, pp. 137–45.

12 We would like to acknowledge the assistance of the many people who have written to us providing local information as a consequence of the 'Hard Luck' exercise. Professor M. J. Pentz also supplied us with his own very useful target list.

13 Ministry of Defence, *Statement on the Defence Estimates 1981*, Cmnd 8212-I, HMSO, London 1981; Ministry of Defence, *Statement on the Defence Estimates 1982*, Cmnd 8529-I, HMSO, London 1982.

14 K. Bullough, Leeds University, private communication.

15 B. Ramberg, *Destruction of Nuclear Energy Facilities in War: The Problem and the Implications*, Lexington Books, Lexington Mass 1980, p. 64.

16 The original 'Hard Luck' targeting plan was devised by O. Greene and N. Turok.

17 British Medical Association, *The Medical Effects of Nuclear War*, Wiley, Chichester 1983.

18 As emphasized, for instance, by Campbell, *War Plan*, p. 432.

19 G. Pattie, *Hansard*, written answers to questions, 203, defence, 6 March 1981.

20 International Institute for Strategic Studies (IISS), *The Military Balance 1982–1983*, IISS, London 1982 p. 113.

21 E. J. Grove, 'Modern strategy and nuclear weapons', *Fission Fragments* 23, Nov. 1978, p. 23/7–23/14.

22 Ministry of Health, Circular No.9/1960 (Appendix B, Civil Defence Sub Regions), 1960.

23 R. Berman and J. Baker, *Soviet Strategic Forces: Requirements and Responses*,

Brookings Institution, New York 1982, table G4, p. 136. In 1955 the USSR had deployed 24 SS3 missiles, 300 Badger bombers and no delivery vehicles capable of reaching the USA. By 1960 it had 48 SS3s, about 200 SS4s and 700 Badgers, together with 4 SS6s and 145 bombers of intercontinental range.
24 D. Campbell, *New Statesman*, 3 October 1980 and *New Statesman*, 6 March 1981. We are grateful to D. Campbell for supplying us with all of the details of Operation 'Square Leg' which he has collected together.
25 Campbell, *War Plan*, pp. 80–1.
26 Ibid., chapters 1 and 2.

CHAPTER 6   ESTIMATING THE EFFECTS OF ATTACK

1 S. Glasstone and P. J. Dolan (eds), *The Effects of Nuclear Weapons*, Castle House, Tunbridge Wells 1980.
2 Ibid., preface.
3 Committee for the Compilation of Materials on Damage Caused by the Atomic Bombs in Hiroshima and Nagasaki, *Hiroshima and Nagasaki: The Physical, Medical, and Social Effects of the Atomic Bombings* (translated E. Ishikawa and D. L. Swain), Hutchinson, London 1981, p. 367.
4 From the Social Science Research Council Data Archive, Essex University.
5 O. Greene, B. Rubin, N. Turok, P. Webber, G. Wilkinson, *London after the Bomb*, Oxford University Press, Oxford 1982, (see appendix 4, pp. 113–19).
6 For a full technical account see S. Openshaw and P. Steadman, 'Predicting the consequences of a nuclear attack on Britain: models, results, and implications for public policy', *Environment and Planning C: Government and Policy* 1, 1983, pp. 205–28.
7 Home Office and Central Office of Information, *Protect and Survive*, HMSO, London 1980, p. 7.
8 *The Effects of Nuclear War*, Croom Helm, London 1980, p. 3.
9 Ibid., pp. 31–2.
10 Ibid. table 5, p. 32.
11 Glasstone and Dolan, *Effects of Nuclear Weapons*, pp. 562–6.
12 A. Qasrawi, *Modelling the Direct Thermal Radiation Effects of Nuclear Explosions on Population*, mimeograph, Scientists Against Nuclear Arms, Birmingham 1982.
13 For details see S. Openshaw, 'The geography of reactor siting policies in the UK', *Transactions of the Institute of British Geographers*, NS7, 1982, pp. 150–64.
14 Glasstone and Dolan, *Effects of Nuclear Weapons*, pp. 114–5.
15 OTA, *Effects of Nuclear War*, figure 1, p. 19; personal communication from P. Sharfman, Director of the Nuclear War Effects Project to A. Macfarlane, Radical Statistics Group, 20 October 1982.
16 OTA, *Effects of Nuclear War*, p. 19.
17 *Hiroshima and Nagasaki*, table 7.9, p. 113.
18 Glasstone and Dolan, *Effects of Nuclear Weapons*, table 12.18, p. 546.
19 Ibid., p. 419.

20 P. R. Bentley, 'Blast overpressure and fallout radiation dose models for casualty assessment and other purposes', Home Office Scientific Research and Development Branch, London April 1981, p. 7.

21 For example the US government WSEG-10 Fallout Model, documented in L. A. Schmidt Jr, *Methodology of Fallout-Risk Assessment*, P-1065, Institute for Defense Analyses, Washington DC 1975, and incorporated in the GUISTO program, as described in L.A. Schmidt Jr, *Development of Civil Defense Damage Assessment Programs*, P-1526, Institute for Defense Analyses, Washington DC 1980. The GUISTO program was used for the calculations presented in W. Arkin, F. von Hippel and B. G. Levi, 'The consequences of a "limited" nuclear war in East and West Germany' in J. Peterson and D. Hinrichsen (eds), *Nuclear War: The Aftermath*, Pergamon, Oxford 1982, pp. 165–87.

22 Glasstone and Dolan, *Effects of Nuclear Weapons*, p. 423.

23 Ibid., table 9.93, p. 430.

24 Ibid., p. 428.

25 Bentley, 'Casualty assessment', pp. 8–10.

26 OTA, *Effects of Nuclear War*, pp. 141–5.

27 A. M. Katz, *Life after Nuclear War: The Economic and Social Impacts of Nuclear Attacks on the United States*, Ballinger, Cambridge Mass 1982, p. 252.

28 Greene et al., *London after the Bomb*, p. 32.

29 J. Rotblat, *Nuclear Radiation in Warfare*, Taylor and Francis, London 1981, p. 92.

30 Greene et al., *London after the Bomb*, appendix 3, pp. 108–12.

31 National Council on Radiation Protection and Measurements (NRCP), *Radiological Factors affecting Decision-Making in a Nuclear Attack*, NCRP Report 42, Washington DC 1974, p. 22. See also C. C. Lushbaugh 'The impact of estimates of human radiation tolerance upon radiation emergency management' in *The Control of Exposure of the Public to Ionizing Radiation in the Event of Accident or Attack*, National Council on Radiation Protection and Measurements, Bethesda Md. 1982, pp. 46–57.

32 British Institute of Radiology (BIR), *Report of the BIR Working Party on the Radiological Effects of Nuclear War*, 1982; quoted in BMA, *The Medical effects of Nuclear War*, Wiley, Chichester 1983, p. 84. See also NCRP, *Radiological Factors*, appendix B, pp. 51–3.

33 BIR, *Report of the BIR*, quoted in BMA, *Medical Effects*, p. 84.

CHAPTER 7   IMMEDIATE CASUALTIES AND DAMAGE

1 Japanese Broadcasting Corporation (NHK) (eds), *Unforgettable Fire: Pictures Drawn by Atomic Bomb Survivors*, Wildwood House, London 1981; M. Hachiya, *Hiroshma Diary: The Journal of a Japanese Physician, August 6 – September 30, 1945* (edited by W. Wells), University of North Carolina, Chapel Hill 1955; T. Akizuki, *Nagasaki 1945* (translated K. Nagata), Quartet, London 1981.

2 S. Openshaw and P. Steadman, 'On the geography of a worst case nuclear attack on the population of Britain', *Political Geography Quarterly* 1(3), 1982, pp. 263–78.

3 See A. Enthoven and K. Wayne Smith, *How Much is Enough?*, Harper and Row, New York 1971.

4 Ibid., p. 207. See also graph from 'US Strategic Offensive Forces in the 1960s' in Commission on the Organization of the Government for the Conduct of Foreign Policies, *Appendices*, vol. 4, p. 139, reproduced in F. M. Kaplan, *Dubious Spectre: A Skeptical Look at the Soviet Nuclear Threat*, Institute for Policy Studies, Washington DC 1980, p. 5.

5 OTA, *The Effects of Nuclear War*, Croom Helm, London 1980, pp. 31–2.

6 Ibid., p. 22. See also S. Glasstone and P. J. Dolan (eds), *The Effects of Nuclear Weapons*, Castle House, Tunbridge Wells 1980, pp. 299–300.

CHAPTER 8   THE AFTERMATH OF ATTACK

1 Patrick Mayhew, Minister of State at the Home Office responsible for civil defence, on BBC Radio 'The World this Weekend', quoted in *The Times*, 7 March 1983.

2 Advertisement for Survival Aids' Survival School, *Practical Civil Defence*, March/April 1983, p. 35. See also B. Popkess, *The Nuclear Survival Handbook: Living through and after a Nuclear Attack*, Arrow Books, London 1980.

3 As for example the Nuclear Protection Advisory Group (NuPAG), *Civil Defence Needs to be Effective*, NuPAG, Hove n.d.; I. Tyrell, *The Survival Option: A Guide to Living through Nuclear War*, Jonathan Cape, London 1983.

4 P. J. Crutzen and J. W. Birks, 'The atmosphere after a nuclear war: twilight at noon' in J. Peterson and D. Hinrichsen (eds), *Nuclear War: The Aftermath*, Pergamon, Oxford 1982, pp. 73–91; see p. 80.

5 S. Glasstone and P. J. Dolan, *The Effects of Nuclear Weapons*, 3rd edn, Castle House, Tunbridge Wells 1980, pp. 196–200.

6 B. Ramberg, *Destruction of Nuclear Energy Facilities in War: The Problem and the Implications*, Lexington Books, Lexington, Mass 1980, p. 64, quoting C. V. Chester and R. O. Chester, 'Civil defense implications of the US nuclear power industry during a large nuclear war in the year 2000', *Nuclear Technology* 31, Dec. 1976.

7 Glasstone and Dolan, *Effects of Nuclear Weapons*, pp. 529–31.

8 S. A. Fetter and K. Tsipis, 'Catastrophic releases of radioactivity', *Scientific American*, 244(4), April 1981, pp. 33–9; Ramberg, *Destruction of Nuclear Energy Facilities*. For estimates relating to Europe see also Ambio Advisory Group, 'Reference Scenario: How a nuclear war might be fought' in Petersen and Hinrichsen, *Nuclear War: The Aftermath*, pp. 37–48; see p. 46 and map inside back cover.

9 A. M. Katz, *Life after Nuclear War: The Economic and Social Impacts of Nuclear Attacks on the United States*, Ballinger, Cambridge, Mass. 1982, p. 99.

10 R. L. Goen, R. B. Bothun and F. E. Walker, *Potential Vulnerability Affecting National Survival*, Stanford Research Institute, Menlo Park California, September 1970; J. Sassen and K. Willis, *Data Base and Damage Criteria for Measurement of Arms Limitation Effects on War Supporting Industry*, ACDA/WEC-242, Metis Corporation, Alexandria Virgina, June 1974. In both studies percentage damage is measured in terms of 'manufacturing value added'.

11 K. G. Wetzel, 'Effects on global supplies of freshwater' in Petersen and Hinrichsen, *Nuclear War: The Aftermath*, pp. 97–107; see p. 105.

12 Home Office Emergency Services Circular ES 1/79, , *Food and Agriculture Controls in War*, Home Office, London 1979. See discussion in D. Campbell, *War Plan UK: The Truth about Civil Defence in Britain*, Burnett Books, London 1982, pp. 352–3.

13 Glasstone and Dolan, *Effects of Nuclear Weapons*, table 5.149, p. 225.

14 Ibid., pp. 622–4.

15 Ibid., pp. 624–7. See also discussion in H. W. Hjort, 'The impact on global food supplies' in Katz, *Nuclear War: The Aftermath*, pp. 147–54.

16 National Academy of Sciences, *Long Term World-Wide Effects of Multiple Nuclear-Weapons Detonations* , NAS, Washington DC 1975.

17 See discussion in Crutzen and Birks, 'The atmosphere after a nuclear war', also OTA, *The Effects of Nuclear War*, Croom Helm, London, 1980, p. 115.

18 E. Teller, 'Deadly myths about nuclear arms', *Readers Digest* 122, Jan. 1983, pp. 21–6; see p. 24.

19 Crutzen and Birks, 'The atmosphere after a nuclear war'.

20 BMA, *The Medical Effects of Nuclear War*, Wiley, Chichester 1983, p. 38. The statistics are for 1978.

21 Dr E. Williams, personal communication.

22 BMA, *Medical Effects of Nuclear War*, p. 124.

23 Ibid. p. 42. See also P. J. Lindop and J. Rotblat, 'The consequences of radioactive fallout' in E. Chivian, S. Chivian, R. J. Lifton and J. E. Mack (eds), *Last Aid: The Medical Dimensions of Nuclear War*, Freeman, San Francisco 1982, pp. 249–79; see p. 277.

24 H. L. Abrams, 'Survivors of nuclear war: infection and the spread of disease' in Chivian *et al.*, pp. 211–33.

25 BMA, *Medical Effects of Nuclear War*, p. 43.

26 The Regional Health Authority for East Anglia has prepared a memorandum on this subject; see Campbell, *War Plan UK*, pp. 395–6.

27 There are by now many accounts of the mental sufferings of the Japanese survivors, of which the classic (in English) remains R. J. Lifton, *Death in Life: Survivors of Hiroshima*, Random House, New York 1967.

28 See for example Glasstone and Dolan, *Effects of Nuclear Weapons*, pp. 590–4; J. Rotblat, *Nuclear Radiation in Warfare*, Taylor and Francis, London 1981, pp. 39–50; Committee for the Compilation of Materials on Damage Caused by the Atomic Bombs in Hiroshima and Nagasaki, *Hiroshima and Nagasaki: The Physical, Medical and Social Effects of the Atomic Bombings*, Hutchinson, London 1981, pp. 186–332.

29 See NAS, *Long Term Worldwide Effects*, p. 105.

30 *Hiroshima and Nagasaki*, pp. 255–76.

31 R. A. Conard, D. E. Paglia and P. R. Larsen, *Review of Medical Findings in a Marshallese Population – 26 Years After Accidental Exposure to Radioactive Fallout*, Brookhaven National Laboratory BNL 51261, Upton LI 1980.

32 J. L. Lyon, M. R. Klauber, J. W. Gardner, K. S. Udall, 'Childhood leukemias associated with fallout from nuclear testing', *New England Journal of Medicine* 300, 1979, pp. 397–402.

33 *Hiroshima and Nagasaki*, pp. 217–33.

34 T. Ohkita, 'Delayed medical effects at Hiroshima and Nagasaki' in Chivian et al., Last Aid, pp. 93–107.

35 For example Nuclear Protection Advisory Group, The Myths and the Realities, mimeo, NuPAG, Hove n.d.

36 P. Harper, 'Genetic effects of nuclear war' in S. Farrow and A. Chown (eds), The Human Cost of Nuclear War, Medical Campaign against Nuclear Weapons, Candiff, March 1983, pp. 29–33. See also Rotblat, Nuclear Radiation in Warfare, p. 50.

37 OTA, The Effects of Nuclear War, Croom Helm, London 1980, pp. 109–13; J. E. Coggle and P. J. Lindop, 'Medical consequences of radiation following a global nuclear war' in Nuclear War: The Aftermath, pp. 59–71 (see table 8, p. 70).

38 International Commission on Radiological Protection, Recommendations of the ICRP, Publication No. 26, Pergamon, Oxford 1977.

39 OTA, Effects of Nuclear War, table 12, p. 111.

40 Calculated from results given in ibid., table 14, p. 113.

CHAPTER 9   HOME OFFICE CALCULATIONS OF THE EFFECTS OF ATTACK

1 P. R. Bentley, 'Blast overpressure and fallout radiation dose models for casualty assessment and other purposes', Home Office Scientific Research and Development Branch, London, December 1981.

2 S. F. J. Butler, 'Scientific advice in home defence' in F. Barnaby and G. Thomas (eds), The Nuclear Arms Race – Control or Catastrophe?, Frances Pinter, London 1982, pp. 135–63.

3 BMA, The Medical Effects of Nuclear War, Wiley, Chichester 1983.

4 Home Office, Protect and Survive,, HMSO, London 1980, p. 7.

5 Bentley, 'Casualty assessment', p. 1.

6 BMA, Medical Effects, p. 71.

7 Butler, 'Scientific advice', p. 145.

8 S. Glasstone and P. J. Dolan (eds), The Effects of Nuclear Weapons, Castle House, Tunbridge Wells 1980, pp. 114–15.

9 Bentley, 'Casualty assessment', pp. 2–4.

10 Home Office and Scottish Home and Health Department, Nuclear Weapons, 3rd edn, HMSO, London 1974, p. 33, table 9.

11 Home Office and Central Office of Information, Domestic Nuclear Shelters: Technical Guidance, HMSO, London 1981, p. 9, fig. 6.

12 Home Office, Nuclear Weapons, p. 35.

13 Home Office, Domestic Nuclear Shelters: Technical Guidance, p. 9, fig. 6.

14 BMA, Medical Effects, p. 61.

15 Home Office, The Control of Civil Defence Operations under Fallout Conditions, Civil Defence Training Memorandum No. 3, HMSO, London 1959, p. 10.

16 See Glasstone and Dolan, Effects of Nuclear Weapons, p. 544.

17 Committee for the Compilation of Materials on Damage Caused by the Atomic Bombs in Hiroshima and Nagasaki, Hiroshima and Nagasaki; the Physical, Medical and Social Effects of the Atomic Bombings, Hutchinson, London 1981, chapters 2 and 10.

18 BMA, Medical Effects, pp. 66–7.

19 British Mission to Japan, *The Effects of the Atomic Bombs at Hiroshima and Nagasaki*, HMSO, London 1946, p. 21.
20 BMA, *Medical Effects*, p. 67.
21 Glasstone and Dolan, *Effects of Nuclear Weapons*, pp. 178–84.
22 BMA, *Medical Effects*, p. 69.
23 Butler, 'Scientific advice', p. 153.
24 BMA, *Medical Effects*, p. 78.
25 Ibid., p. 79.
26 O. Greene, B. Rubin, N. Turok, P. Webber, G. Wilkinson, *London after the Bomb*, Oxford University Press, Oxford 1982, p. 114; cf. also J. Rotblat, *Nuclear Radiation in Warfare*, Taylor and Francis, London 1981, p. 35.
27 Home Office, *Nuclear Weapons*, p. 11.
28 Home Office Scientific Advisory Branch, *Operational Handbook for Scientific Advisers*, Home Office, London 1979, table E10.
29 BMA, *Medical Effects*, pp. 84–7.
30 Ibid., p. 85.
31 Bentley, 'Casualty assessment', pp. 17–18.
32 See Home Office, *Nuclear Weapons*, p. 12.
33 Bentley, 'Casualty assessment', p. 17.
34 Ibid., p. 18, fig. 15.
35 See G. N. Kelly, J. R. Simmonds, H. Smith and J. W. Stather, *The Radiological Consequences of Notional Accidental Releases of Radioactivity from Fast Breeder Reactors*, National Radiological Protection Board Report NRPB-R-87, Washington DC 1979; National Council on Radiation Protection and Measurements, Radiological Factors affecting Decision-Making in a Nuclear Attack, NCRP Report 42, Washington DC 1974.
36 P. J. Lindop 'Radiation aspects of a nuclear war in Europe', paper presented to Conference on Nuclear War in Europe, Groningen, Netherlands, April 1981; quoted in BMA, *Medical Effects*, p. 88.
37 Butler, 'Scientific advice', p. 155.
38 Home Office, *Domestic Nuclear Shelters: Technical Guidance*, p. 17.
39 Home Office and Central Office of Information, *Domestic Nuclear Shelters*, HMSO, London 1981, p. 5.
40 Home Office Scientific Advisory Branch, *Training Manual for Scientific Advisers*, Home Office, London 1977, introduction by J. K. S. Clayton.

CHAPTER 10 CIVIL DEFENCE AND ITS EFFECTIVENESS

1 D. Campbell, *War Plan UK: The Truth about Civil Defence in Britain*, Burnett Books, London 1982.
2 G. Crossley, *Civil Defence in Britain* Bradford University School of Peace Studies Paper No. 7, Housmans, London 1982.
3 Home Office Emergency Services Circulars, distributed to local government officers, civil defence workers, the police etc.; some are confidential or restricted; others are obtainable free on application to Home Office F6 Division. A full list of titles issued between 1972 and 1981 is given in Campbell, *War Plan*, pp. 471–4.

4 Home Office Scientific Advisory Branch, *Trainining Manual for Scientific Advisers*, Home Office, London 1977, chapter 1, para 1.3.

5 Ibid., paras 1.15–1.18.

6 Home Office and Scottish Home and Health Department, *Nuclear Weapons*, 3rd edn, HMSO, London 1974.

7 Home Office and Central Office of Information, *Domestic Nuclear Shelters*, HMSO, London 1981.

8 Home Office and Central Office of Information, *Protect and Survive*, HMSO, London 1980.

9 Ibid., p. 3.

10 Home Office, *Domestic Nuclear Shelters*, shelter types 1a and 1b, pp. 7–13.

11 Home Office, *Domestic Nuclear Shelters: Technical Guidance*, HMSO, London 1981, pp. 73–82.

12 BBC *Panorama*, 10 March 1980; see discussion in P. Bolsover, *Civil Defence: The Cruellest Confidence Trick*, Campaign for Nuclear Disarmament, London n.d., p. 12. Also BBC *QED* 28 May 1982.

13 Home Office, *Civil Defence Review*, Emergency Services Circular ES1/81, Home Office, London 1981.

14 Home Office oral evidence to British Medical Association Inquiry into 'The Medical Effects of Nuclear War', unpublished.

15 See Crossley, *Civil Defence in Britain*, pp. 20–1.

16 Home Office, *War Emergency Planning for the Fire Service*, Emergency Services Circular ES5/74, Home Office, London 1974, pp. 1–2.

17 Mr Patrick Mayhew, Minister of State at the Home Office, reported in *Hansard*, 24 March 1983, p. 1104.

18 Campbell, *War Plan*, p. 141.

19 According to military manuals of home defence; see ibid., fig. 7, p. 144.

20 Ibid., p. 279. A full list of Sub-Regional and Zone HQs is given by Campbell in table 13, p. 280.

21 Home Office, *Machinery of Government in War*, Emergency Services Circular ES7/73, Home Office, London 1973 p. 5.

22 Ibid., p. 5.

23 The general organization of the UKWMO is described in D. Wood, *Attack Warning Red*, MacDonald and Jane's, London 1976. See also Campbell, *War Plan*, chapter 9, pp. 285–93. More recent information was given by W. P. Lawrie, Deputy Director of UKWMO, in a lecture to the Society for Radiological Protection, Middlesex Hospital, London, 12 October 1982.

24 Nuclear Protection Advisory Group (NuPAG), *Civil Defence Needs to be Effective*, NuPAG, Hove n.d.

25 D. Owen, *Negotiate and Survive*, 1980; quoted in Campbell, *War Plan*, p. 156.

26 *The Times*, 2 April 1980.

27 G. Crossley, *British Civil Defence and Nuclear War: A Critical Assessment, with Reference to Economic Consequences*, School of Peace Studies Research Report No. 1, University of Bradford 1980; see pp. 61–6.

28 Home Office, *Food and Agriculture Controls in War*, Emergency Services Circular ES1/79, Home Office, London 1979, p. 3.

29 Campbell, *War Plan*, table 16, pp. 359–61.

30 Ibid., p. 358.

31 Defence White Paper, *Outline of Future Policy*, HMSO, London 1957.
32 Home Office, *The Protection of your Home against Air Raids*, HMSO, London 1938. See Campbell, *War Plan*, plate 10, p. 97.
33 Home Office, *Domestic Nuclear Shelters: Technical Guidance*, type 2, chapter 5 and type 3, chapter 6.
34 See discussion in J. Rotblat, *Nuclear Radiation in Warfare*, Taylor and Francis, London 1981, p. 117.
35 D. Campbell, 'Survival plans abandoned', *New Statesman*, 6 May 1983, p. 4.
36 *The Times* 24 March 1983; also printed in *Hansard*, 24 March 1983, pp. 1087–8.
37 Emergency Services Circular 6/72 *Tidal Flooding in Greater London*; 7/72 *National Arrangements for dealing with Incidents involving Radioactivity*; 7/75 *Major Accidents and Natural Disasters*; 3/77 *National Arrangements for Incidents involving Radioactivity*. See note 3 above.
38 See OTA, *The Effects of Nuclear War*, Croom Helm, London 1980, pp. 45–6; Rotblat, *Nuclear Radiation in Warfare*, pp. 135–8
39 BMA, *Medical Effects of Nuclear War*, Wiley, Chichester 1983, p. 124.
40 Home Office, *Training Manual for Scientific Advisers*, paras 1.19 and 1.8.
41 Ibid., introduction.
42 Home Office, *Domestic Nuclear Shelters: Technical Guidance*, p. 2.
43 Campbell, 'Survival plans abandoned'.
44 See Campbell, *War Plan*, p. 128.
45 Campbell, 'Survival plans abandoned'.
46 See for example the evidence of Professor B. Lown and Dr D. Greer to the Inquiry of the BMA, *Medical Effects of Nuclear War*, pp. 109–10.
47 See discussion in Crossley, *Civil Defence in Britain*, p. 71 and Campbell, *War Plan*, pp. 187 and 196.
48 Home Office, *Protect and Survive*, p. 7.
49 Home Office, *Essential Service Routes*, Emergency Services Circular ES9/73, Home Office, London 1973.
50 R. N. Ormerod, *Nuclear Shelters: A Guide to Design*, Architectural Press, London 1983 is a recent handbook which includes a bibliography. Some official Swiss designs are given in Swiss Federal Department of Justice and Police, Office of Civil Defence, *Technical Directives for the Construction of Private Air Raid Shelters*, 1966; English edn, ed. G. A. Cristy, ORNL-TR-2707, Oak Ridge National Laboratory, Tennessee, n.d.
51 Home Office, *Domestic Nuclear Shelters: Technical Guidance*, type 4, chapter 7.
52 See Ormerod, *Nuclear Shelters*, p. 128.
53 OTA, *Effects of Nuclear War*, p. 50.
54 Ormerod, *Nuclear Shelters*, pp. 129–31.
55 Ibid., p. 191, although Ormerod says that mass production might bring this figure down to between £500 and £700.
56 Home Office, *Domestic Nuclear Shelters: Technical Guidance*, p. 21.
57 Ormerod, *Nuclear Shelters*, p. 192.
58 Ibid., p. 15.
59 R. N. Ormerod, 'Shelter for all?', *Building Design*, 18 March 1983, p. 10.
60 T. K. Jones, *Industrial Survival and Recovery after Nuclear Attack: A Report to the Joint Committee on Defense Production, US Congress*, Boeing Aerospace Co., Seattle, Washington 1976.

61 E. M. Forster, 'The Machine Stops', *The Collected Short Stories of E. M. Forster*, Sidgwick and Jackson, London 1965.

Index